IDEOMOTOR SIGNALS FOR RAPID HYPNOANALYSIS

IDEOMOTOR SIGNALS FOR RAPID HYPNOANALYSIS

A How-To Manual

By

DABNEY M. EWIN, M.D., FACS, ABMH

and

BRUCE N. EIMER, PH.D., ABPP, FAABEHP

To Kathy Sheetz

Dabney Ewin

With a Foreword by

D. Corydon Hammond, PH.D., ABPH

CHARLES C THOMAS · PUBLISHER, LTD.
Springfield · Illinois · U.S.A.

Published and Distributed Throughout the World by

CHARLES C THOMAS • PUBLISHER, LTD.
2600 South First Street
Springfield, Illinois 62704

©2006 by CHARLES C THOMAS • PUBLISHER, LTD.

ISBN 0-398-07628-6 (hard)
ISBN 0-398-07629-4 (paper)

Library of Congress Catalog Card Number: 2005052975

With THOMAS BOOKS *careful attention is given to all details of manufacturing
and design. It is the Publisher's desire to present books that are satisfactory as to their
physical qualities and artistic possibilities and appropriate for their particular use.*
THOMAS BOOKS *will be true to those laws of quality that assure a good name
and good will.*

Printed in the United States of America
SR-R-3

Library of Congress Cataloging-in-Publication Data

Ewin, Dabney M.
　　Ideomotor signals for rapid hypnoanalysis : a how-to-manual / by Dabney M. Ewin and
Bruce N. Elmer ; with a foreword by D. Corydon Hammond.
　　　p. cm.
　　Includes bibliographical references and index.
　　ISBN 0-398-07628-6 -- ISBN 0-398-07629-4 (pbk.)
　　　1. Hypnotism--Therapeutic use. 2. Perceptual-motor processes. 3. Medicine, Psychoso-
matic. 4. Mind and body. I. Elmer, Bruce N. II. Title.

RC497.E85 2006
616.89'162--dc22

2005052975

We dedicate this book with love to David B. Cheek, M.D., FACS, physician, healer, teacher, OB-GYN, therapist, clinical hypnosis pioneer, and courageous visionary into the light.

Dr. Cheek was our mentor and our good friend.

Dabney M. Ewin, M.D., FACS, ABMH
Bruce N. Eimer, Ph.D., ABPP, FAABehP
May 16, 2005

FOREWORD

More than 25 years ago I took my first workshop from David B. Cheek, M.D., on ideomotor signaling and exploration. I was so fascinated by what I learned that I read his book (Cheek & LeCron, 1968) and then began searching out every article he had ever written. As I began applying ideomotor techniques in my hypnosis practice, I was startled at the effectiveness of these techniques. Finally in about 1982, I called David and asked him if it might be possible to consult with him and "pick his brain" for further refinements of technique. He said, "Certainly," and gave me his home phone number. I asked him how much he would charge me for these phone consultations and he said, "I won't charge you anything. If I can be helpful that would be great. Just call me at home, and if I'm busy I will tell you and ask you to understand, but usually I'm not all that busy and we can visit." This led to many hours of telephone mentoring by Dr. Cheek and to my developing a close relationship with this gentle, but humble giant of a man.

Dr. Cheek was an obstetrician and gynecologist. In one of those phone calls, I presented a case to David of a woman who had come to see me in the Sex and Marital Therapy Clinic for anorgasmia, but she also mentioned that she had uncontrollable, recurrent vaginitis. The woman was a nurse. She had seen half a dozen gynecologists, would go on medication, the vaginitis would clear up, and then within three weeks it would be back. No one, including gynecologists at the medical school where I practice, had been able to figure out her case. I asked David if he thought that vaginal infections could have a psychogenic component. He replied, "Absolutely," and went on to describe how emotions or inner conflict could throw off the pH balance of the vagina, allowing infections to develop.

In the next interview, we did ideomotor exploration and discovered that the vaginitis was an unconscious way of the patient punishing herself because of guilt about sexual involvement when she was not married. We worked through her guilt within a matter of minutes and obtained an unconscious commitment that it was no longer necessary for her to continue having problems with vaginitis. In a 15-year follow-up on this case, I learned that in all those years, she had only had one or two episodes of vaginitis.

I could cite many similar "miraculous" cases involving chronic pain and other somatic symptoms, as well as a variety of psychological conditions. It was cases like this that convinced me of the power of the mind to influence the body, and of the power of ideomotor signaling to produce rapid therapeutic change—often allowing the insight-oriented phase of treatment to be dramatically shortened to just one or a handful of sessions.

My approach to psychotherapy and hypnotherapy has always been very eclectic, and I have tried to remain open to learning from a wide variety of approaches to the use of hypnosis. Yet, out of the many dozens of hypnotherapeutic techniques that I have learned and used through the years (Hammond, 1990), the single most valued and valuable hypnosis technique has been ideomotor signaling. I recall a conversation that I had with Ernest Rossi in the late 1980s, just after he published a book (Rossi & Cheek, 1988) with Dr. Cheek—a conversation with which I resonated. He shared that in the field of hypnosis, he had been most intrigued by the work of Dr. Milton Erickson, but that to him the next most fascinating figure in our field was Dr. David Cheek.

Despite my deep affection and appreciation for Dr. Cheek, David knew that I did not agree with him on a couple of points. He believed that there should not be an ideomotor signal for "I don't know," as there was in his original work with LeCron (Cheek & LeCron, 1968). He had come to believe that at some level, the patient did know the answer, and, therefore, that such a signal provided the patient with a "cop-out." However, research (as reviewed in Brown, Scheflin, & Hammond, 1998) has shown that not allowing someone to respond that they "do not know" an answer will result in increased confabulation.

In fact, this is one of the most serious flaws in the hypnosis and memory research on confabulation-research which by its very design, was destined to show increased confabulation, even though it has been documented (Brown et al., 1998) that hypnosis is no more likely to create pseudomemories than waking interviews.

Leading questions, in or out of hypnosis, are what can create memory distortion. Thus, to avoid possible contamination, I have recommended (Hammond, 1997, 1998) that when we utilize ideomotor exploration, we should also include a signal for "I don't know."

David Cheek (1994) also believed (as do Drs. Ewin and Eimer) that valid memories could be obtained for events before the age of three (and even birth or intrauterine memories), even though research has very seriously called this into question (Brown, et al., 1998). Nonetheless, I always encouraged David's workshop attendees who might well believe that such "memories" only represented projection on the part of the patient (which may nonetheless still have potential clinical value and, when believed in, may possibly be a catalyst for therapeutic change) not to allow David's examples and beliefs about this to discourage them from the many other wonderful things that they could learn about unconscious exploration.

I likewise encourage those who are reading this book, despite feeling that such events may only represent confabulation or demand characteristics, to still remain open-minded about the wealth of other therapeutic techniques you can learn from your reading.

Drs. Dabney Ewin and Bruce Eimer are highly experienced clinicians and teachers who studied with Dr. Cheek and who have very extensive experience in using ideomotor techniques. They have provided us with a practical clinical volume that contains invaluable modeling and captivating case examples. There is much to be learned here. Practitioners who utilize hypnosis as part of psychotherapy, or in working with pain or other medical problems, will find that their practice is enriched from studying this manual.

D. Corydon Hammond, Ph.D., ABPH
Professor & Psychologist, University of Utah School of Medicine
Past President, American Society of Clinical Hypnosis
Diplomate, American Board of Psychological Hypnosis

REFERENCES

Brown, D., Scheflin, A., and Hammond, D. C. (1998). *Memory, trauma treatment, and the law.* New York: W. W. Norton.

Cheek, D. B. (1994). Hypnosis: *The application of ideomotor techniques.* Boston: Allyn & Bacon.

Cheek, D. B., and LeCron, L. (1968). *Clinical hypnotherapy.* New York: Grune & Stratton.

Hammond, D. C. (1997). Advantages and safeguards in using the ideomotor signaling technique: A commentary on Walsh and clinical practice. *American Journal of Clinical Hypnosis, 40* (1), 360–367.

Hammond, D. C. (1998). Ideomotor signaling: A rapid method for unconscious exploration. Chapter in D. C. Hammond (Ed.), *Hypnotic induction and suggestion.* Chicago: American Society of Clinical Hypnosis, pp. 113–121.

Rossi, E. L., and Cheek, D. B. (1988). *Mind–body therapy.* New York: W. W. Norton.

PREFACE

ORGANIZATION OF THIS BOOK

This book is about using ideomotor (IM) signals in the rapid hypno-analysis of psychosomatic disorders. In Part I, we cover basic concepts and principles. In Part II, we cover basic applications of the technique, and illustrate their employment. In Part III, we present clinical transcripts of cases to illustrate the actual uses of the technique with psychosomatic patients. This is a "how-to" book. Thus, throughout the book, we provide numerous case examples and illustrations showing specifically how ideomotor analysis techniques are used.

Part I

Chapters 1 and 2 cover the value of ideomotor signals in hypnotherapy and basic principles of hypnotherapy. In Chapter 3, we cover special intake questions for gathering necessary information and preparing a patient for rapid hypnoanalysis. In Chapter 4, we cover treatment planning, and in Chapter 5, we describe in detail, how to efficiently set up ideomotor signals.

Part II

In Chapters 6 through 11, we explain how to use ideomotor signals effectively to uncover and reframe the fixed ideas ("idée fixe" of Janet) underlying one or more of the seven common causes of psychosomatic disorders (Cheek & LeCron, 1968).

In Chapter 6, we discuss applications of ideomotor signaling to direct suggestion in hypnosis (DSIH) and age regression. We specifically cover the seven common causes of psychosomatic symptoms, or "seven keys," in Chapter 7. In Chapters 8 and 9, we discuss the applications of our understandings and the technique to working with surgical patients. In Chapter 10, we cover the treatment of persistent pain, and Chapter 11 covers self-hypnosis.

Part III

Chapters 12 through 16 present detailed case transcripts. These transcripts show the actual use of the technique for resolving specific psychosomatic symptoms.

[handwritten annotation: 1. "FIXED IDEAS WILL MAKE A PERSON SICK" 2. VIOLATING THEM WILL MAKE THE PERSON ANXIOUS 3. SO THESE FIXED IDEAS REMAIN INVIOLATE AND FIXED IN PLACE]

BACKGROUND

As a medical doctor, I (DME) initially became interested in hypnosis after three things occurred. First, I was cured of something myself in a hypnotic trance. Second, my first hypnosis case was a spectacular success. Third, I came to realize that fixed ideas will make a person sick, and violating them will make people anxious, so these fixed ideas remain inviolate and fixed in place.

From the time I was 12 years old, I had a chronic sinusitis. It was actually a vasomotor rhinitis. I couldn't breathe through my nose from the age of 12 until my 30s. Every second or third winter, the swelling would stop up the foramen that drains the sinuses and they would have to fracture into my sinuses and drain the pus out of them.

When I was in my thirties, I attended a hypnosis workshop and volunteered to be a demonstration subject. I asked the instructor if he could do anything about my sinusitis. He took me back to the first time this sinusitis was a problem using hypnotic age regression. We went back to when I was 12 years old and I had a really bad case of sinusitis at that time. I had a headache worse than any pain I had ever had. I had always been an obedient little boy, and this was the first time in my life that I made no attempt to control myself. I was screaming and yelling and my parents brought me to their bed to console me.

Finally at around midnight Saturday night, my parents called our ENT doctor for a house call. Dr. L. was the Chief of ENT at Tulane University Medical School, Chief of ENT at Ochsner Clinic, and the President of the American Academy of Otolaryngology. He was past the time of making house calls but he had been my father's roommate in college and he came.

I was reviewing and reliving these memories in hypnotic regression. "So Dr. L. examined me", and the instructor leans down and asks me, "What does he find?" I answered in trance, "He says I have a terrible case of sinusitis." Instructor: "He'd better find that hadn't he? But, you don't have to have a stuffy nose now to prove that you're not a bad boy, do you?"

Well, I immediately felt my nasal passages open up. I took my nasal spray out of my pocket and put it on the table, saying "I don't need this anymore." Ever since then, I know that if my nose gets stuffy, this signals me that I am feeling guilty about something. So, I can do self-hypnoanalysis and find out what I am feeling guilty about. Thus, the symptom actually becomes an asset. That is because it is specific to a certain emotion and it helps me understand what I am feeling emotionally. Once I've remedied what I've been feeling guilty about, I no longer need the symptom. For example, perhaps I failed to write a thank-you note and it's playing in the back of mind. Once I know what it is and remediate it, I am not guilty anymore and I no longer need the symptom.

Having had the experience of being cured of such a persistently aggravating disorder, I acquired a new attitude that makes me sincerely believe that my patients have the capacity to solve their problems too. In our training workshops and seminars, we tend to emphasize the importance of the patient's believing with conviction the therapy's potential to help him or her heal. However, we often do not put as much emphasis on the therapist's convictions. In 1922, Emile Coué said [Coué] "Conviction is as necessary to the suggester as to his subject. It is this conviction, this faith, that enables him to obtain results where all other means have failed." The Bible says (First Corinthians 14:8): "For if the [Corin 14:8 if the trumpet gives an uncertain sound...] trumpet give an uncertain sound, who shall prepare himself to the battle?"

After my first basic course in hypnosis, my first case was a 6-year-old child with a seizure disorder. His mother told me that his seizures lasted for 20 to 30 minutes at a time. They had started 8 or 9 months earlier, and he had been diagnosed with epilepsy and was on phenobarbital and Dilantin without benefit. He was still having seizures about twice a week. I told her that this sounded strange because a typical epileptic seizure lasts less than a minute. I also mentioned that the next time her son had an episode, I wanted to observe it, since they lived only five minutes away.

The very next day I got a call and this child was in bed with eyes rolled up having tonic activity of all extremities and rolling from side to side on the bed. I put a hand on his shoulder and asked, "Wes, are you trying to tell us something?" He opened his eyes and said "Yes!" I didn't think this was the proper venue to do therapy so I told him, "Good, your mother will bring you to my office tomorrow and you can tell me all about it."

The next day, Wes went easily into trance and told me that his whole family had gone to the emergency room with his first cousin who was having convulsions (due to spinal meningitis), and his cousin died in the emergency room. It became clear the little boy was hallucinating that his deceased cousin Eddie was coming back to take him with him—what we would now call "identifying" with Eddie.

I separated the identification and told Wes that "you are old enough to understand that Eddie is dead and you are alive, and you and Eddie are two totally separate people. Wouldn't it be better to keep your happy memories of Eddie and keep on growing and living a normal life?" Wes opened his eyes and came out of trance and hugged me and said "yes, that's what I want."

I have a 40-year follow-up and he has never had another seizure.

I had an uncle who was a lay hypnotist at the turn of the century. Although he died before I was born, I grew up hearing many stories about his demonstrations and was cautioned many times never to let anyone hypnotize me. This led me as an adult to develop some curiosity about what hypnosis really was.

At the first hypnosis weekend workshop I attended, there was a group induction. I thought I was resisting allowing myself to be hypnotized, but I apparently did drift into trance. Almost immediately, I became quite anxious, nauseated, and had to leave and go to the men's room to vomit.

I had violated a fixed idea that had been imprinted in my subconscious during my childhood. Over the years, I have realized that what we call "resistance" is often a patient's subconscious way of protecting himself against the anxiety of violating his own fixed idea. Resistance has to be worked with therapeutically. Identifying the fixed idea without violating it and presenting better choices is often the key to healing.

too BiG A group someone could become anxious

One of the things I have learned through the years is that I am very careful and even reluctant to do group inductions. This is because if the audience is large enough, there is probably going to be somebody who will have an anxiety attack. And if you think there can be nothing wrong doing a group imagery of going to the beach for example, think again. There is going to be someone there who had a near-drowning. And if you think there can be nothing wrong to take the group to a peaceful forest glen, there is going to be someone in the group who has been bitten by a snake.

% in a group who may have had a neg. experience

In one of my courses with the medical students at Tulane, I thought I could take the group and have each person go to his or her own "laughing place". So I said "you start with a big smile on your face like a clown. Just feeling great." And I always announce before I do a group induction that if anyone has a problem they should feel free to contact me and we will work it out. Well, sure enough, a student had an anxiety attack. I saw her privately later on. She regressed to being three years old. At that time, she had a birthday, and a fellow had a little traveling merry-go-round on the back of his truck and he dressed like a clown. Well, she rode on his merry-go-round and she fell off the truck! And this guy with a big smile on his clown face was picking her up. It was not a good association.

So, even when you think you are doing the most benign imagery, you can run into trouble. Therefore, I am rather leery of group inductions.

It didn't surprise me (DME) that in the Hilgards' studies with the Stanford Hypnotic Susceptibility Scale (Hilgard & Hilgard, 1994), 6 percent of their students, when they came out of taking the test, had headaches. Why would taking a hypnotic susceptibility test that includes a simple induction give you a headache?

As a clinical psychologist, I (BNE) have always been interested in the reasons why people do what they do, and how they do what they do and experience what they experience. I have always believed that every behavior has a reason even though we may not always know what the reasons, or determinants are. Rapid hypnoanalysis enables us to help our patients understand how and why they have been experiencing what they have been experiencing. It enables us to find reasons for symptoms and better solutions to our patient's problem. That is why I became involved in the practice of this remarkable technique of hypnotherapy, and why I chose to help Dr. Ewin write this book.

In the last 15 years, managed care and its exclusive focus on "cost efficient" psychological treatment has come to dominate the mental health field. As a result, psychotherapies have been made briefer at the expense of deeper. Briefer is desirable, but superficial is not. Yet, superficial "quick fix" therapies have come into favor. One problem is that many of these therapies have become the equivalent of applying a pressure tourniquet to a gunshot wound! Yes, you first have to stop the bleeding, but then you need to clean out the wound and repair the tissue damage.

When behavior change and symptomatic relief are focused on to the exclusion of insight and changing beliefs, the results of the therapy are often superficial. The majority of adjustment problems people have are relatable to their subconscious beliefs and fixed ideas.

In today's managed mental health care environment, clinical hypnosis has become popular as a tool for alleviating symptoms quickly. The emphasis has often been placed on suggestive and behavioral approaches which have limited utility with deep-rooted problems. Unfortunately, many presenting problems are deep-rooted problems.

After having experimented with a wide range of rapid, behavioral and symptom oriented therapy techniques and approaches (Eimer, 1988; Eimer & Freeman, 1998), I (BNE) became aware years ago that something deeper was needed. I searched the literature and came up with the work of David Cheek and Leslie LeCron (Cheek, 1994; Cheek & LeCron, 1968) who pioneered the hypnoanalytic approach covered in this book. I later met my co-author (DME) at a clinical hypnosis conference and we became friends. Under his tutelage, I discovered firsthand, the power of clinical hypnosis and hypnoanalysis for uncovering pathogenic, fixed ideas and changing them.

While modern "cognitive" approaches to brief therapy purport to address fixed beliefs which they term "schemas" and "core beliefs," these approaches often require a year or more to work with people who are very depressed or who have personality disorders (Eimer, 1989; Eimer & Freeman, 1998). I have discovered that one of the major shortcomings of the cognitive-behavioral approach is its almost exclusive focus on the conscious part of the mind. The problem with cognitive therapy is that it is too cognitive! It largely emphasizes "left brain" thinking and behavioral strategies.

Quite to the contrary, most psychological problems are difficult to change because they are imprinted in the "right brain." So, to access and change these "imprints," what is needed is a way to access state-dependent memories (Rossi, 1993; Rossi & Cheek, 1988) stored in the brain's right hemisphere, release the attendant affect, and then change or reframe these memories, thus creating new memories at the cellular level (Rossi, 2002).

Rapid Hypnoanalysis is a technique developed by Cheek and LeCron (1968), and refined by my co-author (DME) over the past 30 years. It makes it possible to accomplish the above with elegance. It puts the feeling back into brief therapy without taking out the logic or the efficiency. It addresses the whole brain.

I (BNE) have discovered through personal experience that Rapid Hypnoanalysis works. It can help both the healer and the healer's patients. When the healer is healed, it gives the healer conviction in the value of what he is doing. Much of that conviction has been losing steam over the past 15 years as treatment manual guided, "empirically validated therapies" focus exclusively on behaviors and conscious automatic thoughts. Rapid hypnoanalysis offers a refreshing alternative that allows therapists to go deeper while being even briefer. Rapid hypnoanalysis is not difficult to learn to practice and is very satisfying to practice because you get to see results.

B.N.E.

A major shortcoming of cognitive-behavioral approach is its almost exclusive focus on the "left brain", conscious part of the brain

INTRODUCTION

The technique we describe in this book is applicable to treating sane patients with psychoneurotic disorders. It is a method of doing deep therapy briefly using hypnosis. Sigmund Freud abandoned hypnosis early in his career because his hypnotic method was to employ direct suggestions and authoritative hypnosis. He found that his suggestions just wouldn't hold and he got symptom substitution. His problem, at the time he was using hypnosis, was that his technique didn't help the patient develop any understanding of what the problem was. Freud's emphasis on sex overlooked the fact that reproduction is only the second law of nature, and the first is self-preservation. It was good that Freud wasn't a good hypnotist and went on to develop deeper understanding of psychodynamics through psychoanalysis.

Our technique helps us uncover and reframe the pathogenic fixed idea/s underlying the patient's problem and symptoms. We have found that by analyzing when and where the symptom started, and under what circumstances, we have been able to achieve long-term cures for many presenting problems in about five visits.

Nothing Happens for No Reason at All. Nothing happens for no reason at all. There's a reason why somebody has got a headache. There's a reason for whatever goes on. In psychosomatic problems, such as headaches, itching, stomach aches, irritable bowel, chronic coughs, and asthma, the "reason" is usually subconscious, and the patient cannot verbalize it. The patient doesn't know what the reason is. But all behavior, and all symptoms have a reason.

We view it as our job to find the reason and reframe it–to appropriately *re-interpret* the need for the presenting dysfunctional behavior. This can then lead to replacing the symptom with a more appropriate functional behavior, or helping the patient accept that the behavior can be modified or eliminated without the necessity of replacing it.

Symptoms as Inappropriate Coping Methods. Symptoms and symptomatic behavior are viewed as inappropriate, negative coping methods; leftover dysfunctional behaviors that started as a way of coping with some stressful situation (Zarren & Eimer, 2002). They continued because of repetitious imprinting and habit formation. When they are no longer needed as methods of coping with external reality, they are behavioral remnants from the past. They are viewed as a continuing attempt to cope with an old emotional wound in a manner that is no longer needed.

Throughout this book, we use the term *subconscious* rather than *unconscious* because some patients assign a negative connotation to the term "unconscious." By "subconscious" we refer to the nonverbal part of the mind that is involved in implicit learning. The patient knows it, feels it, believes it, and acts on it, but cannot express it verbally. It is usually associated with the right hemisphere of the brain and self-preservation.

It is the duty of the subconscious mind to protect the person. Sometimes we call it "instinct." Sometimes we call subconscious responses "intuitive" or "reflexive." Once you've heard the screech of brakes, you have an implicit, self-protective, mental and muscular reflex to the next screech, even if it's way down the street.

We know that when we change an idea, we can often change an illness. It is in the subconscious that fixed ideas are imprinted and reside. Insight-oriented psychotherapy is often more effective and permanent in facilitating change than suggestive and behaviorally-oriented therapies. This is because insight-oriented therapy addresses the subconscious fixed ideas that keep people from getting well.

When we do rapid hypnoanalysis, we want to find out what fixed idea the patient is clinging to that is making him or her sick. Often, it is NOT what seems apparent to the therapist or the patient's family, nor is it consciously available to the patient. After setting up ideomotor signals as described below in detail, our first request for an ideomotor response (IM) is *"Is it all right with your deepest feeling mind for me to help you with this problem?"* The usual (sometimes hesitant) "yes" response to this seems to seal the therapeutic alliance, and in our experience, therapy then proceeds more easily.

After this, we can start right in to questioning the patient about the seven common causes of psychosomatic illness so well described by Cheek and LeCron (1968). These are "conflict, organ language, motivation, past experience, identification, self-punishment and suggestion."

Most pliable at the moment of insight!
*Each session ends c̄ debrief * Note may still be in lt Tran,*
Light Trance *Introduction* xxi

The optimum time to reframe the pathogenic fixed idea is when it is first identified–it is most pliable at the moment of insight! Often, we are able to accomplish successful therapy with this technique in 3 to 5 visits. *Office Visits*

The first visit is devoted to conducting the intake evaluation and giving the patient his or her first brief experience of a hypnotic induction. The second and third visits focus on uncovering, identifying and reframing the fixed idea/s that have been hinted at in the intake. IM signals are set up in the second visit and are employed for reviewing the patient's sensitizing experiences and diagnosing the fixed idea/s. The information obtained in the intake is drawn on and consolidated into the analysis.

Each session is ended by debriefing and verbally processing the session with the patient who, at that point, may still be in a light trance state. The fourth or fifth session is devoted to debriefing with the patient about the therapy and consolidating any remaining unfinished business into the reframed fixed idea/s. If it is indicated, we make a personal self-hypnosis tape for reinforcement at home.

On occasion, it is possible to conduct a "marathon session" (3 to 5 hours) in which all 4 or 5 of the above sessions are combined into one long session. Marathon therapy has the added advantage of really "striking while the iron is hot."

This approach is not like psychoanalysis in terms of aiming to change the overall personality. It is directed at one specific problem at a time with attention being devoted to solving that problem. For example, if a patient comes in with a number of complaints such as migraines, obesity, and insomnia, we ask the patient the following: *"If you could solve only one problem right now, which would it be?"* All the succeeding questions in the intake are built around the initial question, *"Tell me about your problem."*

We do this so that we can have a goal by which we can measure success. Frequently in the process of getting to this goal, some of the co-existing problems clear up too.

A useful metaphor for this approach is a computer metaphor. The patient comes in with a complaint or series of complaints that, unbeknownst to the patient, are driven by a pathogenic fixed idea. This is analogous to a bad line in a computer program that gives an error message every time the program is run. The cure is to find the bad line and to correct it.

Milton Erickson said "the symptom is a solution" (Erickson, 1986). We need to find the very FIRST time the patient subconsciously got the idea that the headache, cough, etc., (whatever the symptom is) was a solution, rather than the problem that it is now. The goal is to help the patient accept on a feeling level that even though it may have worked at a time in the past, it now has outlived its usefulness and no longer has any value.

ACKNOWLEDGMENTS

We gratefully acknowledge our patients who have entrusted us with their secrets in the hope that we might help them obtain relief from their symptoms. In our efforts to help them, we continue to gain valuable experience that we can pass on to our students. We also thank our students whose questions continue to stimulate our search for more efficient and compassionate ways of helping. Teaching and doing therapy and hypnosis keep us young. We are grateful to our students and our patients for teaching us.

Bringing a good book to fruition requires the help of a good publisher. We gratefully acknowledge Michael Thomas of Charles C Thomas for recognizing the value of this work and continuing to support this project.

We also gratefully acknowledge the expert assistance of Claire Slagle who made our manuscript more readable.

We both express our heartfelt appreciation to David B. Cheek, M.D., the father of modern ideomotor hypnoanalysis techniques, for his kind and gentle guidance as a mentor and friend to both of us.

Last but not least, we thank our families, my (DME) wife Marilyn, and my (BNE) wife Andrea, and my (BNE) mother Cecile, for their loving support and encouragement.

Disclaimer

The clinical evaluation and treatment methods described in this book are NOT intended as substitutes for appropriate, individual, medical, psychiatric, or psychological, evaluation and care. This book is NOT intended to replace the professional recommendations of licensed physicians and other licensed health professionals who are familiar with a given case. If expert medical or psychological assistance, counseling, therapy, or hypnosis are needed, the services of a competent health professional should be sought.

This book is designed to provide accurate and authoritative information in regard to the subject matter covered; clinical hypnosis and hypnoanalysis. It is intended to offer usable information that can enhance the effectiveness of the reader/clinician in helping his or her patients.

However, it is written and sold with the understanding that no book can replace attendance at live workshops, individual supervision and consultation, clinical experience, and therapy.

Although this book is intended primarily for experienced health care clinicians, as a source of practical, usable information about how to do hypnoanalysis using ideomotor methods, we recognize that this book may be of interest to the intelligent layperson with an interest in hypnosis.

However, we do not support the *lay* practice of hypnosis, or the training of *laypersons* in the use of hypnosis. By "practice" we mean providing hypnosis, or offering to do so, to individuals or groups, whether for a fee or for free. By "layperson" we mean a person (a) with NO accredited professional education or clinical training in a licensed health care discipline, and (b) who has NOT pursued a degree, from a regionally accredited institution, in a recognized, professional health care discipline.

Note that the identities of all patients described in the case examples and transcripts presented in this book have been disguised to protect and preserve patient confidentiality.

For simplicity, throughout this book, instead of using "he/she" and "his/her" to refer to a single patient, we will use the male pronoun.

Dabney M. Ewin
Bruce N. Eimer

CONTENTS

IDEOMOTOR SIGNALS FOR RAPID HYPNOANALYSIS

PART I
BASIC CONCEPTS

Chapter 1

IDEOMOTOR SIGNALS: THEIR VALUE IN HYPNOTHERAPY

One of the casualties of the limited time in our basic workshops is that we must gloss over the remarkable value of ideomotor (IM) signals, noting only that they can be useful, giving a short demonstration, and admonishing participants to read about the details of the technique. It is easy, the uses are many, and the time use is efficient.

IM signals are body language, and anyone can read the "yes" and "no" language of ideomotor signals, as opposed to the complicated art of reading body language in general, which is a science unto itself. In the diagnosis and treatment of nearly every patient, there is a place for this form of nonverbal communication.

Insight-Oriented Therapy. Insight-Oriented Therapy is often much more effective and permanent than direct or indirect suggestion. We know that when we can change an idea, we change an illness. But what is the fixed idea that the patient clings to that makes him sick? Often, it is NOT what seems apparent to the therapist or the patient's family, and it is not consciously available to the patient.

Repeating for emphasis what we said before, our first request for an ideomotor response is to ask, *Is it all right with your deepest feeling mind for me to help you with this problem?* The usual (sometimes hesitant) "yes" response to this seems to seal the therapeutic alliance, and in our experience, therapy goes more easily than it did before we started using this as an opening question.

After this, we can start right into questioning about the seven common causes of psychosomatic illness so well described by Cheek and LeCron (1968). These are conflict, organ language, motivation, past experience, identification, self-punishment, and suggestion. The optimum time to reframe the idea is when it is first identified—it is most pliable at the moment of insight!

Deepening Trance. Deepening trance with these signals saves valuable treatment time. While we are setting up each signal, we add: *And every time your feelings answer a question you will become more aware of your deepest, most heartfelt feelings.* It is unnecessary to spend further time on deepening, because deepening progresses with each answer about the seven common causes.

Repetitive Subconscious Review. Repetitive subconscious review of a memory occurs when searching for the date of origin of a fixed idea. In order to give an ideomotor answer "yes" to the question, *Did it happen before age 20?* the patient must first do a subconscious review of some sort. Then, *Before 10?* and *Before 5?* to the "no" at age four, means the patient has done four subconscious reviews of the experience before even focusing in on what happened at age four. This makes the subsequent regression to age four much easier for the patient. Note that numbers are emotionally neutral and are not repressed.

Confirming Depth of Trance. Confirming depth of trance is useful. If therapy has been going slowly, we may open a session with an eye-roll induction and the suggestion, *Each breath you take, you will go deeper and deeper, and when you are deep enough to solve this problem, your "yes" finger will rise.* It may take two or three minutes of silence before the "yes" finger rises, and the patient is often in such a deep trance, that he is unaware that it rose. For that reason, we always touch the finger and push it back down so the patient gets both tactile and verbal feedback from the therapist.

That's right, you know that you are deep enough to solve this problem, and as we approach it together, I'll make sure that you are safe.

Incomplete Therapy. Incomplete therapy can result in apparent failure (erroneous). When we think we have solved the problem, we need agreement from the patient and wholehearted acceptance of the new idea. Before alerting, we ask, *Is there any other problem you feel we should deal with that might keep you from getting well?* A "yes" signal to this requires attention. Most often the last sticking point is a reservation or fear of expecting good things because of previous disappointments. We counter this by pointing out that there's no need to be optimistic or pessimistic. We ask, *Would it be all right to just be neutral, and see what happens?* A "yes" signal to this question lets therapy end on a good note.

Regression to Preverbal Memories. Regression to preverbal memories cannot be done in the waking state, but subconscious ideomotor review will bring to consciousness what the patient believes happened. We know that if a person believes something to be true, it IS true for him, and he will behave as if it were true. It is depressing for a girl to be born believing that her parents wanted a boy. An unwanted child often suffers, even if adopted at birth. The human personality is molded during the first few years of life, and hurtful ideas from those early years can be explored and reframed after identifying them with ideomotor review.

Hearing Under Anesthesia. Hearing under general anesthesia has been confirmed experimentally to the satisfaction of all of us who do not belong to the flat earth society. Bennett's (1988) human studies with blinded tape recordings of operating room sounds for verification are seminal. Weinberger et al. (1984) demonstrated that one can do Pavlovian conditioning of rats to a sound heard under general anesthesia. Skeptics attribute recall to insufficient anesthetic, and that is plausible in the cases where what was heard can be recalled verbally in or out of trance. Experimenters who fail to get recall in hypnosis simply ask for verbal responses, and do not use ideomotor review.

David Cheek developed the ideomotor technique for recall (Cheek, 1959, 1960c, 1962a, 1962b, 1962c, 1962d, 1964, 1966a, 1981, 1994) and I (DME) wrote it up in detail (Ewin, 1990). If you're having a hernia operation and hear your surgeon say "Uh oh!" can you imagine ignoring that as meaningless (even though he may have simply dropped a hemostat)?

When an otherwise good and supposedly curative operation leaves a patient with a painful scar, post-operative depression, or other unexpected residual symptoms, it is appropriate to do an ideomotor review for sounds heard under anesthesia that might have left an imprint.

Dream Interpretation. Dream interpretation can be enhanced nicely with ideomotor signals when the meaning is not readily apparent. By asking for "yes" or "no" answers about the emotional tone—is it fear, anger, sadness, frustration, etc., the stage is set. Who are the people in the dream—self, father, mother, spouse, God, etc. What triggered the dream? Is it something current, or was it from long ago?

One of the most valuable uses is for self-analysis. We find it easy to set up our own ideomotor signals and use them to analyze our own dreams. If a dream wakes one in the morning, one can use ideomotor signals while it's fresh and one is still half asleep, and should not leave it until he feels he understands the message the dream was imparting (sometimes not much of anything).

Suicide Prevention. Suicide prevention may help the therapist more than the patient. We don't treat patients who are clearly suicidal. We refer them to a hospital-based psychiatrist. But some patients worry us. They're not sick enough to make a big deal over sending them to the hospital, but they seem fragile enough that some untoward event might push them over the edge. We dread getting a phone call that the worst has happened. If a patient starts talking about "ending it all," but has no plan of action and is not really convincing, we can induce a good trance and ask for ideomotor assent to the question, *No matter how bad you may feel, will you agree to let it be IMPOSSIBLE to take action against yourself without first contacting me or whoever is on call for me?*

If we cannot get a "yes" to that question, we must refer. If we get a clear "yes," we can sleep well. In our combined 65 years of practice, neither of us has lost a patient to suicide (to our knowledge).

Chapter 2

PRINCIPLES OF HYPNOTHERAPY

If [affordable] psychotherapy is ever going to come to the public,
it will have to be through hypnosis.

–Sigmund Freud

When a patient is reacting to a situation in a dysfunctional way, it's the psychotherapist's goal to help the patient find better choices. Early on in the movie *Forrest Gump,* the little crippled boy Forrest is being chased by a bunch of bullies throwing rocks at him. He is in a terrified, emotionally focused state (hypnoidal) not knowing what to do. His little girlfriend shouts "Run, Forrest, run!" He does run and he gets away. This acts as an imprint (fixed idea), and from then on, he has a subconscious solution when faced with stress–he runs. While this was effective at the time the idea was implanted, it quickly outlived its usefulness. What started as a solution ends up becoming a symptom, and later in the movie, Forrest is shown running across the entire United States, ending up exhausted. He needs better choices.

The Symptom as a Solution

This brings to mind Milton Erickson's comment mentioned earlier that "the symptom is a solution" (Erickson, 1986), but it is a solution to something that happened long ago, and it is inappropriate to the stress at hand. In other words, the symptom has outlived its usefulness as a solution. As clinicians, when we get ready to diagnose and treat the symptom, *we have to find out what problem this symptom would solve and under what circumstances it originated.*

9

Symptoms occur when something in the internal or external environment triggers a memory. This invokes the original state in which the symptom was imprinted, and the symptom is triggered as a conditioned response. We assume that when the original or sensitizing event occurred, the patient experienced a powerful emotion (e.g., fear, guilt, sadness) that was appropriate at the time. This powerful emotion was imprinted in the patient's subconscious.

Subsequent events that the patient perceived and experienced as similar to the originating event activated similar emotions which were further imprinted in the patient's subconscious by repetition. Even though the originating circumstances are no longer happening, similar emotions continue to occur along with similar attempts to cope with the anxiety. The patient's original choice of coping may have been appropriate at the time, or may have been the only choice available then. However, at the time the patient seeks our help, this form of coping has become dysfunctional, and a problem for the patient.

Body Language

All body language; every frown, nod, smile, crossed arms and legs, etc., is a form of subconscious, nonverbal communication. Reading body language is a science unto itself because each person has his own. Body language expresses feelings that you are not consciously aware of, or that you want to withhold. It conveys a person's true feelings, and it may affirm what a person is saying, or may contradict it. As such, it is an essential ingredient in our therapeutic search for the "fixed idea."

Ideomotor Responses

Ideomotor (IM) signals as we use them in hypnosis (e.g., *yes* and *no*) are simply a form of directed body language that most people can read without studying the science of body language. Whether we are "high hypnotizables," "medium hypnotizables," or "low hypnotizables" (Spiegel & Spiegel, 1987), we all have body language, and we all have "yes" or "no." Each person has his own body language. Different movements mean different things to different people. For example, one person may wrinkle his forehead when he says something he doesn't believe, while another might smirk or blink. Regardless of other differences, head nodding is an almost universal body language for "Yes," and head shaking for "No."'

Ideomotor. Ideomotor means that a subconscious idea is being expressed as an involuntary or automatic motor signal. In hypnosis, we can specify that raising one finger means you feel "yes," and a different finger means you feel "no."

Ideosensory. *Ideosensory* means that a subconscious idea is being translated, or transmuted into a sensation or feeling. Sometimes when ideomotor responses don't seem to be working, we can tell the patient that if there is a feeling such as a tingling, or just an awareness of the "yes" or "no" finger, to consciously raise it so that it can be seen. This works just as well as good ideomotor responses.

The Pathogenic Fixed Idea

Underlying most psychosomatic disorders is a fixed idea that was imprinted at some emotionally focused time in the patient's life. It could be the patient's own idea or one introduced by some other person. Often, it's a simplistic, child-like solution to an immediate perceived danger. It's survival oriented. For example:

Case 1. A teenage boy has been secretly smoking for a year. He decides to light up right in front of his parents after dinner. This can be a highly emotional moment with the boy prepared to defy his father, who smokes. Instead of becoming angry, the father says, "Oh son, don't start smoking, because you'll never be able to quit." The boy has already started a year ago and so, what the father has inadvertently implanted is the fixed idea that *you'll never be able to quit,* which is already the father's problem. This patient starts his intake by saying "I can't quit smoking."

Case 2. A man falls off a roof and sustains a concussion. While he is falling he is afraid he will die. He has a terrible headache and in the stupor, this is the only way that he knows he is still alive. He subconsciously gives himself the idea that *as long as I am aware (i.e., have the headache) I can't be dead yet.* When he comes out of the stupor, and has all the usual ways to know he's alive, his protective subconscious continues to reassure him that he is alive by maintaining the headache. The symptom is a solution only in terms of "trance logic."

Remember, however, that not all fixed ideas are dysfunctional. For example, the first law of hypnosis is "never start an induction if the

therapist or the patient needs to go to the restroom." This is an imprinted fixed idea from our earliest toilet training; "don't wet your pants."
The subconscious attempt to control this will likely override whatever
is going on in the therapy.

Listen to Your Patient and Use the Patient's Own Words

Left-brain thinking is turned off in a good trance. We know that in a
good trance, a subject will not *initiate* speech, but will reply when told
to, or when asked a question.

The right brain thinks in pictures and the verbal left brain puts a title
under it. The right brain is used to getting its verbal input from its own
left hemisphere. So, if the patient's left hemisphere is turned off, then
the therapist's voice becomes the verbal input and the source of the
title under the patient's picture (Pedersen, 1984, 1994). Miscommunica-
tion can occur because some 70 percent of the words in Webster's Dic-
tionary have more than one meaning.

I (BNE) had a patient who was talking to his son and referred to his
son's friend as "bad," meaning "no good." However, his son took that to
mean that his friend was "cool." This patient was working on improving
his rapport with his son and we had to work on his developing a better
understanding of his son's language. So, in talking with someone, we
may both use the same word, but not be thinking about the same thing.

One of the lessons we must learn from that is to listen to our patient,
because he's telling us his picture, and putting a title under it. Keeping
this in mind, if the patient tells you, "I stammer," don't talk to him
about "stuttering," because that brings up another picture. He stam-
mers and other people stutter. The fact that you may consider them
synonyms is meaningless to the patient at a subconscious level. So,
always use your patient's own words when you are talking to him.

Remember that, from our first contact with our patient, we are talking to both his conscious and subconscious mind (left and right brain).
This also means that when we are taking the patient's history, we need
a double diagnosis. When the patient says that he has asthma, or
migraines, or leg or back pain, that's what he's told the last ten doctors.
We know what a migraine or an asthma attack is like. We need to formulate a psychodynamic diagnosis. We want to know whether it's a
conflict, an imprint, or any of the other seven causes we will discuss.

When the patient is giving us a history, he is giving us two histories.
The patient's left brain is communicating with our left brain in words

and titles. At the same time, if we are alert to it, his right brain is communicating by his tone of voice, his facial expression, his tears, his crossed arms, and so forth. That's the second history. Sir William Osler, the father of medicine in America, said, "Listen to your patient. He's telling you his diagnosis." Listen left brain and listen right brain.

When you hear a patient rationalizing, and you spot it, what he said is not the truth. It tells us that we need to find out what the truth really is. For example, a person who is phobic of elevators, and walks up ten flights of stairs, may say he does it to get exercise. Usually, people who exercise regularly have a planned program, but he only walks up ten flights when he wants to get to the tenth floor! That is not an exercise program. It is a rationalization of why he avoids the elevator. When we resolve his fear of elevators, he'll no longer need the rationalization, and he no longer will need to walk up the ten flights.

Left Brain versus Right-Brain Thinking

"Left-brain thinking" is verbal, logical, abstract, temporally oriented, analytic, planned, and optimistic. It is one of the things that is distinctly human and constitutes the human characteristic of consciousness called "the will."

In contrast, "right-brain thinking" is nonverbal, illogical, concrete, immediate, reflexive, global and synthetic, intuitive and instinctive, creative, emotional, sensual, and inherently pessimistic. We share this with the rest of the animal kingdom, and all of these attributes are involved in "the imagination." Animals communicate nonverbally with all five senses.

The right brain is survival oriented. When survival is at risk, we shift into right-brain thinking. The reason we have fire drills is to turn left brain, logical knowledge into right brain, automatic behavior. In an emergency, when the "fight or flight response" is triggered, if there is a lack of effective prior training in what to do, we will revert to ineffective, illogical, and instinctual responses. An old U.S. Marine slogan (read suggestion) states that "to fail to plan is to plan to fail." So, we use our left brain to develop a logical plan to get to safety, and then we train to implement that plan automatically and reflexively, if it is ever needed in a real emergency.

Military and law enforcement firearm training (Rementer & Eimer, 2005), requires lots of technical and practical left-brain knowledge, and then lots of practice applying that knowledge in the performance of reality-based drills. These drills prepare the professional to automatically apply the logical knowledge in a life or death, critical incident. In crisis, adrenaline is pouring into the bloodstream, the heart is pumping faster, and blood is being shunted to large muscles for quick gross motor action. In such an event, the military or law enforcement professional who has a logical plan, and who has been well-trained to reflexively implement it, will survive an assault.

The subconscious is smart about what it's smart about and dumb about what it's dumb about (O'Hanlon & Martin, 1992). What this says is that there is no wise, all knowing subconscious that hasn't already been trained. In ordinary life, the subconscious can perceive danger where it doesn't exist and keep us in a state of hypervigilant anxiety.

Preparing the Patient for Hypnosis

It is important for both you and the patient to create in the waking state some logical sense about what is going to happen. This creates a mindset for accepting what happens in hypnosis—an "anticipatory trance state" (Zarren & Eimer, 2002). Leo Alexander's (1971) paper on "pre-hypnotic suggestion" described a difficult intake on a patient who stuttered very badly. He told the patient, *We can make this easy for you. I will hypnotize you and you will be able to give me your history easily without stuttering.* This is exactly what happened. All stutterers have periods when they don't stutter at all.

Lay mythology presents hypnosis as a master-slave relationship that may be threatening to people who are concerned about losing control. Such a counterproductive idea about what hypnosis is needs to be reframed at the outset of the hypnotic relationship. By "reframe," we mean change the way the patient thinks and feels about hypnosis so he understands that it is a collaborative teacher-student relationship.

We seek to prepare the patient for hypnosis by helping the patient to rethink, or reframe, beliefs, feelings, and behaviors that could inhibit his responsiveness and suggestibility. The goal is for the patient to have the expectation that he will be helped by participating in the hypnotic experience.

As in any teacher-student relationship, we have some "A" students, more "B" students, lots of "C" students, and rare "F" students who really don't want to learn. Our job as a teacher/therapist is to lead the patient to self-understanding, and help mobilize the patient's own assets and inner resources to solve the presenting problem, using hypnosis and language as tools. This discussion is essential for getting the patient on the right track and developing an acceptable level of rapport so that we can continue our work collaboratively.

The Law of Dominant Effect

Therapeutic hypnosis is about changing bad ideas to good ones in the subconscious. Obviously, we are all susceptible to forming good or bad fixed ideas. Emil Coué, the father of self-hypnosis, who taught patients *Self Mastery through Conscious Autosuggestion* (Coué, 1922), said that bad ideas come without effort, and our good ideas should come without effort also.

One of Coué's laws was the "Law of Dominant Effect," which stated that when the imagination (read, subconscious) and the will (read, conscious) are in conflict, the imagination tends to win. A corollary to that is that a stronger emotion always counteracts a weaker one. These principles inform our rationale for employing therapeutic hypnosis. Hypnosis makes it possible for good ideas to come without effort.

The elevator phobic person who walks up ten flights rather than take the elevator consciously says to himself, "get in the elevator, it's not dangerous, everyone else is." However, his unconscious says, "don't get in there!" He can get in, he can force himself in, but he'll have an anxiety attack—he'll be in the elevator with his pulse racing, in a cold sweat, pumping out adrenaline. In other words, he'll be violating the equivalent of a post-hypnotic suggestion, a fixed idea that he believes strongly. When he violates that fixed idea, he does so at the expense of his comfort. He has an anxiety attack. So, rather than bring on an anxiety attack, he'll understandably do almost anything else.

Hypnotizability and Trance Depth

Our hypnosis work is grounded in the belief that you do not need deep trance to do deep psychotherapeutic work for lasting change. Milton Erickson (1961) and David Cheek (1994) both believed that people "enter hypnosis as they mentally review sequential events" (Cheek, 1994, p. 1). Cheek (1994) wrote, *"A Hypnoidal state is entered when [remembering sequential events such as: recalling a tune, remembering the visual images of waves breaking on a beach, the movements of a candle flame, and the words of a poem"* (p. 1)]. Thus, a basic mechanism for inducing a *hypnotic altered state* is the review or processing of a sequence of sensory impressions or memories (Zarren & Eimer, 2002).

No Hypnotizability Testing. Our type of insight therapy differs from direct suggestion in hypnosis (DSIH) in a fundamental way. DSIH patients need to be chosen by their hypnotizability, and some "lows" may not even be candidates for hypnotherapy with DSIH. To the contrary, everyone communicates with body language, and ideomotor signals are just a directed form of body language, equally as useful for "lows" as for "highs." When we are going to use ideomotor signals, we rarely test for hypnotizability, because it is superfluous.

"Low hypnotizables" and "high hypnotizables" are both capable of communicating with body language, and the ideomotor analysis technique seems to work equally well regardless of a patient's suggestibility. We think that this is because the patient is being helped to solve his own problem by getting insight into a solution that is not dependent on the therapist's direct suggestion.

One of the standard tests of hypnotizability is the Spiegel Eye Roll Test (Spiegel & Spiegel, 1987/2004), which includes an open eye roll induction. Since we are going to use hypnosis and do ideomotor analysis, we don't test for hypnotizability, and we don't want an open eye roll test to lead us to make a prejudgment on what to expect from the patient hypnotically. If we have a low expectation, we're likely to get it. Therefore, we do a closed-eye-roll induction.

In fact, we prefer to treat "low hypnotizables" since, with "low hypnotizables," once we get a cure, it is long-term. This is because "low hypnotizables" are the least susceptible to future suggestions that could undo the new ideas that have been formed and accepted by their subconscious as a result of our treatment. On the other hand, "high hypnotizables," being very susceptible to waking and hypnotic suggestions, are susceptible to future waking suggestions that could undo the cure.

Both of us have had the experience of treating patients with migraine headaches who became better. Then, they have a subsequent experience that in the past would have caused a headache. Someone expresses surprise that the patient does not have a headache, and then they have a headache! "High hypnotizables" keep coming back to the hospital (Evans, 1991, 2001). With lows, once they get well, they tend to stay well.

The First Induction

We think it is important for the patient to experience a simple induction at the *first visit*. This seals the rapport because it communicates that we are going to do something different, and that hypnosis is both safe and easy. People are often scared and very curious when they first come to a hypnosis clinician. They usually come to our offices feeling that they've exhausted all other possibilities. They have been worked up and interrogated ad infinitum at other clinics, and are typically disillusioned with doctors. Therefore, if you want your new patient to show up for the next visit, it is important that you do more than just repeat what everyone else has done, which has been to conduct an intake and obtain the patient's history.

In the last five minutes of the intake, we typically say to the new patient: *I think you ought to experience what hypnosis feels like so you feel comfortable with it.*

We go through a simple induction with progressive relaxation, and then add some encouraging suggestions such as: *Some part of your mind knows that you can improve your life, and you'll find it easier and easier to get more comfortable and relaxed with every session.* Then, we alert the patient. Almost none of our patients fail to return after the first visit. The patient has come for hypnosis and has gotten hypnosis, and looks forward to the next visit.

"Imagination" versus "Daydreaming"

Hilgard (1986, 1991) described hypnosis as "believed-in imagination." We agree with this definition. However, we have learned to avoid using the words "imagine" and "imagery." It is not uncommon for psychosomatic patients to have already been told, "its all in your imagination," or "you're imagining things." As a result of what they've been told, the word "imagine" may be interpreted by their subconscious as meaning "to make up," or "it's not real." Thus, some patients dislike the word or resent it.

We don't know any difference between imagination and daydreaming, but most people think they control their daydreams, but not their imagination. Imaginations run wild. So, we tell patients, as we begin to do a trance induction, to *Just shift into daydream-type thinking. Just as we can daydream bad things, we can daydream good things.* Patients find this reframe very acceptable.

Relaxation Is Not Hypnosis

A mistaken idea is that relaxation is hypnosis. It is not hypnosis. Hypnosis is mental. Relaxation is physical. The mental part of hypnosis is very much like daydreaming. It is often called imaging, but we like to compare it to daydreaming, and everyone tends to daydream best when they are relaxed. So, these two ideas do go together.

When we get deeply relaxed, we are likely to drift off into daydreams; to shift into daydream-type thinking, and go into trance. Conversely, if we drift off into daydreaming, unless we are daydreaming something terrible, we are likely to get very relaxed.

A person can also be in deep trance and not be relaxed. For example, being in deep trance daydreaming that one's body is a board (body catalepsy), a person can then be placed across two chairs and have someone stand on him. He is not physically relaxed, but yet, he is deeply hypnotized. In the waking state, he would probably deny that he could do this.

"Habit"

"Habit" is repetitious activity without conscious thought (Zarren & Eimer, 2002). If a conscious choice is made, then it is not habit. Part of effective brief therapy for an undesirable habit is the suggestion, *Let it be impossible to . . . without first becoming aware and making a conscious choice.* For example, with nail biting, we might say, *Let it be impossible to put your fingers in your mouth to bite your nails without first looking at your hand and making a conscious choice.*

Now, we always want to make sure that the conscious choice is the positive alternative. For example: "Yes, I have a plan, to take care of my nails and do something else with my hands." In contrast, the negative choice would be: "Poor me. I'm helpless." In a free country, you can make a negative conscious choice, but it's still not habit.

Characteristics of the Trance State

An ordinary epileptic seizure lasts less than a minute, but in a condition known as status epilepticus, the generalized spasm continues indefinitely (including the muscles of respiration). Some of these people may die. It was found that on EEGs, these patients have reverberating circuits from one hemisphere to the other via the connecting tracts of nerve fibers known as the corpus callosum (Drislane, 1996).

Split Brain Studies. In animals, researchers found that they could surgically divide the corpus callosum, and the animals seemed to be normal (Gazzaniga, 1998; Ivry & Robertson, 1998; Tramo et al., 1995; Trevathern, 1990). In order to save lives, the procedure was done on humans in order to interrupt the reverberating circuits. The epilepsy cleared, and the patient seemed normal. For the first time, one could study how each hemisphere processed the same information without any input from the opposite hemisphere.

Roger Sperry and his associates won the Nobel Prize in 1981 when they set out to study these patients (Sperry, 1964; Trevathern, 1990). They found that each hemisphere processes the same incoming information differently (Hoptman & Davidson, 1994). The left hemisphere processes information in words, and the right hemisphere processes information in pictures and in all five senses. They found that the functions of the left hemisphere included speech, logic, abstract thinking, time keeping, analytical thought and optimism. They found that the functions of the nonverbal right hemisphere included imagination, intuition, thinking in pictures, controlling reflexes and instinctive behaviors, interpreting sounds, physical coordination, global and metaphorical thinking, seeing the big picture, emotionality, and pessimism.

Right-Brain Dominance in Trance

Sperry's work led to great interest in the study of the role of each hemisphere in controlling different states of mind (Hoptman & Davidson, 1994; Kolb & Wishaw, 1996). Hypnosis is an altered state of consciousness. One of the things that appears to happen when a person is in a hypnotic trance, is that the functions controlled by the right cerebral hemisphere, or the "right brain," become dominant, and the functions controlled by the left hemisphere, or "left brain," are relatively turned off or down (Watzlawick, 1978).

In a good trance, a person will not initiate speech, is undisturbed by logical incongruity (trance logic), thinks concretely as opposed to abstractly, thinks globally, overgeneralizes rather than analyzes, loses track of time, and tends toward pessimism unless directed otherwise. The left brain attributes are suppressed.

Therefore, when the patient is in trance, we have to remain very conscious of how we word things. Well-intentioned, but poorly thought out and worded statements tend to be accepted by the patient's subconscious mind in a way that is opposite of what is intended–that is to say, in a negative or pessimistic manner.

This is illustrated by something that happened when I (DME) was teaching a small group practice in a Basic Workshop. A woman had no partner, so I told her she could hypnotize me. She asked me what I enjoyed for leisure, and I told her I like to go fishing; so she took me on her idea of a fishing trip. She had me out in the middle of Lake Michigan, but in my imaging I was in my small bass boat that I use in the bayous of Louisiana. She said, "You're *sinking* deeper and deeper . . ." and as I visualized my boat going under and was up to my waist in the water, I alerted spontaneously feeling quite anxious.

Principles of Suggestion

A good suggestion is like a title of a picture. It should be short and preferably contain ten words or less. The classic ten words are Emil Coué's famous autosuggestion, *Every day, in every way, I'm getting better and better.* Repetition helps. For most direct suggestions, three repetitions suffice. Coué used twenty repetitions twice a day.

Suggestions should be worded so that they are set in the immediate future rather than in the present. This gives them time to be absorbed and take effect. For example, if we want to remove a headache, we would not say, "Your headache is gone." This would be contrary to the immediate fact that the patient still has a headache. Instead, we would use wording such as, "Your head will begin to clear and soon the ache will dwindle away and be gone." (Cheek & LeCron, 1968, p. 60).

Any suggestion changing physiology such as analgesia, coolness, warmth, appetite, etc., should have an end point such as, *until it is healed,* or *until you no longer need it.*

A question is often an indirect suggestion, and an indirect suggestion is usually better than a direct suggestion.

It is also important to reinforce the patient's motivation for the acceptance of an idea. For example, we would suggest to a smoking cessation patient that, *You came here today to become a nonsmoker, because you want to be a nonsmoker. Isn't that so? Therefore, when you leave here, you will no longer have any desire to smoke. You will no longer care for cigarettes, or want them at all. Smoking is not something you will ever want to do again.*

It is also a good idea to limit the number of ideas, or suggestions, you give at any one time to two or three, so as to avoid overburdening the subconscious.

Ambiguous Suggestions

Cheek's *Law of Pessimistic Interpretation* (Cheek, 1994) says that if a statement can be interpreted optimistically or pessimistically, a *frightened* person will interpret it pessimistically. When I (DME) go into the recovery room after surgery, I may hear the nurse say something like, "Wake up Mr. Jones. It's all over." That instruction is way too vague. The words, "it's all over," may be interpreted by the patient's subconscious as what happens at death and traumatize him. I (DME) say to the patient instead, "Mr. Jones, your operation is completed and you're okay." It is best to assume that every patient is frightened and to avoid ambiguous suggestions. Be precise in how you word your suggestions so that they cannot be misinterpreted.

For example, how many of us have had patients with persistent pain tell us that their doctor told them that they "have to learn to live with their pain"? In an emotionally focused state (i.e., in a naturalistic or spontaneous trance), the doorway to the patient's subconscious is open opened (Zarren & Eimer, 2002). A doctor's statement, often made in frustration, "you have to learn to live with your pain," is likely to be interpreted by the patient's subconscious as the iatrogenic suggestion, "the only way to get rid of the pain is to die"! This bad idea is what gets imprinted in the patient's subconscious.

The characteristics of left-brain thinking are all human characteristics; they are not shared with the rest of the animal kingdom. Ergo, the global, emotional, synthetic thinking of the right brain is primordial and archaic. It's survival oriented. In emotional or stressful situations, right-brain-type thinking tends to become dominant. As previously noted, we have fire drills so that in an emergency we don't have to think logically, because we have a plan that will automatically lead to safety. Emergency and law enforcement personnel are put through repetitive, emergency response training drills so that the desired responses become imprinted in muscle memory (Rementer & Eimer, 2005).

Avoid the Word Try!

Trying is the most logical thing you can do. If something isn't working, logic says that you should try harder. However, logic is in the left brain. The ordinary patient has already tried as hard as he can to solve the problem. If trying solved the problem, the patient would not be in our office. Visualize yourself in your dentist's office, and he says, "Try to relax." Trying takes effort. Relaxation is effortless. So, trying to relax is an oxymoron. How much better it would be if the dentist would just say "relax." We never use the word "try" unless we don't want it to happen! The Nike advertisement says, "Just do it!"

Emile Coué's *Law of Reversed Effect* (Coué, 1922) stated that if someone wants to do something but feels he can't, the harder he tries, the less he will be able to do it. Two common examples that involve trying to do something that nature will do for you effortlessly are trying to fall asleep and trying to have an erection.

Types of Suggestions

There are waking suggestions and hypnotic suggestions, and they both are most effective when they are short and bring up a picture. Waking suggestions are usually in the form of adages, such as "A stitch in time saves nine"; "Strike while the iron is hot"; and Ben Franklin's, "Early to bed, early to rise makes a man healthy, wealthy and wise." The best known hypnotic suggestion is once again, Emile Coué's classic auto-suggestion, *Every day in every way I'm getting better and better*–ten words! As stated above, repetition helps to fix a hypnotic suggestion in place in the subconscious, and three repetitions usually suffice.

Negative Suggestions

Negative suggestions should be avoided because the subconscious mind has no picture of something *not* happening. The normal reaction to *don't* think of an elephant is to first think of an elephant so you know what *not to do*. There are many positive verbs that directly imply an action that is the opposite of the undesirable action, such as, "You will reject"; "You will refuse"; "You will avoid"; "You will ignore"; or "Let it be impossible to . . ."

For example, your subconscious can picture "I reject a cigarette." On the other hand, if you suggest, *I won't want to smoke,* you have to first think about smoking to know what you need to avoid. The subconscious handles the statement *don't look in this hole* as though the *don't* were not in the sentence. If you pass it, you will almost invariably look in the hole!

Loss of Sense of Time In Trance

In a good trance, a person loses track of time. There is time distortion. This can be manipulated therapeutically. An hour of real clock time can feel like a few minutes, and conversely, a few seconds of real clock time can be experienced as several hours, depending upon the needs and motivations of the patient. This can be effectively utilized in a number of ways.

You can say to a patient in trance to take as long as he needs in trance, to do whatever is clinically relevant (e.g., review an issue or experience, enjoy comfort, etc.) even though you have a limited amount of external, or clock time. You can stretch out the time that goes on in between recurrent episodes of migraines for example and shorten the perceived time of the episodes.

You can also use this characteristic of trance in rousing up a patient who is reluctant to alert from trance because it feels so good. If he wants to stay like this for six more hours, you can say something like, "Fine, you can stay like this for six more hours. Every time I count a number, an hour will have passed. Okay. One . . . two . . . three . . . four . . . five . . . six. Wake up." And the patient will wake up.

Age Regression

When we suggest (after obtaining permission) that a patient close his eyes and orient his mind back to a particular incident in his life, this is *age regression.* It capitalizes on the phenomenon of time distortion in trance. Thus, a patient can review an important experience in only a few seconds of real clock time. It is a central facet of our work.

Cheek and LeCron (1968) described in detail different techniques for inducing complete and partial age regressions. They pointed out that it is much easier to obtain partial regression. This is all that is necessary for most therapeutic work. Their simplest verbalization for this is to say, "you will count to three and the patient will then be at the suggested age, seeing the scene. This can be elaborated, stating that he will see it becoming clearer and will see the people present. He can be asked to describe the clothing worn by anyone present, with other minor details brought out which tends to develop the reliving of the experience further" (p. 52). Ideomotor (IM) finger signals are employed to punctuate the experience, deepen it, and communicate with the therapist.

Cheek and LeCron point out that repeated reviews of an important experience help the patient learn how he feels about what took place and discharge the emotions tied to it. This makes the therapy deeper and more involving. It is a progressive desensitization process. The objective is to change the fixed ideas that were formed at the time and that are no longer adaptive.

Chapter 3

SPECIAL INTAKE QUESTIONS FOR HYPNOANALYSIS

Obviously, we need factual information about the presenting problem (left brain information). We also need emotional information (right brain information). We need to ask questions to make a double diagnosis. The presenting problem, such as asthma or chronic pain, may be the main symptom and reason for the visit. However, we also need to formulate a psychodynamic diagnosis of the underlying fixed idea that is producing the symptom. If you can change the fixed idea, you can change an illness. That is the reason for asking the following special intake questions.

   1. Tell me about your problem. This is not a question. It is a direction and is literal. We already know what an asthma attack is like, or a headache, or being overweight, or having irritable bowel. We are interested in learning about *the problem*. The patient will often give an answer that, if taken literally, will describe the ultimate subconscious diagnosis. Consequently, this should be written down verbatim or audiotaped. The patient may volunteer a gratuitous clause, a repetitive phrase, or an apparently irrelevant reference in answering this question. For example:

To elicit subconscious info

- *Doctor it's hard to answer this question.* You hypothesize he probably has a sexual problem.
- *To be perfectly concrete, I don't know what the problem is.* We didn't ask about concrete and the patient volunteered a phrase that subsequently turned out to relate to a fall on a concrete sidewalk.
- *I get the urge and go out and drink and drink and drink, or I get the urge to eat and eat and eat.* It may turn out that the patient is sexually starved. "Urge" is a sex word–the urge to merge.

- *I can't quit smoking.* Obviously anyone can quit smoking. All you have to do is put them on an island where there are no cigarettes. This statement of belief typically reflects that the speaker is carrying out the common fixed idea or imprint, "Don't start, you'll never be able to quit smoking."

The symptom is protecting the patient all the time, and the underlying problem is usually sitting right there on top of the brain ready to bounce out, if someone just listens literally to the patient!

This initial directive is very different from "how can I help you?" or "why are you here?" because these questions don't elicit any subconscious information.

2. When did it start? The true answer should be a date. Often the patient says something like: "Ever since I was in the hospital," or "Ever since my accident," or "Ever since my parents divorced," and then may not even give an approximate date until asked. Our notes should include these volunteered clauses because that is the emotional input. If the patient gives an exact date, follow up with ***What was going on in your life at that time?*** As opposed to a date, if the patient relates it to an incident, follow with ***What change took place in your life at that time?*** Keep in mind that the patient is unlikely to volunteer that psychodynamically important information unless you ask for it!

One blinding headache patient answered "About 6 months after my sister died." This was obviously not grief at his sister's death which should have started immediately. His reply to the question about what change took place in his life when his sister died was "that's when mother came to live with us."

Remember, in working up the case, you are like a detective searching for clues. You have to think like Sherlock Holmes. Ask yourself: *What would I have to believe and feel to say what the patient just said?*

3. When did it become a problem? Sometimes a symptom that has been a minor discomfort gets exacerbated into a major problem by an illness or incident that exposes a weakness or vulnerability. This is often an issue with an incorrigible smoker who has a heart attack or is put on oxygen for pneumonia or COPD and is confronted with the fact that he *must* stop smoking, but it is not happening. It also can occur when a parent who smoked dies of cancer. The patient may be identifying with the parent and daydreaming that they used to smoke together, and so it brings up a pleasant memory. The patient cannot keep

A date vs Eversince Link

mom or dad alive, but he can keep the relationship alive in reverie by smoking (trance logic—obvious incongruity). Patients often do not see smoking as a problem [it's a solution] until all of a sudden they have to "quit" and they have trouble "quitting."

When a patient uses the word "quit," we ask him to take that word out of his conversational vocabulary because the goal is going to be to *stop,* not to quit. We are taught from childhood on, not to be a "quitter." Quitting school, a job, or a marriage are big decisions. We "stop work at 5 o'clock," or "stop at a red light" with very little emotion (even though some people may get road rage when having to stop at a traffic light!). The word "quit" is typically associated with a lot of resistance because it is associated with violating a universal fixed idea.

4. What makes it better? Aside from medicines, are there circumstances, times of day, times of the week, times of the year, certain dates, when it's better? Is it better on vacation? Better at work? (If it's better at work, there is probably something going on at home!).

5. What makes it worse? As above, except that if nothing makes it better and nothing makes it worse, you are going to need to look for a perceived "near-death experience." This is because if a person is emotionally "dead," nothing makes any difference.

6. If you were cured, what would you do that you cannot do now? The answer to this question tells you what the symptom keeps the patient from doing and what problem it seems to be solving. If the patient says "I wouldn't *do* anything different. I would just enjoy life better by not being bothered by it," then the patient is not motivated to have the symptom. He is just being aggravated by it. If the patient answers the question with things he would do if he didn't have the symptom, then, it will likely show up later as a secondary gain. If the patient gives you a list of things he would do, the last one is the one he least wants to talk about and therefore the most important.

At this point in the interview, we are getting ready to ask a series of emotional, right brain questions. Up until this point, the questions have been left brain and emotionally neutral. Now we want to get on a more intimate level. We ask the patient, **What do you like for your friends to call you?** and whatever the answer may be, we ask: **May I call you that?**

This is very literal. We have learned though long experience that many people don't like their names, or too much informality. A man named Joseph may not like for people to call him Joe. A woman may have a pet name like "Missy" that she likes for special people to call her. When you ask permission to use the name the patient likes for his friends to call him, it's also an indirect suggestion that you would like to be thought of as a friend (because you are getting ready to ask some very intimate questions that he might not confide to anyone but a friend).

Before each question, we say the patient's name.

7. <Name>, in your entire life (pause), what's the worst thing that ever happened to you? Often, the answer is not something that actually happened to the patient, but describes a situation in which the patient experienced helplessness, perhaps for the first time (e.g., a parental divorce, a sibling's death, the trauma that brought on the symptoms, etc.). Whatever the answer, it usually has life changing emotional stress. After asking the question, you can almost see the patient momentarily go into spontaneous trance, perhaps doing a reflexive eye roll as the patient accesses a devastating experience.

After a few seconds, say: **First thought?** so that the patient does not shift back into left brain analysis of trying to analyze the first worst and the second worst and the third worst thing that ever happened. We are interested in what comes to mind as a first thought–what is sitting on top of the brain.

8. <Name>, in your entire life (pause), what's the worst thing you ever did? This question accesses the kind of thing that makes the patient feel guilty. Sometimes the patient will balk, or say "nothing." This usually means that's the problem (i.e., it is repressed). Later on, in trance, using IM signals, we will want to ask again **Would it be all right to know if this symptom is a form of self punishment?**

Sometimes the patient will report some childish or childhood transgression like, "I stole a candy bar from the drugstore." This tells us what a highly developed conscience the patient has about stealing. You can safely leave your wallet on the desk if that's the worst thing he ever did! Almost everyone has stolen something trivial as a child. It's the ones that get caught that will answer the question in this way, because getting caught early on emotionally imprinted that **YOU DO NOT STEAL!** They probably don't even pocket sweeteners at Starbucks!

9. <Name>, in your entire life (pause), what's the most frightened you've ever been? Adrenaline release imprints memories (Weinberger et al., 1984), and the answer is often informative. There is a strong sense of helplessness that goes with being afraid. It is the most unpleasant of all the emotions, and causes the physiological changes of fight or flight–increased blood pressure, faster heart rate, cold sweat, increased blood sugar levels, etc. These are potent imprints.

10. <Name>, in your entire life (pause), what's the most angry you've ever been? Be alert to the knowledge that the emotional energy of *fear* is often transduced into *anger* because we are more comfortable with anger than we are with fear. At least we can release it by cursing or suing.

11. <Name>, in your entire life (pause), what's the most embarrassed you've ever been? This is particularly poignant for patients who limped or stuttered or were fat as a child, because children are naturally cruel to each other, and even take delight in making fun of other children.

Frequently, the answer to one or more of questions 6 though 11 will coincide with the time that the symptom started, which gets our attention.

12. <Name>, have you ever known anyone with the same or a similar problem? This question is asked because patients model their symptoms and behavior after people who are influential in their lives. This may give a clue to the origin of the patient's symptom complex. Note however, that if the patient brings up someone who has no personal emotional meaning or attachment in their lives, then the answer is unlikely to be pertinent. You wouldn't *model* after somebody like that.

13. <Name>, what's the best thing that ever happened to you? We use this later in ego strengthening and optimistic expressions of the patient's future. A healthy ongoing relationship is a useful predictor of a good outcome. If the patient answers, "Nothing good ever happened," that's a bad prognostic sign of severe depression and taking away the symptom may be taking away the last solution the patient has got! Such patients may need to be referred to a hospital-based psychiatrist. They may be suicidal. They may not be good candidates for hypnosis.

14. If I had a magic wand, and one wish would come true, what would you wish? If the patient says "world peace," we note that and give the patient another wish. However, later on, we can use this again in ego strengthening by pointing out what a fine person the patient really is to have such an altruistic wish instead of something selfish. What we are hoping the patient will really wish for is *to get well*. We need the patient's attention focused on the problem. If the first three wishes don't include getting well, we ask, *How many wishes would I have to give you before you wished to get well?*

This usually brings the patient back into why we are having the session. If he answers something like 14 wishes, we usually give a direct suggestion for symptom removal and dismiss the patient with the counsel that if that does not suffice, to come back at a later date when the wish to get well moves up to number one. In such a case, we are dealing with a patient who is not very motivated, or who might even be negatively motivated.

15. Is there anything else you think I ought to know? This is the most important question of all. If the patient answers it, he is telling us what the subconscious problem is. In effect, his subconscious is saying, "you had an hour to ask the right question, and since you didn't, I'll go ahead now and tell you what the problem is!" If his answer is "No," his subconscious is saying, "I have already told you, and what's important is already in the answers to the previous questions."

Here are all 15 intake questions without the explanations. An intake worksheet is provided in Appendix 2 for your clinical use.

1. Tell me about your problem.
2. When did it start? [What was going on in your life at that time? What change took place in your life at that time?]
3. When did it become a problem?
4. What makes it better?
5. What makes it worse?
   If you were cured, what would you do that you cannot do now? [What do you like for your friends to call you? May I call you that?]
7. <Name>, in your entire life (pause), what's the worst thing that ever happened to you?
8. <Name>, in your entire life (pause), what's the worst thing you ever did?
9. <Name>, in your entire life (pause), what's the most frightened you've ever been?
10. <Name>, in your entire life (pause), what's the most angry you've ever been?
11. <Name>, in your entire life (pause), what's the most embarrassed you've ever been?
12. <Name>, have you ever known anyone with the same or a similar problem?

13. <Name>, what's the best thing that ever happened to you?
14. If I had a magic wand, and one wish would come true, what would you wish?
15. Is there anything else you think I ought to know?

Chapter 4

TREATMENT PLANNING: ANALYZING THE HISTORY

When you get a block on any of the emotional questions (Questions 7 though 11, see p. 28) while taking the history, it means the patient feels so bad about that feeling, that he cannot even talk about it, and resists even feeling it. In trance, this will be something that has to be addressed.

We formulate a treatment plan by listening to our patient. After the intake, we take a break to look through our notes. We review the intake notes we took and use a red pen to circle phrases that the patient has used more than once, or that carry emotional impact. We pay attention to special words that reflect ABSOLUTES, such as, "constant," "always," "all my life," and so forth.

- A constant symptom cues us to look for a psychological "death." This is heard in answers like, "Nothing makes it better or worse," "I live with it," and "It never goes away." It means the symptom is associated in the subconscious with being alive; to be without it, means to die.
- "All my life" tells us we are going to have to regress to birth.
- "As long as I can remember" tells us the imprint was probably laid down before age three.
- Words such as "urge," "satisfied," "scared stiff," "on and off," "it's hard," "it comes in spurts," "heads or tails," and "stuffed," cue us to look for sexual issues.
- A sigh after a phrase negates the phrase. A sigh before the phrase indicates that the patient didn't want to say it because it had a lot of emotion in it. The polygraph studies taught us that.
- We look for volunteered negatives, for example; "I don't steal" (You'd better keep your hand on your wallet!). In response to the question,

"What's the worst thing you ever did?" if the patient answers, "I've never killed anybody!" he's probably thinking about it! It's not responsive to the question. We didn't ask the patient what he *never* did; we asked him what he *did*.

• We look for conditional clauses, particularly statements that negate, or undo, what the patient just said, such as "I guess," "I suppose," and so forth. For example: Question: "How do you feel about having this operation?" Response: "Okay, I guess." The "I guess" leads us to wonder about what the patient's fears and reservations are, and relieves him from having lied by just saying "Okay."

• Nonresponsive answers include volunteered negatives and vaguely related, oxymoronic or tangential associations. For example, the stutterer who is asked "When did it start?" and answers, "All my life," is giving an illogical answer, since he couldn't talk at birth.

We have to go through the intake notes as if we are analyzing the data from a projective test such as a TAT or Rorschach Inkblot Test. We are making connections between outstanding and repetitive phrases, and forming hypotheses about the hidden meaning of these phrases.

From all of that, we formulate a tentative psychodynamic diagnosis. For example, we may be looking for a "sex" problem, or a "psychological death" problem.

We also place the problem on a time line (e.g., "When did it start?"). If the puzzle begins to fit together by the response to "What's the worst thing that ever happened to you?" coming right before "When did it start?" we associate this trauma with the symptom.

The IM analysis with regression in trance validates or invalidates our presumptive psychodynamic diagnosis. If we need more information, we conduct an inquiry of the seven common causes of psychosomatic disorders (see Chapter 7). In trance, we conduct the IM questioning using the "seven keys" (Cheek & LeCron, 1968). This is akin to doing a "lab work-up." It helps us prove or disprove our clinical-presumptive diagnosis. If our presumptive diagnosis is incorrect, the IM questioning using the "seven keys" will frequently lead to the correct diagnosis. The correct diagnosis will lead to the appropriate treatment options.

The essence of Rapid Hypnoanalysis is to *listen to the subtleties* and *to listen with your "third ear."* Sir William Osler, the father of modern medicine said, "Speech was given to conceal thought," meaning listen to what the patient doesn't say or leaves out. He also said, "Listen to your patient, he's telling you his diagnosis," meaning listen to what he does say.

The "Anamnesis"

"Mnesis" means memory in Greek. "Amnesia" means no memory. *Anamnesia* is what the patient didn't repress or forget. What the patient tells us is the anamnesis, not the history. We call it a history when the patient tells us what happened, but in truth what the patient tells us is what he didn't forget or repress. Regarding repression, if the patient tells you a series of things, it's the last thing the patient told you that matters most because it was saved until last. For example:

I (DME) was treating a woman who said her children were driving her crazy for the past two weeks. I asked "How many do you have?" and she replied, "three boys, 14, 12, and 16," My question then was, "What's wrong with the 16-year-old?" (the one she obviously did not want to talk about!) She replied, "He was expelled from school two weeks ago for drugs".

If the patient answered the last intake question ("Is there anything else I need to know?"), that is most likely to be the core of the problem. If the patient didn't answer it, then we better go through our notes carefully again.

Basic Steps of Rapid Hypnoanalysis

These are the basic steps of rapid hypnoanalysis which represent the essence of the technique:

1. Do your intake and have the patient <u>tell you about "the problem</u>." Then conduct further questioning to find out: when did it <u>start</u>; <u>what was happening</u> at the time; what makes it <u>better</u> and <u>worse</u>; what <u>difference</u> a "cure" would make; what <u>name</u> the patient likes his friends to call him; the <u>worst</u> thing that ever happened to him and the <u>worst</u> thing he feels he ever did; what was the most <u>frightened</u>, <u>angry</u>, and <u>embarrassed</u> he's ever been; if he ever knew <u>anyone else</u> with a similar problem; the best thing that ever happened to him; <u>one wish</u>; and if there's <u>anything else</u> you should know.
2. After the intake, orient the patient to trance.
3. Induce trance and set up the ideomotor (IM) signaling system (see Chapter 5).
4. In trance, obtain permission to help the patient with "the problem."

5. Regress the patient to the onset of the problem and have the patient do a subconscious review using ideomotor signaling.
6. Regress the patient to the onset of the problem and have the patient do a conscious review with IM signaling and verbalization of memories.
7. If necessary, use IM questioning to identify which of the "seven causes" of psychosomatic symptoms are active (see below and Chapter 7). Regress and review active causes.
8. Using IM signaling, have the patient subconsciously and then consciously review the original and/or sensitizing experiences.
9. Restructure or reframe the experience/s and active causes.
10. Give direct suggestions in hypnosis (DSIH) for healing.
11. Return to the present and alert the patient.

Sidebar. In essence, if we have a good working diagnosis from our intake, that is, we have a good guess about what we are likely to find, we go for that first in regressing the patient. However, if we do not get it, we then go for the "seven causes" or "seven keys" (see Chapter 7).

Regress to the onset of the problem. In trance, we in essence do an "Affect Bridge" (Watkins & Watkins, 1997) by first bringing up the negative emotion and then saying to the patient: "Orient your mind back to the <u>first</u> time you experienced this feeling." Even though the affect may have been experienced many times since, the important affective experience to access is the first time the affect was imprinted in state dependent memory.

Subconscious review of the experience. Ideomotor signals (IM) are finger movements chosen to nonverbally indicate a positive or "yes" <u>feeling</u> by raising one finger, and a negative, or "no" <u>feeling</u> by raising another. These are analogous to nodding the head "yes" and shaking the head "no" in nonverbal response.

The hypnotic subconscious review involves raising the "yes" finger as the subconscious mind begins to review its perceptions about the experience, raising the "no" finger every time something emotionally important to the patient occurs, and signaling with another finger (usually the thumb) when the subconscious review is complete.

We must do at least one or more subconscious IM reviews before the patient can bring the material up to consciousness. Patients cannot usually verbally describe the incident until they have done the subconscious review. If they could, they would have given it to us in the waking history!

When the patient begins his subconscious review, we usually observe autonomic changes in breathing, neck pulse, and/or facial skin color, indicating that emotions are being accessed. The muscular IM signals tend to follow the autonomic activity. The way we know we are getting into a good review is when we first see the autonomic changes noted above.

Conscious review with verbalization of memories. After several subconscious reviews, the question is asked: *Would it be all right to bring this up to a conscious level so you can tell me what happened?* When the answer is "yes," a standard regression with verbalizations of memories is done.

Reframe the fixed idea. The most propitious time to reframe a fixed idea is when the patient has just given a verbal description of the problem. Good common sense and training in psychology need to lead the therapist in teaching the patient to take a lemon and make lemonade.

Return to the present. Note that when a patient is regressed and we say "return to the present," or "return to today," the regressed patient is in what he perceives as the present and today. Therefore it is best to specify the actual date. For example, we say, "Return to today, April 2, 2005.

FOUR IDEOMOTOR SEARCH
METHODS

The "Seven Causes" or "Keys"

David Cheek (1994) credited Leslie LeCron for developing the method of using ideomotor signals to explore the "seven common causes" of psychosomatic disorders (Cheek & LeCron, 1968). Cheek pointed out, and it has been our experience, that many events located as the beginnings of a problem have been preceded by earlier events that made the patient vulnerable or sensitized. Therefore he recommended that, following discovery of the first reported incident, it is judicious to check for earlier sensitizing events by asking, *Is there an earlier experience that could have made you vulnerable or sensitive to what you have just told me?*

Retrograde Search

This method, which Cheek (1994) also credited to LeCron, allows the patient to gradually move back in time to a traumatic event. It gives the patient protective distance, and also, enables the patient to do multiple subconscious reviews which can have a desensitizing effect. The method is illustrated in our transcripts wherein we ask the patient in trance to answer with the fingers questions pertaining to the age when the causal event happened. For example, using ideomotor signals, ("T" is the therapist and "IM" is the patient's IdeoMotor signal):

T: Was it something that happened before you were 20 years old?
IM: Yes.
T: Before you were 15 years old?
IM: Yes.
T: Before you were 13?
IM: No.
T: Were you 13 years old?
IM: Yes.

In this example, the patient would have had to have done four subconscious reviews.

Chronological Search

This method involves finding a safe starting point from which to have the patient go forward in time to the moment when something important related to the problem is happening. Then we progress forward in time from one significant event to another.

Direct Approach

The "direct approach," which we often favor, involves telling the patient in trance to go directly back to something we hypothesize might be important. We base this on the information we have gathered in the intake. With the direct approach, it is still necessary to ask the patient "if there might be some earlier experience that could have set the stage or created a vulnerability to the initially selected trauma" (Cheek, 1994, p. 92).

Chapter 5

HOW TO SET UP IDEOMOTOR SIGNALS

Ideomotor signals are set up by first telling the patient in trance: **I am going to teach you a way to signal how you feel about a question without even talking.** It is then suggested that a designated finger will rise if he has a positive "yes" feeling in response to a question, and that a different finger will rise if he has a negative "no" feeling in response to a question. The designated fingers should be stroked gently and passively raised, so that the patient gets sensory feedback that goes with the "yes" and "no" feelings.

In the past, we were taught to introduce this by inviting the patient to experience a positive "yes" feeling and seeing which finger moved spontaneously, and doing the same with feelings of "no," "I don't know," and "I don't want to answer." This technique has many drawbacks and is unnecessarily long and confusing. When every patient has different fingers on both hands being signaled, the therapist must reorient with each patient and be continually looking back and forth from one hand to another. Looking from one hand to the other, the therapist doesn't get to observe the patient's facial expression and other subtle cues as much as is desirable. We simply work with one hand. It makes no difference which hand is used. We choose the hand that is closest to the therapist.

Direct Suggestions in Hypnosis (DSIH)

Since these signals are set up when the patient is already in trance and able to take suggestions, we simply suggest the same thing to all of our patients. That is, that the index finger on the hand nearest the therapist signals "yes," the middle finger on that hand signals "no," and the thumb signals "I'm not ready to answer that question yet," or "I don't want to answer."

I Don't Know?

We were originally taught to have a finger signal to indicate "I don't know," but we have abandoned that because patients use it as a dodge to keep from answering important questions that they subconsciously do know the answer to.

Therapists who are concerned about confabulation include an "I don't know" signal, and that is appropriate for forensic work where confabulation can cause serious problems. However, in clinical work, all we are interested in is how the patient *feels* about something regardless of its factual accuracy.

If you ask a patient if he loves his wife, and he signals "I don't know," you should not want to hear that baloney because that's a cop-out. You want him to signal with his thumb that "I do not want to answer that question" (taking the Fifth!). That will tell you that you are onto something significant in his life and that at some point in therapy you are going to have to address the issue.

One signal that we have found very valuable, but is omitted in most instructions is:

If anything crosses your mind that you want to talk about, or if you want to ask a question, just raise your hand and we'll talk.

This is important because a patient in a good trance will not ordinarily initiate speech, but will initiate movement. Patients free associate in trance and may think of something important they want to communicate, but may have forgotten it later on when alerted. If the patient raises his hand, say: **Speak to me and tell me what's on your mind.**

When a patient REALLY doesn't know the answer to a question, he will not signal with any of the fingers, and after some hesitation, he will raise his hand and when asked, say "I don't know." In addition, we sometimes ask confusing questions, and the patient will raise his hand and say, "I don't understand." Then, we re-word the question and usually get a response.

False Memories: The Experimental and Factual Issue of Confabulation of the Truth

Every question, waking or ideomotor, involves memories. In clinical work, what matters is what the patient believes to be true, regardless of whether or not it is factual. In forensic work, the actual truth is critical, and setting up an "I don't know" finger is valuable, as recommended by Brown, Scheflin, and Hammond (1998) and Hammond and Cheek (1988). Our book is about how we practice clinical hypnotherapy. Since our book is not about forensic or experimental work, and while we are aware of the potential for confabulation, we don't care if what the patient believes is factually verifiable. What matters is that the patient believes it because he will act as though it is true.

Since a question is an indirect suggestion, it is imperative to avoid specific questions that could implant a false memory. We never ask a question like "Have you been sexually abused?" Instead, we regress to a time of trauma, and ask, "What is happening?" We think that therapeutically, we are obliged to deal with what the patient gives us (utilization).

Arm Positioning

The physiology of muscles is such that they can only contract and relax. Like a string, they cannot push; they can only pull. Consequently, if the wrist is straight or extended, the muscles are relaxed and require a significant contraction to produce a finger movement. If the wrist is flexed, and the extensor muscles are tight, the slightest muscular contraction will produce a visible movement of the finger.

In a reclining chair, it is helpful to have the patient place the hand on the abdomen with the elbow on the side and the wrist flexed (Figure 5.1). In a sitting position, you can let the wrist flex over the end of an armrest (Figure 5.2), or with the elbow resting on the armrest, simply raise the patient's forearm (Figure 5.3), and say: **You'll find your hand is more comfortable in this position and hold it right here.**

Preparing the Patient for Hypnotic Induction

The first thing we ask the patient is: *Do you have any questions before we start?* If the patient says "no," we ask, *Are you afraid of hypnosis?* If the patient says "yes," we obviously talk about it to allay the patient's fears and misconceptions. If he says "no," we ask:

> *Do you know what it is that you are most likely to do that will interfere with this?*

The patient usually says "No, I don't". We then answer:

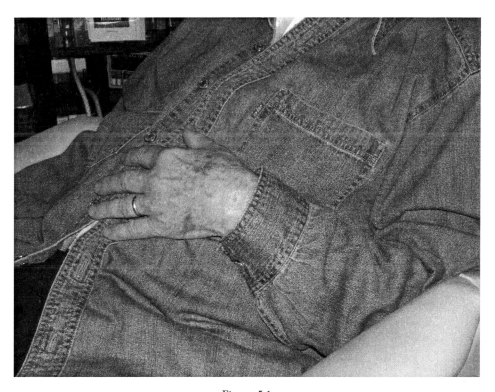

Figure 5.1

You are likely to try too hard. If you start trying to be the best patient I ever had, or wondering if you are doing it right, or if you start thinking things like should I feel like I am floating, or should I hear other noises, you have to be out of trance to analyze if you are in trance, and that's my job. Your job is to just do what I ask you to do, and shift into daydream type thinking, and don't give a hoot whether you do it right or not.

If the patient asks, "what if my mind wanders?" we answer:

Great. That means you are shifting into daydream-type thinking which can wander anywhere it likes!

Remember that if the patient is asking about it, he is trying to analyze it, and he has to go back into left-brain thinking to do such analysis. Therefore, we have to clear up any misconceptions that the patient has about hypnosis. After doing so, we induce hypnotic trance with a short induction, an example of which is scripted below.

The philosophy behind what we do is that we want to be able to spend our time doing <u>hypnoanalysis</u>. Therefore, the more efficiently we can do a rapid induction and set up IM finger signals, the more time

Figure 5.2

we have available to do the actual therapy. So, we start with a rapid induction and use IM signals for deepening.

Common Misconceptions about Hypnosis

As discussed by Cheek (1994), there are four false ideas that often need to be corrected.

1. The Idea that Some People are Not Hypnotizable. Anyone who can daydream can be hypnotized if he is <u>willing</u>. Nobody can be hypnotized against his will. If a person is not willing to cooperate, he cannot be hypnotized. However, the idea that some people are just not hypnotizable is INCORRECT. Some patients may initially have problems with feeling that they may lose control in some unacceptable way. This may lead them to intellectually second-guess and overanalyze what is going on. Thinking too much will interfere with relaxing enough to enter trance.

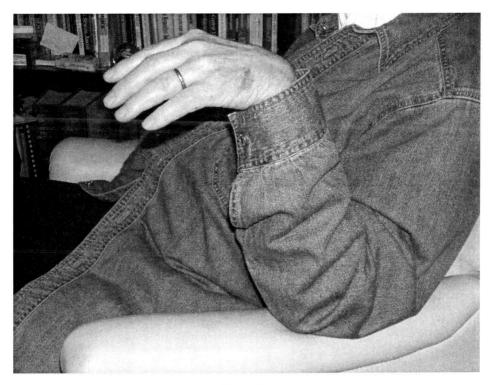

Figure 5.1

Hypnosis is NOT about the hypnotist controlling the patient. It is about the patient gaining more control over himself. Once the patient realizes that experiencing hypnotic trance will (a) help him feel how he wants to feel and do what he wants to do, AND (b) actually give him more control and power than he previously had, he will stop overthinking, let it happen, and become a good subject.

2. The Idea that Hypnosis Can Weaken the Mind. Hypnosis does NOT weaken the mind. On the contrary, it helps people use more of their mind's potential. It helps people access their inner strength. The subconscious mind is protective. Hypnotized people will accept suggestions that are acceptable, and reject suggestions that are not acceptable. Suggestions must be worded in a form and language that the patient's subconscious can understand.

3. The Idea that Hypnosis is a Truth Serum. Hypnosis CANNOT be used to find the truth, or make a person tell the truth. Hypnosis is NOT a truth serum. First of all, the hypnotized subject retains enough awareness and control to NOT say anything that he doesn't want to make known, or isn't ready to make known. Secondly, human memory is inherently inaccurate and unreliable both in and out of hypnosis (Brown, Scheflin, & Hammond, 1997). Hypnosis can help a willing patient get deeper in touch with his deepest and most heartfelt feelings. But feelings are NOT facts. Recollections that come to mind in hypnosis are colored by the patient's feelings. We use hypnosis to find the truth about how the patient feels about something, NOT the truth about what really happened.

The hypnotist or therapist CANNOT make the patient find out, or talk about, how he feels about something, unless the patient feels comfortable and totally safe, and is ready.

4. The Idea that Hypnotized People Behave like Zombies. Hypnosis is NOT about ZAP you are under my power like Svengali. Hypnosis is a collaborative and cooperative teacher-student relationship. Hypnosis is NOT sleep. When a person is in hypnosis, he is relaxed and aware of his surroundings. He hears the sound of the therapist's voice and will remember more or less of what the therapist says.

The hypnotized subject or patient is NOT asleep. He is relaxed, comfortable, focused, and in a state of daydream-type thinking. His analyzing thinking mind (Conscious mind) is turned off and his feeling and intuitive and creative mind (Subconscious) is aware of everything that is going on. A hypnotized subject cannot be made to do anything he is not willing to do. A person must be a willing and cooperative subject for hypnosis to work.

Trance Induction

We don't worry about trance depth because you can actually do ideomotor work in the waking state. In fact, when a person simply nods "yes" in the waking state, he is doing body language (i.e., ideomotor signaling). The value of inducing trance before setting up IM signals is that the patient will take the suggestions to use particular fingers as directed to signal his subconscious responses. The following script of Ewin's Rapid Eye-Roll Induction illustrates a typical, effective, rapid trance induction as verbalized to the patient:

> *Get comfortably relaxed. Close your eyes, and keeping your eyelids closed just as though they are glued together, roll your eyeballs up as though you are looking at the top of your forehead, looking way, way up. . . . Now, take a deep,*

deep breath, the deepest breath you've ever taken, and hold it . . . hold it. Feel it pressing against your chest. One . . . Two . . . Three [about a 5-second pause concentrates the patient's mind on holding the breath]. . . . *And as you let it all out . . .* [drop your voice tone as you also pace by exhaling a deep breath] *. . . just like a balloon collapsing, draining all the tension out of every nerve and fiber in your body. . . . Your eyes relaxed and going deeper, deeper relaxed than you've ever been. . . . Going inside to find that part of you that knows you're precious, that your feelings matter. . . . And that you own your own body, and it has to do what you tell it to do. . . .*

Paying attention only to the sound of my voice. Any other sounds you hear will be very pleasant in the background and just help you to get more comfortably relaxed. It's comforting to know that the rest of the world is going on about its business while you and I are doing ours. . . .

Eyes relaxed . . . jaws unclenched . . . shoulders droopy . . . arms limp and floppy, your neck and back comfortably supported by the chair. . . . And you can let all those muscles relax . . . abdomen soft . . . each breath you take as you exhale, just picture yourself blowing all your worries and stress, all your stress and tension, out into the atmosphere, never to return . . . your legs all loose and limp and lazy-like, and your mind as relaxed as your body . . . (shifting to a positive emotion) feeling calm . . . safe . . . peaceful . . . and in control . . . comfortable . . . precious . . . confident . . .

Confident because you own your own mind, and it must think what you tell it to think. Confident because you own your own body and it must do what you tell it to do. Confident because you own your own feelings and they have to feel what you tell them to feel. Way, way, way down deep.

A "Laughing Place"

If we get into very traumatic or upsetting situations in treatment (which is not always possible to predict), it's good to have a safe mental retreat available as a precaution. Most hypnotherapists like to use what they describe as a "safe place" to visualize for this purpose. We prefer to call it a "Laughing Place" because laughing is therapeutic and healing, as well as safe. Norman Cousins' experiences of laughing himself into health are well documented (Cousins, 1979). We set this up using the following suggestions:

For starters, I want to help you find your "Laughing Place," because laughing is healthy and drives out misery. Everybody has a laughing place. You can start by making a smile come onto your face. Even if you don't feel like it, see what happens if you tell the muscles in your face to make a smile . . . [pause and wait and validate the patient's response]. . . . *See what happens. You can do it. That's right. And as the smile comes on to your face, notice the feeling that goes along with it. And just let that feeling go down to your heart [pause] and spread over your entire body. . . . And as you begin to feel this pleasant sensation, just let it happen . . . just let it happen. . . . Now, I wonder if you can make yourself feel like laughing even if you haven't felt this way in a while. . . . Because laughing is healthy and drives away misery. . . . Just do it and see what happens. . . . Just do it and see what happens. That's right. You may even enjoy that feeling more than you expected . . . and as you feel more like laughing, it may bring up a happy memory of a time when you felt like laughing.*

And you may begin to experience some of the sensations that go along with these feelings . . . the scene, the place, the colors, the shapes, the people you are with, or the quiet peacefulness of solitude . . . the sounds . . . the shared laughter, the music, or perhaps the voice of someone who loves you . . . the smells that are here . . . the scent of perfume or flowers, the smell of clean fresh air in the outdoors, the delicate aroma of a good wine . . . the taste of your favorite food or drink . . . the touch and caresses of someone who loves you; all the things that make <u>your</u> laughing place, your laughing place, so good . . . so free of any cares, or worries, or duties. . . .

And while you are enjoying your laughing place, nothing can bother, nothing can disturb you. . . .

When your inner mind knows that you are so concentrated on your laughing place that nothing can bother, nothing can disturb, just give me a little nod of your head so I'll know you've found it. . . . And having found it, take a mental snapshot of it now, so that at any time when we're doing therapy together, we can instantly shift back to this picture for comfort (It usually takes 30 to 60 seconds for a confirming head nod response, and then you can go on with the ideomotor set-up procedure).

Alerting

Often this is as far as we get in the first visit. Remember, that after we do our intake, we want to leave enough time to give the patient a short and pleasant experience of hypnosis. Proper alerting will be important at the end of every session. Sometimes, suggestions of analgesia or residuals of a traumatic regression may still linger with a patient, and we like to administer a general "wipeout suggestion" that covers all possibilities. If a patient is suggestible enough to have accepted any bad ideas during the session, he is also suggestible enough to accept the "wipeout."

We verbalize:

> *In a moment, I am going to alert you by counting slowly from one to three. When I say three, blink your eyes and open them, and come back fully alert, sound in mind, sound in body and in control of your feelings. One . . . rousing up slowly . . . two . . . and three. Wide awake, alert, refreshed, and feeling great.*

If you are sound in mind, you are not goofy. If you are sound in body, you are physically intact. For example, you don't have any residual anesthesia, or any other sensory or perceptual changes that you have experienced in trance, and if you are in control of your feelings, you're not anxious.

An alternate alerting technique is to use a double bind by suggesting:

> *When your deepest mind knows that you can control this symptom (or keep processing this), you'll blink your eyes and come back fully alert, sound in mind, sound in body and in control of your feelings.*

This gives the patient a choice between staying in trance forever or accepting the suggestion.

Ideomotor Set-Up

After inducing trance, we set up ideomotor (IM) signals for doing hypnoanalysis. It goes like this: ("T" is the Therapist, "P" is the Patient, and "IM" stands for Ideomotor signal.)

T: *I'm going to move your* [right or left] *hand.* [That is the hand we are going to work with. Always tell the patient before touching! Otherwise it can startle the patient.] *And you'll find it's more comfortable in this position, and hold it right here.* [We position the arm with the wrist in flexion. See Figures 5.1, 5.2 and 5.3.]

T: *Now I am going to teach you a way to signal how you feel without even talking. So if I ask a question, and it feels YES, you agree with it, it's okay, that's good, the answer's YES, this finger* [gently stroke the patient's index finger, passively raise the finger, and then lower it] *will slowly rise to signal that the answer's yes, that you agree.*

T: *Do you like for your friends to call you* [say the name your patient has told you he likes for his friends to call him.]?

IM: The YES finger will rise.

T: [After it rises, touch it and gently push it back down and say] *Sure. You've already told me that you like for your friends to call you* . . . [This gives both tactile and verbal feedback which is important because later, the patient may go so deep in hypnosis that he is unaware that a finger has risen.] [Then say]

T: *Every time your feelings answer a question, you'll notice a wave of relaxation go over your entire body and you'll go deeper inside and get more in touch with your deepest and most heartfelt feelings.*

[**Comment.** This sets the stage for each IM answer to become part of a deepening technique. Often this first answer to the "yes" question is not a true IM signal–it's volitional, but it is training the finger. If the finger is raised with a smooth rapid movement, it is usually volitional. As the patient goes deeper, and the responses become more involuntary, the movement becomes slower and tremulous. If the signals start by being volitional, as the patient goes deeper, they will become more and more involuntary and subconsciously meaningful.]

T: *If I ask you a question and you disagree, you have a NO feeling about it, you don't even have to know why, it just doesn't feel right, this finger* [gently stroke the patient's long finger, passively raise the finger, and then lower it] *will slowly rise to signal that you have a NO feeling about it, you disagree.*

T: [Now ask a question that you know is "NO" such as:] *Is today the Fourth of July?*

IM: NO finger rises.

T: [Gently stroke the NO finger and push it back down and say:] *No, of course not, this isn't the Fourth of July, today is* [State today's date as in the eighth of April, 2005].

T: *If I should ask a question that you're not ready to answer* yet, *or don't want to answer, you just signal with your thumb and that's okay* [gently raise the thumb on the same hand, and then lower it].

[**Comment.** Since we don't know a test question for this, we don't test it. The word "yet" is important though, because later, if we get a thumb signal, we can structure our response by saying: *Even though you are not ready to answer this yet, would it be all right to dream about it or to answer it on your next visit?* We often get a "yes" to that. We next say:]

T: *And if something crosses your mind, you want to talk to me, or ask a question, just raise your hand* [Gently lift the patient's hand and let it fall back] *and we'll talk.*

[**Comment.** Remember that the patient in trance tends not to initiate speech, so if you get a hand signal, say: "Speak to me and tell me what's on your mind." Since we sometimes ask confusing questions, the patient will occasionally raise his hand, and when we say "Speak to me" he says "I don't understand." Then, we re-word the question, and we get a response.]

T: [We then ask our first question which is to ask for permission from the patient to help him with the problem.] *And my first question is, is it all right with your feeling mind for me to help you with this problem?*

IM: [If patient respond YES, then say:]

T: *Okay. And you answered yes.*

I (DME) have only acquired a "no" answer to this question once, and in that case, I followed up with the question, *Would it be all right for you to solve the problem yourself?* The patient signaled "yes." So, I said, *Fine. I'll be quiet while you go deeper and deeper and find your own solution.* In a few minutes, the patient had a substantial abreaction. This man was an incorrigible smoker and I (DME) have a three-year follow-up indicating that he stopped smoking for good. So, you can still do this work even if the patient initially says "no."

A "yes" answer to this question, however, is a contract between the patient and you that the patient will cooperate. It's a good starting question to initiate the ideomotor analysis.

Distinguishing Between Conscious and Subconscious IM Signals

A subconscious IM signal does not occur immediately. There is a delay of a few seconds to as long as 45 seconds before the finger begins to twitch slightly and slowly rise tremulously in repetitive up and down motions. This is similar to the body language of nodding the head to signal "yes." We almost never nod just once, but in giving assent, we nod several times.

A signal that starts almost immediately and rises smoothly, rapidly and up high is equivalent to a consciously spoken "yes." In our experience, when we initially get a conscious response, we still use it as a deepening technique, but we do not attribute subconscious meaning to it. After two or three questions, conscious responses tend to move into typical subconscious signals.

For example, in response to our first question, *Is it all right with your subconscious mind for me to help you with this problem?* we often get a conscious "yes" signal. Then, we push the finger back down and say, *That's nice, and every time your feelings answer a question, you'll go deeper and deeper and get more in touch with your deepest most heartfelt feelings.*

PART II
BASIC APPLICATIONS

Chapter 6

IDEOMOTOR APPLICATIONS TO DIRECT SUGGESTION IN HYPNOSIS (DSIH) AND AGE REGRESSION

Ideomotor techniques can be employed to facilitate both direct suggestion in hypnosis (DSIH), and uncovering work that involves age regression.

Direct Suggestion in Hypnosis (DSIH)

I (DME) had two patients whose white blood cell count dropped below 2,000 from chemotherapy treatment. This put them at risk for infection, and further chemotherapy would have to be discontinued until the count returned to at least 4,000, which could take a week or more. There are now drugs that help some with this. I was not the treating physician in either of these cases, but had previously treated each of these patients with hypnosis.

Case #1. A 34-year-old housewife with a melanoma, from out of state, came to New Orleans for treatment cycles in the hospital. She usually received two rounds of chemotherapy on a trip to save expense. Her leukocyte (white blood cell) count was under 2,000 after the first treatment. Nothing was to be gained by staying in the hospital for a week.

For lack of anything in the literature, I simply did a trance induction and gave the suggestion *"Get your white count up."* I then asked her to *go deep and get in touch with your bone marrow and blood forming organs, and when you know you can do this, give me a "yes" signal.* I obtained a "yes" in one to two minutes, and the next morning, her white count was above

53

5,000. She got her chemotherapy and has had a five-year cure, which is rare for melanomas.

Case #2. A 45-year-old female with bilateral breast cancer was seen for hypnosis. She was a deep trance subject, and I had done pre-operative hypnosis with her. She had both breasts excised without requiring a blood transfusion. After chemotherapy, her white count fell below 2,000. Using the same DSIH and IM regimen given to Case #1, her white blood cell count rose to above 7,000 in two days. She has had no recurrence of cancer after ten years.

These case anecdotes provide evidence that blood-forming organs can be activated by direct suggestion in hypnosis (DSIH) assisted by IM signaling.

Age Regression vs. Symptom Regression

Age regression and symptom regression require different techniques. We use *age* regression when we have been alerted to a particular time (age) or incident by the patient's answers to the intake questions. With a headache patient, the question, "What's the worst thing that ever happened to you?" might elicit the answer, "When I fractured my skull at age 13." We know that has to be significant. We must review that episode in trance, and will plan an *age* regression to age 13.

With a *symptom* regression we are blind to the time and circumstance the subject will produce. We are searching for the *first* time a symptom was experienced, and we bring up the feeling (affect) of the symptom and do an *affect bridge* (Watkins & Watkins, 1997) back to the first time the patient ever experienced this emotion. Since most emotions are *first* experienced before age three, we regularly encounter something that was omitted from the history and was unavailable to the patient's conscious mind.

Symptom Regression

> Luke Skywalker: "I don't believe it."
> Yoda: "That's why you fail."
>
> –George Lucas, *The Empire Strikes Back*

Many cases of symptom regression have been reported where the patient's response to the request to go to the *first* time he had this symptom (headache, asthma, hives, rage, fear, guilt, anger, etc.), was to go to an early illness or trauma, a birth experience, an intrauterine experience, or a past life. This can clash with the world view of the therapist, causing feelings of disbelief and uneasiness with the treatment, and abandonment of this approach to therapy.

I know this feeling. In fact, in my (DME) foreword to David Cheek's last book (1994), I commented on my first encounter with his workshop: "I heard Cheek talk about regression to birth. My first reaction to this was more than disbelief; it was a judgment that I might be associating with kooks! I 'knew' that I couldn't recall my own birth, and concluded that no one else could either, and simply pigeonholed it as the idiosyncrasy of an enthusiast. The rest of the information made sense. The credentials were there, and I pressed on with my education."

Later, I experienced my own regression to the twelfth day of my life, when I was taken off of breast feeding. I was able to confirm the gist of the episode from hospital records, and I reported it (Ewin, 1994). Since then, I have located a good deal of scientific evidence that imprints occur in human babies.

Humans are part of the Animal Kingdom, and Konrad Lorenz received the Nobel Prize in 1973 for demonstrating birth imprints in birds. Gidro-Frank and Bowers-Buch (1948) reported the reappearance of a positive Babinski reflex when a healthy adult was age regressed in hypnosis to the first six months of life. This reflex is pathological in an adult, but normal in the first six months of life. I (DME) have replicated this finding in several demonstrations with somnambulists. Anyone interested in prenatal imprints should read Thomas Verny's delightful book, *The Secret Life of the Unborn Child* (Verny & Kelly, 1981).

DeCasper and Fifer (1980) reported in *Science* their studies showing that newborn infants recognize their mother's voice (DeCasper & Spence, 1986; Querleu et al., 1984). Madrid and Schwartz (1991) demonstrated in a controlled study of asthmatic children that 26 of 30 asthmatics were not bonded with their mothers at birth, while 22 of 30 healthy matched controls were bonded (p<.001). Cheek (1974) reported sequential head movements during birth regressions that mimicked the movements recorded in the delivery room records.

Raine et al. (1991) studied patients with combined birth complications and early maternal rejection, and found that while they were only 4.5 percent of the study group, they accounted for 18 percent of violent crime (p<.0001). They conclude "The findings . . . suggest that prenatal, perinatal, and early postnatal health care interventions could significantly reduce violence." We (DME & BNE) conclude that our jails are filled with unwanted children. Buchheimer (1987, p. 52) states emphatically, "We now have enough empirical evidence to demonstrate clearly that human beings can and do recall birth events with validated accuracy. I am speaking of validated memories, not recollections of older members of the family that have been told within the family, or personal fantasies."

The important thing is not whether or not the therapist believes it really happened, but rather, that these regressions are therapeutic when appropriately reframed. If a person believes something to be true, it *is* true for him. What the patient brings up is what he believes, and it comes from him, not the therapist.

These regressions are often quite emotional, and they can be life-changing in that they frequently reveal painful insights that have never been fully identified and comprehended. The regressions allow the subconscious material to be clarified and understood. The result is often the promotion of a new and profound therapeutic empathy on the part of the patient towards his infantile ego state and parents, and child-parent bonding.

Age Regression

Age regression is simply taking the patient back to a specified episode at an *age* that has been previously identified in the history. We select times that appear pertinent to the patient's answers to our intake questions. This may be the answers given to the questions, *When did it start?* or *What's the worst thing that ever happened to you?* or *Is there anything else you think I should know?* or volunteered information relating to a specific time or incident in the patient's life.

The technique for doing an age regression is described and illustrated in detail on page 84. A 14-year-old girl with herpes simplex that recurred with every menstrual period since menarche was regressed to her first period at age 12. When this appeared to be bland, she gave IM signals that something happened earlier to sensitize her to what she would later learn about the meaning of menstruation.

Another detailed description of the technique for doing an *age* regression starts on page 184 with the annotated transcript of the videotape *One Visit Cure of a Hypersensitive Scar.* Baby Elizabeth had a pin through the femur (thigh bone) for skeletal fixation in a body cast after hip surgery. When asked if there was anything else she thought I needed to know (remember, if this question is answered, it is invariably the cause of the problem), she replied "the pin fell out once, while I was in the crib." The *age* regression to that episode led to the imprint of her father's voice saying "Be careful with the scar." If an imprint can be inserted, it can be removed, but only after you find out what it is.

Symptom Regression

When doing a *symptom* regression, neither the patient nor the therapist knows what they will find, or what the time frame will be. Once in a while, as we search for the *first* time he felt this way, a patient will go to a previous life. We will have gone through the series of questions:

T: Before 10?
IM: Yes.
T: Before 5?
IM: Yes.
T: Before birth?
IM: Yes.
T: In your mother's womb?
IM: No.

(Since it was before birth, and not in the womb, the only logical question is:)

T: Was it in another life?
IM: Yes.

This is not leading the subject, as some people suggest, because the therapist has asked no leading questions, and has no preconceived ideas to impose on the subject. It does require that the therapist have an open mind.

Past Life Example

An illustrative case is X.Y., a 25-year-old woman with chronic, severe, right-sided headaches without any aura, nausea, photophobia, or other symptoms of migraine. She had been diagnosed as a migraine variant and treated with the full array of anti-migraine therapy without significant improvement before she sought hypnotherapy. She said it had been a problem "All my life."

After my (DME) usual intake, which failed to render any good clues, I set up ideomotor signals, got the signal that it was all right for me to help her, and that it was all right to go to the *first* time she felt this way. We went through the above time questions, and she indicated that it was in a previous life. The session went as follows:

DME: Let your thoughts and feelings find what is happening when you first have this pain in your head. When you start reviewing it, your *yes* finger will rise, every time you encounter something emotionally important your *no* finger will rise, and when you have completed reviewing it, you will signal with your thumb.

Patient: Over several minutes shows autonomic signs of distress with rapid breathing and speedy pulse, then *yes* finger rises, then *no* finger rises two times, and then thumb rises.

DME: Would it be all right for you to tell me what you have just experienced?

Patient: IM: Yes. (Note literal ideomotor answer, no verbalization)

DME: Speak to me, and tell me about it.

Patient: (Summarized) She says she is a little girl about 5 years old, living on a farm in rural Pennsylvania. She is an orphan, and a farmer and his wife have taken her in, but she notes that "they don't love me." One day she is playing in the hayloft of the barn, and she falls out, striking the right side of her head on the iron rim of the wagon wheel (first *No* signal). She lies there unconscious. The farmer finds her, and says, "She's going to die." (second *No* signal).

DME: (Still in past life regression, and using present tense as though it is really happening.) Since you can hear what he says, and have a headache, does your feeling mind know that you are still alive?

IM: Yes.

DME: Does this little girl actually die from the head injury?

IM: Yes.

DME: But until she actually dies, does the headache let her know that she hasn't died yet?

IM: Yes.

DME: Leaving that life behind, and coming back to this time, here in my office, let your deepest subconscious mind look at all the

Even if it seemed like a good idea in the past can you see that it ( ) has out lived its usefulne then let it go. Would it be all right to let it go.

Ideomotor Applications to Direct Suggestions 59

facts: that was a long time ago, at another place, in a different body, and you are 25 and she was only a child. The past is past. Just because the headache helped a little girl know she was still alive, does it follow that a healthy woman in this life needs a headache to prove she's still alive?

IM: [After about a minute of quietness] No.

DME: Of course not. You have all the usual ways of knowing you are alive—you got up this morning, got dressed, came to my office, you go to work, you have friends. Even if it *seemed* like a good idea in the past, that headache has outlived its usefulness. Would it be all right to just let it go?

IM: Yes.

DME: Then just let it go, and let your head feel clear and normal in every way. Want it to happen, let it happen, and it will happen. And when you know you can let it happen, blink your eyes and open them, and come back fully alert, sound in mind, sound in body, and in control of your feelings.

She alerted slowly, and stayed in my office for about 15 minutes in a hypnogogic state. The next day she called to tell me she felt great and had no headache. I lost her to long-term follow-up.

We tend to find a certain consistency about *symptom* regressions that go to a past life; the cause of death in the past life is allegorical to the present-day symptom. Thus, if a soldier in the past life was bayoneted in the abdomen, the patient complains of a chronic stomachache, or if the past life character died of tuberculosis, the patient has an unexplained cough. These are unsolicited past lives, and they identify themselves as ordinary people. It's in the solicited past lives that we read about grandiose reincarnations of Julius Caesar or Cleopatra.

Early Life Experience

A *symptom* regression to an early post-natal experience is illustrated by the case of A.G. which is detailed on page 131. Earlier we said, "With a *symptom* regression we are blind to the time and circumstance the patient will produce." That was the situation in this case. At age 42, A.G. complained of having a headache "As long as I can remember," which literally means it is after her birth (she would have said "All my life" if it were due to a birth experience), but she could not verbally give an age or incident.

go back as an observer

In hypnosis, I (DME) asked the patient A.G. first to review on a sub-conscious level her memories of what caused the headaches and what it meant to her, giving an IM signal with her thumb when she had com-pleted this task. Then we did a retrograde search to find out <u>when</u> it was. She brought up a trauma at age 10 days that gave her head pain and caused her family to fear she might die. After reframing, she became symptom free, and 11 months later, she sent me (DME) a note stating that she hadn't had a headache since being treated.

If I (DME) had already known how old A.G. was when she got hurt, I would have done an *age* regression to that time. I started without either the <u>time</u> or the <u>circumstance</u>, only the symptom, and "As long as I can remember."

Birth Regression   Cerebral palsy

H.X., a 16-year-old boy from another state was seen by me (DME) on an experimental basis for <u>treatment of cerebral palsy</u>. His aunt was a valued long-time employee, and he had a summer job filing in our office. Cerebral palsy patients have <u>involuntary spasm of both flexor and extensor muscles</u>, as though they are "scared stiff," like a deer caught in the headlights. They cannot coordinate their muscles to work together. His spasm was mainly in his neck, throat, and mouth, interfer-ing with speech. His grandmother could hardly understand anything he said on the telephone, but would pretend that she heard. Years of speech therapy had been of no avail. His IQ was normal, and he made good grades in school and participated in sports by being the team manager.

He had had a traumatic birth with a forceps delivery, was born with a hematoma on his right forehead, required an intracardiac injection of adrenalin to resuscitate him, had two Jacksonian (total body) seizures, and he didn't cry for nine hours (I was able to obtain a copy of his birth record to verify all of this).

On the first two visits, I got ideomotor "No" answers when I asked for permission to do an age regression to birth. It is hardly surprising that he <u>was unwilling to relive what had happened</u>. On the third visit, I <u>asked if it would be all right to go back to his birth</u> as an observer in the delivery room. He <u>would know everything that HX was experiencing, but only as an observer,</u> and I got an IM "Yes." He did the regression without much emotion, and described much of what I noted above (which he had probably been told about by his family, even though he said little in his waking history). What was good about the regression as an observer was that I could then say (reframe):

DME: Knowing now that you survived okay, and it only *seemed* (seemed is such a good word in hypnosis) that you might die, would it be all right at our next visit for you to go back and review your own birth experience, knowing that I won't let anything happen to you, and that you already know you will make it through the difficulty and survive?

IM: [after some hesitation] YES.

The next visit was videotaped, and a copy of that tape which includes a 14-year follow-up is in the American Society of Clinical Hypnosis (ASCH) video lending library. His regression included an impressive abreaction, with turning of the head as he is extracted, complaint of head pain, two Jacksonian convulsions (which I asked about), and a startle reaction. I asked what startled him, and he said, "They're sticking me," but indicated his left arm rather than his heart. (nobody's perfect and not all memories are accurate). The following is a partial transcript of the regression and the handling of his abreaction:

DME: The next question is related to the onset of this involuntary muscle spasm around your mouth. Let your fingers answer this question. And the question is, is this a reaction to something that happened at your birth experience? Is this spasm around your mouth a reaction to something that happened when you were born?

IM: Yes.

DME: And the answer's *yes*. Every time you answer a question you are going to go deeper and deeper and deeper relaxed. Is it the result of fear? Is it the type of thing we're talking about when we say someone is "scared stiff" and his muscles go into spasm? Is it the result of fear? Is fear the important thing that happened at your birth experience?

IM: Yes, finger starts twitching.

DME: Your finger's twitching. Let it rise. Give me a good clear signal. Is fear the important thing that happened?

IM: Yes.

DME: Deeply, deeply relaxed. Are you still being affected by some fear that is buried in your subconscious mind? Is your subconscious mind still being affected by some fear from this experience?

IM: Thumb.

DME: Your thumb's saying you don't want to answer that question. It's all right. Deeply, deeply relaxed. Take a deep breath and let it ALLLLL out. Way, way, way down deep. That's right.

DME: The next question is if you can completely remove all of the fear that you experienced when you were born, will you be able to speak clearly? Will you be able to get well? (DME repeats question four times)

IM: Yes.

DME: And that's a good clear signal, and the answer's *yes.* Deeply, deeply, deeply relaxed. You can get well. You can completely remove all of that fear that you experienced that you still feel deep inside.

DME: The next question is, is it all right for you to go back to your birth experience and relive it, knowing that you got through it all right? Knowing that you are here today, knowing that you got through it all right, is it all right to go back and relive it? To know everything that happened? To feel it, to see it, to hear it. For you to go back and relive it, knowing that you got through it, even though it seemed very dangerous, even though you were very frightened? To go back and relive it? So that you can get rid of this and get well? Knowing that you made it safely. Knowing that I'll be with you. I'll keep you out of trouble. You're going to make it through.

IM: Yes.

DME: Okay. You've got some hesitation about it, but you're giving me the yes. So, we're going to go to it, because this is the way you can get all this fear out of you. I'm going to be holding your hand and you know you made it through and you're going to be all right.

DME: I want you to go back though time, back through the years, back through your teens, back through your youth, back through your babyhood, back to the time when you're just getting ready to be born, just getting ready to be born. Everything's dark. Everything's black. You can feel yourself being squeezed, your whole body being squeezed. Something is happening. It seems very difficult. It seems very difficult. It squeezes and then relaxes. And you get squeezed and then relaxed. Little itty bitty baby. Then something's happening. What's happening to your head?

What's happening to your head? What does it feel like? What does it feel like? Something's happening. Speak up and tell me what's happening.

P: Tight pressure.

DME: Tight pressure?

P: Tight pressure.

DME: Tight pressure. Speak up and tell me what it feels like. What does it feel like?

P: Tight . . . pressure.

DME: Does it hurt?

P: YES.

DME: Where does it hurt?

P: It hurts.

DME: Where does it hurt?

P: My head!

DME: Your head hurts?

P: Yes.

DME: Your head hurts. Tell me about it. What are they doing to you?

P: My head!

DME: Why does it hurt so much?

P: Squeezed.

DME: Squeezed? You're being squeezed?

P: YES.

DME: Squeezed. Does it pull?

P: Pulled.

DME: Now what's happening?

P: I can't breathe

DME: You can't breathe? Why can't you breathe?

P: I can't breathe.

DME: You feel like you can't breathe. All right, do you get out now? You're trying to breathe.

P: I can't. It won't let it me.

DME: It won't let you. What won't let you?

P: The cord.

DME: The cord? What's it doing?

P: It's around my neck.

DME: The cord is around your neck and you can't breathe. Are they doing something about it?

P: Cut the cord.

DME: They cut the cord? Now you've got to breathe. Can you breathe now?

P: It's too hard to breathe.

DME: It's too hard to breathe?

P: Too hard to breathe.

DME: Well you're going to be able to breathe. Keep on trying. Keep on trying.

P: [Gasps for air. Breathing is labored. Breathing becomes easier and smoother]

DME: Now what's happening? What do you feel like?

P: Muscles are stiff.

DME: Your muscles are stiff? All of your muscles? Your whole body?

P: Out of control.

DME: Out of control and stiff? Your whole body? Your whole body? How about your neck?

P: Stiff.

DME: Your neck is stiff. Are they helping you to breathe?

P: Helping me breathe.

DME: What does the doctor say? Can you hear what he says and what he does?

P: Yes.

DME: Yes. What does he say? What's happening? Tell me what's happening.

P: Flinches.

DME: What's happening?

P: Needle.

DME: A needle?

P: A sharp pain.

DME: A sharp pin?

P: Sharp pain.

DME: A sharp pin and sharp pain. Take one finger and show me where he puts it. Where's the pain?

P: [Points to left arm] Right in there.

DME: All right. Why are you smiling? Are you smiling or crying?

P: Starts crying.

DME: Do you feel like crying? What happens with the pin?

P: [Sobs] It hurts.

DME: It hurts?

P: It hurts.

DME: Do you cry out when it hurts?

P: No, cause they won't let me. I want to.

DME: They won't let you?

P: YES. They won't let me.

DME: You want to but they won't let you. Do you want to cry out?

P: Yes.

DME: Are you frightened?

P: Very frightened.

DME: You're very frightened.

P: Very frightened.

DME: You're very frightened. Do you want to call for help?

P: Yes.

DME: You want to call for help. You didn't do it before, did you? Why don't you call for help now? You can call for help now.

P: Call for help?

DME: You can call for help now. Help is here. Call for it.

P: [Sobs]

DME: You don't have to hold in what you want to say. You feel like crying?

P: Nods.

DME: You're frightened aren't you? You scared?

P: YES.

DME: What are you scared of? What are you frightened is going to happen to you?

P: Die.

DME: What?

P: Die.

DME: You're afraid you're going to die?

P: Yeh.

DME: That's very frightening. Why don't you call for help?

P: Help!

DME: Come on. Get some help!

P: Help me. I need help! I'm gonna die!

DME: You don't want to die do you?

P: No!

DME: All right, you want to live don't you!

P: Yeh. I wanna live!

DME: Sure you want to live. Sure you want to live, and the help is here. And I'm holding you, and you're going to be ALL RIGHT. The help came with the shot. It was a shot of adrenaline. And it picked your heart function up and you're breathing. And as soon as you get over being a little frightened here you're going to be all right. Because you're important and you're valuable. Everybody's going to come to your help and make sure you'll be all right. Because you're safe and in good hands. And everybody cares. Go ahead and cry because it was very frightening. But you made it through. You made it through and you survived. You made it through and you're going to be all right. So go ahead and cry.

P: [Sobbing]

DME: That cry for help was answered. And you're breathing all right. You're breathing all right. Notice how each breath comes easier and easier now. Your normal breathing is beginning to come in all right. Your heart rate's leveled off and you're doing very well. But it frightened you a lot and in the first few hours you may even have some times when you get stiff. Just go on through that.

P: [Patient is convulsing]

DME: Your muscles are tightening up. You're reliving this. Go on through it because I want you to get all of this out of your system. Be this little baby. They're going to put you in the incubator now. Tell me what's happening now? What happens next? What is it that's happening?? Your fingers are trying to signal something. Tell me what's happening. You're in the incubator. Are you safe?

P: [Convulsing]

DME: All right. That's just working off of fear. That's going to clear, and when it does, the fear's going with it. Work it on out. This little baby's scared stiff and all his muscles are tight and when they relax, he's going to be well. When they relax, he's going to be well. He's working off all that fear. Working off all that fear.

P: [Patient calming down and relaxing.]

DME: Take a deep deep breath and let it ALLLL out. Oh boy, feel all those muscles go loose and limp. Your face, your mouth, your neck, your shoulders, your chest, your arms, your legs, your whole body, and relax. Oh . . . each breath you get more and more relaxed, because you're safe now. You made it through it all. . . . And whenever you want to speak, . . . it's going to be perfectly easy, because there's not going to be anymore fear, fear that your going to die and fear that you can't call out for help . . . Because you called for help, and you got it!

You can speak your thoughts and say "no" to anybody. Each day you're going to get better and better. You're going to abandon any bad habits of speech that you have, so that you can hold your head erect, looking at someone, speaking clearly and effortlessly, naturally. You're just going to be yourself. You'll be comfortable being with other people. . . . Talking with them naturally. And if you have any bad habits of speech, just like we have different habits, you can practice them some to change them; to make them more like you want them to be. But you're going to be able to speak naturally and normally with confidence and self assurance whenever you want to. . . . Deeply, deeply, deeply relaxed now. Way, way down deep. You went through that very very nicely. I want you to come back to today now. I want you to let your fingers answer the question. I want you to scan from the depths of your inner mind, because sometimes when something is this big and is this important and has had this much effect on your life, sometimes you have to go through it more than once to completely get all of the emotion out of it. And your inner mind knows the answer to this question, and I want you to let your fingers answer it. I want you to think about it a minute, because the question's going to relate to whether or not you've gotten it all out. Because if you haven't gotten it all out, we can go back over it again and get the rest of it. It's easy. You saw the way we already went through that.

The next question is. . . . Were you able just now to completely release all the tension you need to release to get well? Have you let out all the tension you needed to in order to get well? Have you let all of it go that you need to in order to get well? Have you done all you need to do in order to get well?

IM: NO and then I'M NOT READY TO ANSWER YET (Thumb).
DME: That answer's equivocal. I know you don't relish going through this again, but you got through it all right. I'm here with you. You got through it okay. Is it all right to go back through this whole thing again to get out all the remaining tension that you need to get out to get well? Is it all right for you to go back through this whole thing again to get rid of any tension that's left in order to get well? Give me a good clear signal. Deeply deeply relaxed.

IM: I'M NOT READY TO ANSWER YET (Thumb).

DME: Let me change that question. You don't want to answer that question. I'm assuming that it's not all right to do it today so I'll change my question. If it turns out that you're not completely well from this, would it be all right to go back through this again at a later time? Because at some point, it'll just become a memory. There won't be anything frightening to it at all. Would it be all right for you to go back through it again at another time if you need to?

IM: Yes.

DME: Okay, and the answer's *yes.* Way, way, way down deep. Deeply relaxed. Now I want you to come back to today here, to January 25th, 1974, and my next question is, is there anything you want to ask, anything you want to say, before I rouse you up?

IM: No.

DME: No. Okay. Deeply deeply deeply relaxed. In a moment, I'm going to count to three, and when I say three, I want you to blink your eyes tightly and open them wide and rouse up wide awake, fresh and alert, comfortable. . . . ONE, Rousing up slowly now, Two, THREE.

P: [Opens eyes and sits up]

DME: How do you feel?

P: How'd I do?

DME: You did fine.

DME: Now, how did it feel? Tell me what you remember of this.

Outcome. The patient's speech improved noticeably. He returned home to finish his senior year in high school. His long-time companions expected him to be like he always had been, and he met their expectations and slipped back to where he was by Christmas. Then he came back to New Orleans for the summer between high school and college, and we repeated the regression, this time exhibiting much less emotion.

He improved nicely, and went on to attend a small college where no one had preconceived expectations. This time he did not slip back. He went on to get his Ph.D. in Biology, and the last I (DME) heard, he was teaching in a State College. The family said that his grandmother could understand him on the phone, and he said that his students did not complain about his lectures. He still grimaced some when he spoke, but in a 14-year follow-up video, he recited the Gettysburg address quite understandably!

David Cheek's Approach

Dave Cheek, as detailed in his books (Cheek & LeCron, 1968; Cheek, 1994) often asked his patients for permission with IM signals to explore their birth impressions with a focus on whether or not they felt welcome at birth.

He would have patients review in hypnosis their feelings about their mother's reactions to learning that she was pregnant. Then, if appropriate, he would have them move forward chronologically to the moment when their father was told about the pregnancy. He would have them sense their parents' emotional reactions. If these reactions were negative, Cheek would often suggest that the patient review it "as it would have been" if their mother had better preparation and a positive attitude.

He would also attempt to soften the feeling of being rejected by asking if the mother had an unconscious desire to be pregnant when she conceived. He would also ask if there were times during intrauterine development when the patient recognized maternal and paternal acceptance.

After establishing IM signals, Cheek (1994) would ask the patient:

Cheek: Would it be all right for us to review your birth?
IM: Yes.
Cheek: Let your inner mind go back (or "orient back") to the moment your head is emerging into the outside world at the end of your mother's labor. Your "yes" finger will lift to indicate you are there. ["Head movements and the recognition of which arm came out first were indications that she was getting physiological memories." (Cheek, 1994, p. 106)]
Cheek: "Is your mother able to speak at the moment of your birth?"
IM: Yes.
Cheek: "How does your mother feel when she sees you?"
P: [Verbal response]
Cheek: "How does the baby feel?"
P: [Verbal and/or physical response]
Cheek: "Please go back to the moment your mother realizes that she is pregnant with you. When you are there, your 'yes' finger will lift. As it lifts, please tell me how your mother is feeling when the doctor tells her."
P: [Verbal and/or non-verbal response]
Cheek: "Go to the moment she tells your father that she is pregnant."

Cheek points out that when Mother's attitude was negative about the pregnancy, that "it is important then to impress the patient with the fact that this attitude on the part of the mother was her problem and was probably based on the mother's early relationship to her parents and siblings" (Cheek, 1994, p. 107).

He also utilized the patient's suggestibility in trance to reframe the patient's birth impressions on an emotional level. He stated, "Sometimes it is possible to have the patient review the moment of her unhappy mother's diagnosis of pregnancy and have the mother think to the little embryo the kind of feelings that would have made her baby feel welcome. This is turning the concept of being a baby into being the mother. It curiously is possible for troubled patients to hallucinate the sensations of feeling welcome and nurtured when there was none of this in the early experience" (p. 107).

Chapter 7

THE SEVEN COMMON CAUSES OF
PSYCHOSOMATIC DISORDERS

There are <u>seven common causes of psychosomatic disorders</u> and symptoms. In doing ideomotor reviews of which ones are active with a particular patient, <u>patients often say "yes" to more than one</u> of these causative factors. The seven common causes are Conflict, Organ *language* language, Motivation, Past experience, Identification; Self-punishment, and Suggestion, and collectively spell the mnemonic, C.O.M.P.I.S.S. In our chart, when we get ready to scan through the seven common causes using IM signals, we just write the mnemonic vertically down the left margin to organize our notes.

Cheek and LeCron (1968) deserve credit for disseminating this useful model and ideomotor questioning technique for rapid hypnoanalysis. <u>Milton Erickson knew about it and used it to some extent</u> (Erickson & Rossi, 1981). <u>He didn't distrust it,</u> but he moved on to doing more complex and <u>layered, improvisational therapies.</u>

This technique is remarkably simple and easy to use. It will frequently produce insights that are sufficient to get the patient well quickly without complicating or lengthening the therapy.

1. Conflict (WANT vs OUGHT) (PULLED IN TWO DIRECTIONS)

We explain to the patient:

T: One of the things that causes symptoms is what we call a <u>conflict</u>. A conflict occurs when you feel like you <u>want</u> to do one thing, but you ought to do the opposite. You're pulled in two directions. That uses up a lot of energy. [The patient is asked to answer with his fingers:] So, my question to you is do you sense that you are being affected by a conflict? That you're being pulled in two directions?

IM: If the answer is no, we pass on. If the answer is yes, then we ask:

T: Would it be all right for you to know at a conscious level what the conflict is?

IM: With a yes answer to that, we say:

T: I'll be quiet while you scan your feelings, and when it comes to your conscious mind, your yes finger will rise.

IM: When the yes finger rises, ask:

T: Is it all right for you to tell me what it is? [Some things are private and we must respect the patient's right to keep things private. However . . .]

IM: If the patient signals "yes," we say:

T: Speak to me and tell me what you're experiencing.

P: Once the patient has identified and verbalized the stressful conflict, we typically point out:

T: A conflict is a problem in indecision. You are being pulled in two directions and you are suffering from a problem in indecision. So, you need to decide which choice to make, abandon the thoughts about the opposite choice, and get on with your life. Which choice you make has to be your own. But having made one, I can help you feel comfortable carrying it out.

The Treatment   *make a decision*

Since a conflict is a problem in *indecision,* the treatment for the conflict is to make a *decision.* Often the choice is not a medical choice. If someone feels like he wants to get a divorce but ought to stay married, it is not a medical issue. It is a personal decision. There are usually family members, religious advisors, and lifetime friends, who are people who know the patient far better than the doctor or therapist. Such individuals can usually proffer personal advice. Our point to the patient is:

> *The conflict is resolved when you make a choice and start carrying out your decision. There are changes that go with making a choice, and I can help you deal with whatever you choose. Another choice you can make is to decide to put off making a decision until a more appropriate later date. Sometimes you don't have enough information to make a wise choice. So, it's sensible to postpone making a serious choice until you have more factual information. If you decide this is not the right time to make a decision, then put the issue out of*

your mind until a more appropriate time. This is still a choice, and it will give you relief from the symptom in the meantime.

In our experience, the common, ordinary tension headache is usually caused by a conflict.

Conflict Case Example

I (DME) saw a 22-year-old Emergency Room nurse limping, and asked why. He showed me a two-inch diameter plantar wart on the ball of his foot. I inquired, "What's going on in your life that stresses you?" and he replied "Aw, Doc, I'm in love, and I ought to walk away from it." I saw him in my office the next day. He had been treated for the wart for about three months with topical Podophyllin and Salicylates with minimal response. After my regular intake, and photographing the wart, I induced trance and set up Ideomotor Signals:

DME: One of the causes of symptoms is what we call a Conflict, which occurs when you feel like you want to do one thing, and you ought to do the opposite. Or, you feel you ought to do something, and you want to do the opposite. You are pulled in two different directions. Do you feel that you are being affected by a conflict?

IM: (ideomotor signal): Yes.

DME: Is it all right for you to know at a conscious level what the conflict is?

IM: Yes.

DME: The thought will cross your mind, and when you know what it is your YES finger will rise.

IM: After 10 to 20 seconds, the YES finger rises.

DME: Is it all right for you to tell me what it is? (Note that sometimes the patient feels it is too private or embarrassing to tell us. Then, we have to handle it differently. See * below.)

IM: Yes.

DME: Tell me. (Note that he doesn't speak until I say to.)

---

* In the rare instance where a patient indicates that it is not all right to tell us, we go right to the comment that "Conflict is a problem in indecision . . . ," then "Does it make sense. . . ," and finally "Can you solve this for yourself without having to tell me what it is?" So far, in our experience, that answer has been YES, and these patients recovered without our ever knowing exactly what the conflict was (though the intake gave us a likely diagnosis).

Patient: Doc, I'm in love and want to get married, but she won't do it until she gets her college degree. She's a sophomore now. (Listen in "literal." {She won't do it}).

DME: Are you living together?

Patient: No. We're both Catholic, and neither of us has ever had intercourse. I'm very horny.

DME: A conflict is a problem in indecision. It's like turning on the engine in your car, and not shifting into forward or reverse. You can use up a whole tank full of gas sitting in neutral, and you're still right where you started. Conflict stresses your immune system, and that energy could be used to heal this wart. You need to make a decision, and I can help you either way you decide. If she's really the right girl for you for a lifetime, you can stand three more years of being in love and being celibate. That's your decision to make, but either way there will no longer be an emotional conflict depressing your immune system, and your body will use that energy to heal this virus infection that causes the wart.

DME: Does it make sense to you that you need to make a decision about this conflict?

IM: Yes.

DME: Does your subconscious mind feel there is any other problem we need to deal with that would interfere with healing this wart?

IM: No,

These are the key questions and responses that took place in three 45-minute visits. He decided to "walk away from it," and six months later, he married another girl and had a successful marriage. His wart became pain-free the day he made his decision, and the lesion cleared completely in about a month. I did not see him to get my follow-up photo until three months after the last visit (see Figures 7.1 and 7.2, before and after). There was no recurrence at five-year follow-up.

2. Organ Language

There are many phrases in our everyday conversation that include mention of a body organ in a negative way. For example, we often hear people say things like: "I feel like I've been stabbed in the back"; or

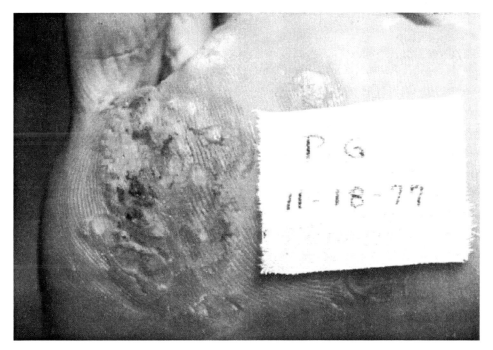

Figure 7.1

"My boss is a pain the neck"; or "I can't stand on my own two feet"; or "I can't swallow that"; or "I'm itching to get out of this relationship."

At a subconscious level, these metaphors can be internalized literally and be turned into a symptom, or these types of expressions can reflect the underlying psychodynamics of the symptom. We explain to the patient:

T: One thing that can cause symptoms is what we call "organ language." This refers to phrases in our everyday conversation that include mention of a body organ in a negative way. [In giving examples to the patient, we try to include a phrase or two that might be applicable to the patient's symptom that mentions the patient's target organ as an example. For instance, if the patient has headaches, we might give an example such as:] For example, we sometimes hear people say things like: "My job is a real headache," or "My boss is a pain the neck." If taken literally by your subconscious, these types of phrases can be converted into an actual symptom. [Having explained what "organ language" is, we use IM signals to ask the patient:]

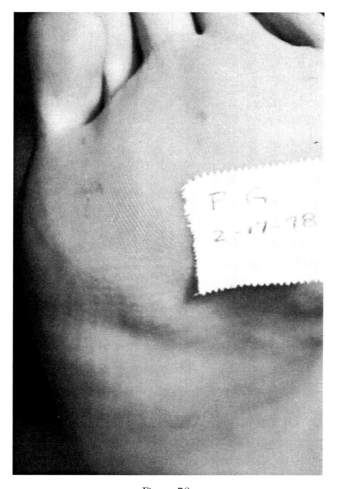

Figure 7.2

T: Do you sense that you are being affected by organ language? Answer with your fingers.
IM: If the answer is yes, we then ask:
T: Would it be all right to bring your specific phrase that's affecting you to a conscious level?
IM: If the answer is yes, we then ask:
T: Would it be all right to tell me the phrase?
IM: If the yes finger rises, we say:
T: Speak to me and tell me how it's affecting you. [Allow time for the patient to bring the material up and say it.]

The Treatment

The treatment for "organ language" is to accurately re-word the phrase omitting the name of any organ. For example:

T: The fact is that your boss is an unpleasant person to deal with, and you need to work out a way to deal with him and still maintain your comfort. [You remove any organ reference from the phrase] Would it be all right with your subconscious to come up with another way to deal with him and still maintain your comfort?

IM: If the yes finger lifts, say:

T: Let your subconscious review this issue, and I'll be quiet, and when you come up with a way to cope with this problem and still be comfortable, your yes finger will rise.

IM: When the yes finger rises, say:

T: Now lock in on that with every cell in your mind, and body and feelings.

Want it to happen, let it happen, and it will happen (An elegant admonition from Dave Elman, 1970).

Organ Language Case Example

A 53-year-old celibate priest had the typical itching, well-demarcated, pigmented plaques of neurodermatitis (alternately known as lichen planus or scratch dermatitis) on both forearms and hands, present for about eight days. After my intake and photographing the lesions, I (DME) induced trance and set up Ideomotor Signals (see Figure 7.3).

DME: One of the causes of symptoms is what we call Organ Language, which occurs when a common saying that includes some organ in the body is converted by the subconscious mind into a disorder of that organ. The saying "I feel like I've been stabbed in the back" may become an actual chronic back pain when a person is feeling betrayed. Or the feeling "This job is a pain in the neck" can cause a painful wry neck every day at work. Do you sense that you are being affected by an Organ Language saying?

IM: Yes.

DME: Do you feel like you are "itching to . . ." do something?

IM: Yes.

DME: Would it be all right to go back and review what was happening when it started?

IM: Yes.

DME: Take a deep breath and relax, and let your thoughts and feelings go back to what was happening when this started. When you start reviewing it, your yes finger will rise, every time you come to something emotionally important your no finger will rise, and when you've completed reviewing it your thumb will rise.

IM: Goes through the review with one NO signal.

DME: Is it all right to tell me what happened?

IM: Yes (Note the literal answer. He will not initiate speech until I ask him to.)

DME: Speak to me, and tell me what happened.

Patient: An attractive woman in my congregation told me her husband was out of town, and invited me to visit her. She said she'd like to know me better.

DME: That sounds to me like she'd like to "know" you better in the Biblical sense. Did that cross your mind?

Patient: Yes, but I didn't go.

DME: Is that what you started itching for?

IM: Yes.

DME: But you didn't do any thing but itch?

IM: Yes.

DME: Nobody's perfect. But didn't God create males of every species to be alert to receptive females, to encourage his instruction to "be fruitful and multiply"? Isn't this symptom interfering with how well you go about doing God's work?

IM: Yes.

DME: Would it be all right to forgive God for making you a male, and ask him to forgive you for feeling like one?

IM: (15 seconds of hesitation) Yes.

DME: If you do that, can you picture yourself putting this problem in the past, and getting back to feeling like a Priest, and setting a good example for your flock?

IM: Yes.

DME: Let it happen. Do you sense that there is anything else in your subconscious mind that would interfere with your getting well?

IM: No.

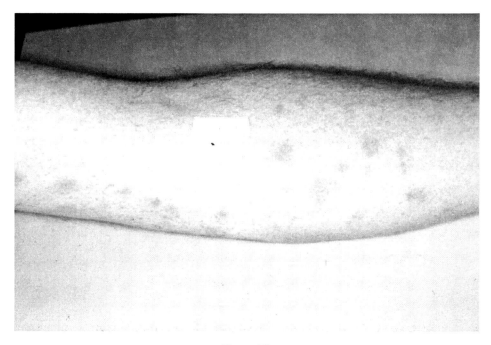

Figure 7.3

DME: Want it to happen, let it happen, and it will happen. Then, my
usual alerting suggestions.

He left my office comfortable, and returned at my request for follow-up photos three days later, at which time the lesions were about 75% cleared, and there was no more discomfort (see Figure 7.4). The symptoms did not recur.

3. Motivation

Sometimes a symptom solves a problem for a patient or at least seems better than what might occur. Halitosis is better than no breath at all. In psychological terms, we often refer to this as "secondary gain." Patients understand it better when we discuss it as being *motivated* to have the symptom because it's not all bad; there's something beneficial about it too. We tell the patient:

T: A person can be motivated to have a symptom because it seems to solve a problem. One of the causes of symptoms may be that they serve a subconscious purpose. These symptoms may even be self-

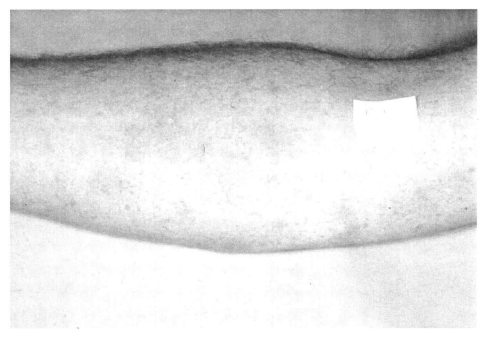

Figure 7.4

protective such as when students get sick around exam time, or when soldiers get sick when especially dangerous missions are about to be undertaken. Do you sense that you are motivated to have this symptom? That it somehow serves a useful or protective purpose for you?

IM: A yes answer to that calls for asking:

T: What possible good could come in your life from having this problem? How is it possible that this symptom is helpful or protective to you in any way?

In answering this question, the patient exposes what he needs help with. At this point, the therapist can refer back to the answer to the intake question, *If you were cured, what would you do that you can't do now?*

Patients often feel guilty about having these symptoms and tend to be reluctant to admit to them. They are more likely to "medicalize" and rationalize their origins and continuance. One must probe ever so gently to avoid being confrontational or appear being judgmental and losing rapport. In truth, patients are very grateful once you help them get it out and when you have not made a judgment on them.

The Treatment

This form of disorder is nonadaptive. The problem that needs solving is still there. The treatment is to find a better and healthier way to cope with the problem, or to change the way the problem is perceived. When you find out the problem the patient is trying to solve, you can reframe the solution to a healthier and more adaptive alternative that makes it unnecessary to be sick.

Motivation Case Example

A 42-year-old Vice-President of a large chemical corporation presented with a cluster of 41 venereal warts on his penis, nine on the glans, and the rest on his foreskin, that had been present for three months (see Figure 7.5). He was seeking a cure that did not involve burning or freezing, and was referred by a dermatologist who knew I'd (DME) had success with treating warts. Intake history revealed that he was married and had two children. He was involved in a stale affair, and said he intended to end it. He had not had intercourse since the warts appeared. After intake and photographing the lesions, I (DME) induced trance with a rapid eye-roll induction and set up ideomotor signals.

DME: Sometimes it *seems* to the subconscious mind that a symptom can solve a problem, and we are motivated to use it that way. At a feeling level, do you sense that somehow you are motivated to have these warts to help solve a problem?

IM: Yes.

DME: Tell me—If you didn't have the warts, what would happen?

Patient: She'd go to bed with me.

DME: Who'd go to bed with you?

Patient: My girlfriend. But I need to break up with her and get back with my wife.

DME: What does your wife think about the warts?

Patient: She thinks I've got some kind of nasty disease, and she won't sleep with me either.

DME: That doesn't sound like a good solution to anything. The traditional way to break up with a girlfriend who hasn't hurt you is to give her some money, or a job, or a fur coat, or something you know she'd like. You couldn't have gotten to be Vice-Pres-

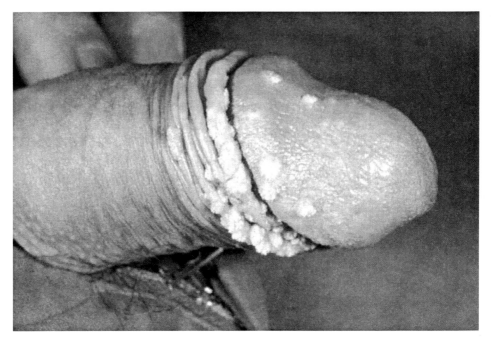

Figure 7.5

ident of a big company without being a problem-solver. Can't you think of a way to break up with your mistress without hiding behind a bunch of warts?

Patient: (5–10 seconds of quiet, then a big sigh) "Yes."

DME: Then do it, and let the warts go.

He was alerted, and left with a knowing look on his face. He kept a requested three week follow-up appointment, and on follow-up, there was no sign he'd ever had a wart (see Figure 7.6). This is an incomplete report, because I got so involved in getting my follow-up photos that I never found out if his girlfriend got money, a job, a fur coat, or something else.

4. Past Experience

There are two kinds of past experiences from a psychosomatic point of view. Obviously, every symptom started at some point in the past. Ordinarily this is a time of being emotionally focused. Sometimes, the experience is so powerful that the symptom starts right then and there

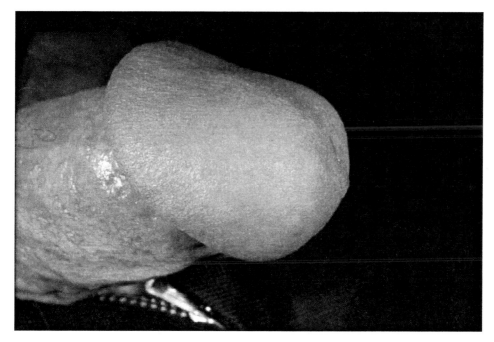

Figure 7.6

and continues to manifest itself. The other case is when an experience triggers a subconscious memory of a previous sensitizing past event that has not been producing symptoms. At this point in time, the symptom manifests. The initial idea and feelings were implanted long ago, and that past event sensitized the patient to react to subsequent similar circumstances.

The Treatment

The treatment for past experience in either case is to *regress* and *reframe* the fixed idea. When regressing to the onset of the symptom, it is always useful to ask the question, *Did something happen prior to this to sensitize you?* That way you pick up what happened earlier. This enables you to distinguish between the two types of past sensitizing experiences. We ask the patient:

T: Do you sense this problem started with a significant experience in your past?

IM: In response to a yes answer, we ask:

T: Is it all right to go back and do a subconscious review of everything that was significant to you in this episode?

Repetitive Subconscious Review

If you get a "yes" at this point, repetitive subconscious review is valuable because the more you review it, the clearer your memory of it is. Also, a graduated regression (i.e., "retrograde search") to uncomfortable repressed material is often less threatening to the patient. So, we go on as follows:

T: Did it happen before age 20?
IM: The patient must first do a subconscious review of some sort to answer "yes."
T: Before age 10?
IM: Another review to answer "yes."
T: Before age 5?
IM: A third review to answer "yes."
T: Before age 4?
IM: Another review, and this time the answer "no" would tell us that it happened at age 4.
T: Is it all right to orient your mind back to what happened at age 4?
IM: With a "yes," say:
T: Okay. Let your mind orient back to the very beginning. And when you start reviewing it, your yes finger will rise. Every time you encounter something emotionally important to you, your no finger will rise. And when you have completed reviewing the episode, you'll signal with your thumb.

After this review, we ask the patient:

T: Is it all right to bring it up to a conscious level and review it again and tell me what's happening?
IM: If the patient signals, "yes," say:
T: Speak to me and tell me what's happening. [At this point, the therapist must use common sense to reframe whatever trauma is described into a healthy, realistic experience from which the patient can learn and move on.]

After that regression and discussion in trance, it is worthwhile to ask: *Did anything happen before this to emotionally sensitize you?* If "yes," then

Retrograde Search

follow a similar procedure to identify and review the sensitizing event and reframe it appropriately.

Sidebar. Here we get into a technical issue. Some therapists believe it is best to regress to a safe time just before the sensitizing episode and then progress forward into it (i.e., "chronological search"). The theory is that if the experience is very traumatic, the patient will avoid going to it directly. In our experience, that is rarely necessary, and we usually go directly to the incident. If the patient resists this, then we see what happens by going to a safe period before the incident. Since the patient has already been asked if it is all right to regress to the incident and said "yes," we find that patients seldom resist doing this.

If the patient's YES finger lifts indicating it is all right to go back to the sensitizing incident, we do a "retrograde search." We say: *Did it happen before you were age 3? Age 2? Age 1? At birth?* When we get a "yes," we repeat the IM review procedure illustrated above.

Very Emotional Regressions. In very emotional regressions, the no finger will often twitch first almost like a startle response, but then the yes finger will rise, as the review starts, and the no finger will rise one or more times as the patient's subconscious review takes place. We count the number of times the no finger rises because if there are three emotional instances, we are going to want to deal with and reframe each of the three at the time of the regression.

If the patient's no finger lifted three times during the IM review, then after he completes the IM review, we say: *Now go back and review it again and tell me what's happening.* We need to hear three things that are emotionally significant because we want to make sure each is reframed. So, we instruct the patient: *As you speak, your "no" finger will rise each time you encounter something emotionally important.*

If there are several no signals and it appears complicated, we will say to the patient: *You got through it all right, but let's go over it again as though you read the headlines last time and now you are going to read the fine print— all about it, the details, who's there, what they're saying, how you feel, and what's happening.* And then start another review.

The first time David Cheek used this technique to recover sounds heard under general anesthesia he had to do thirteen subconscious reviews to get the material up to consciousness (Cheek, 1994). We do as many reviews as necessary. Next we ask:

T: Is it all right to review it one more time and speak and tell me what is happening?

IM: With a yes answer to that, we say:

T: Speak to me and tell me what's happening, and every time you come to something emotionally important, your NO finger will rise while you're speaking.

[Note that this is in the <u>present</u> tense as though it is happening right now.]

This was a time when the patient was very vulnerable. It could be a major rejection or loss, a death of a loved one, a rape or robbery, an auto accident, being under a general anesthetic, a fall, etc.

Past Experience Case Examples

Sometimes the Ⓐsymptom starts immediately at a time of significant emotion. But sometimes the subconscious mind just can't handle it at the time Ⓑstores it, and is prepared later for anything that activates the memory. Physically, it's analogous to the first shot of penicillin causing no reaction because the body has never dealt with this foreign substance. However, it can make antibodies, and the second shot of penicillin may produce a strong antigen-antibody reaction.

Delayed Onset

A psychiatrist referred to me (DME) a 14-year-old girl for treatment of insomnia and nightmares. Drugs were altering her liver function. She was failing in school. She came in with a large fever blister on her upper lip, which she said recurred with every menstrual cycle since her first at age twelve. She was very self-conscious about it, and was more interested in treating the herpes than the insomnia. She felt (erroneously) that its presence informed others that she was menstruating. After intake and photographing the lesion (see Figure 7.7), I induced trance with a rapid eye-roll induction and set up ideomotor signals. Utilizing her priorities, I went first to what bothered her the most.

DME: One of the causes of symptoms is a very emotional episode that occurred in the past that is still affecting a person. Do you feel that you are being affected by a Past Experience?

IM: Yes.

DME: Would it be all right for you to go back and review at a subconscious level everything that was important to you at the first time you had a fever blister?

[margin handwritten note: Conscious Permission to Review @ Sub C. Level]

Feeling Mind (handwritten)

IM: Yes.

DME: Each breath you take, you'll go deeper and deeper, as your feeling mind reviews the whole episode. When you start reviewing it, your yes finger will rise, every time you come to something emotionally important your no finger will rise, and when you have completed the review you will signal with your thumb. (I touch each of these digits as I refer to it).

[Comment: She did the review with very little sign of emotion, and one NO signal.]

DME: Would it be all right to review it again in more detail, and this time speak to me and tell me what's happening?

Permission to speak (handwritten)

IM: Yes.

Patient: (Summarized) She was a country girl, and her first period started on a weekend at home. Her mother told her what she knew about hygiene, that it would happen every month, and that it meant that she was growing into womanhood and was old enough to have babies. She had the first fever blister the next day.

[(Comment) She described a comfortable mother–daughter encounter. It was bland, and I couldn't detect what was emotionally important enough to have caused the no signal.]

DME: Did something happen before this to sensitize you?

IM: Yes.

["Retrograde search"]

DME: Did it happen before you were twelve?

IM: Yes.

DME: Eleven?

IM: Yes.

DME: Ten?

IM: No. (Note that she had to do three subconscious reviews to locate age 10. Also, questions about numbers do not evoke emotion or repression, and are answered readily.)

DME: Are you at home?

IM: No.

DME: At school?

IM: No. (The episode is on her mind, and I have shifted into the present tense as though it is happening now. She's not at either of the two places a 10 year-old girl is most likely to be.)

DME: Are you alone?

IM: No.

DME: Are either of your parents there?

IM: No.

DME: Is there more than one other person there?

IM: Yes.

DME: More than two?

IM: Yes (We determined there were four teenaged boys there.)

DME: (Putting two and two together, since the symptom onset is related to vaginal bleeding . . .) Do they do any thing to you sexually?

IM: Yes.

(**Comment:** This became tedious because she would only answer with finger signals. It finally occurred to me that they might have done what molesters and rapists often do, and I asked the right question).

DME: Did they threaten to hurt you or someone you love if you ever told anyone?

IM: Yes.

DME: But you didn't tell me. You just wiggled your fingers. They didn't say that if you ever wiggled your fingers they'd hurt you. You're safe here, and it's all right to speak and tell me what happened.

(Note that to a terrified, vulnerable, 10-year-old, the threat was like a post-hypnotic suggestion, and she had carried it out compulsively. She never told her mother, her father, or her school counselor, and she couldn't tell me until I removed the suggestion. She had been gang raped at the point of a knife, and told that if she ever told anybody they'd rape her again and kill her.

Now her mother's words have new meaning. A 12-year-old country girl knows what causes babies, and she's had intercourse with four boys, and if she gets pregnant, she'll have to tell someone, and then they'll kill her. That's stressful menstruation!)

DME: When your mother says menstruation means you're old enough to have babies, does that bring up the memory and stress you?

IM: Yes.

DME: You will learn in biology that menstruation means that a woman is *not* pregnant. You also need to know that a woman has to have intercourse within the last 48 hours in order to get pregnant. You haven't had intercourse in four years, your menstruation means you are not pregnant, and you are physically intact.

[I added:] No one can hurt you emotionally without some kind of agreement or consent from you. A psychiatrist named Viktor Frankl survived the death camp at Auschwitz in World War II, and came out as a functioning physician. He wrote, "The facts of our lives are not as important as our attitudes towards them." No one can change the fact that you were assaulted, but you need to get on with your life, feel strong and unafraid, and find your happiness. You need to change your attitude towards it.

Can you picture yourself leaving this episode in the past, and getting on with looking forward to something good each day?

IM: Yes.

DME: Want it to happen, let it happen, and it will happen.

After alerting, I showed her one of my (DME) treasures. During the war, Helen Keller was active visiting service personnel, and inspiring them with her bravery in spite of being blind and deaf. I was in the Navy in 1944, and met her. I had a copy of Keller's autobiography, and she inscribed on the foreleaf, "For Dabney Ewin, who will find that obstacles are things to be overcome, if we are to live strong and unafraid. Affectionately, Helen Keller." A picture is worth a thousand words.

The patient was returned to the care of the referring psychiatrist, who had indicated that she was probably schizophrenic, with a poor prognosis. However, the insomnia and nightmares cleared, she finished high school, and graduated on the Dean's list from a small but accredited college. The menstrual herpes stopped completely (see Figure 7.8). She had one recurrence of herpes when she visited the town where the rape occurred, and still gets one outbreak every year the first time she goes out in the summer sun. I have no explanation for that. She is married and has several children.

Immediate Onset

A 22-year-old medical student volunteered for a demonstration to the class. He stated that he got hives when he ate chocolate for "as long as I can remember." After taking an abbreviated history, I (DME) asked if there was anything else he thought I ought to know. He replied with-

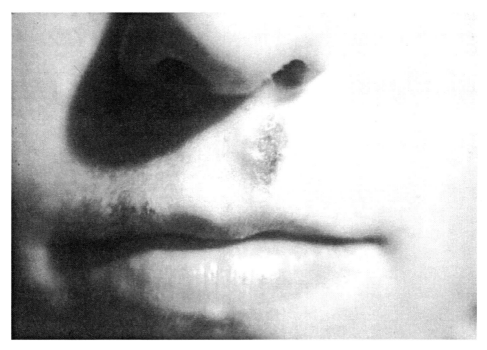

Figure 7.7

out hesitation, "Yes, I'm phobic about snakes. If one comes on TV, I have to leave the room or turn off the TV." I had just lectured on history taking (anamnesis), and made the point that <u>if a patient answers that last question, it is the key to the solution</u>. So I was stuck doing a demonstration with a patient who gets hives eating chocolate, and the problem is snakes. I could not imagine any connection between these ingredients. I induced trance with a rapid eye roll and set up ideomotor signals.

DME: Do you sense that you are being affected by a Past Experience?
IM: Yes.
DME: Would it be all right to go back at a subconscious level and review this episode?
IM: Yes.
DME: Did it happen before you were five?

[**Comment:** I picked the age 5 for starters because I was searching for a time that went back as far as he could remember.]

IM: Yes.
DME: Four?

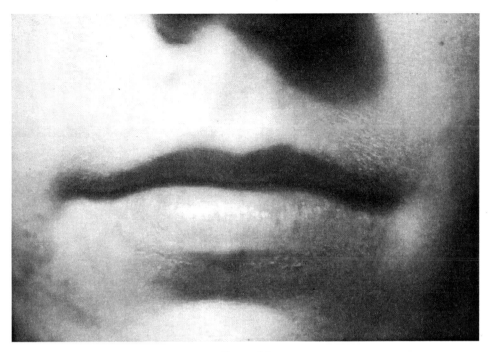

Figure 7.8

IM: Yes.

DME: Three?

IM: No.

DME: Let your thoughts and feelings go back at a subconscious level to review everything that is important about what happened when you were three years old. When you start reviewing it, your YES finger will rise. Every time you encounter something emotionally important to you, your NO finger will rise, and when you have completed the review you will signal with your thumb. (I touch each of these digits as I verbally refer to it).

[**Comment:** He did the review with autonomic changes of increased rate of breathing, speeding of pulse rate in the neck veins, and signs of arousal. There was one prolonged NO signal.]

DME: Would it be all right to review it again, and this time, speak and tell me what is happening?

IM: Yes.

Patient: (Summarized) It was a sunny Saturday in the spring, and my parents took me to Audubon Park. We stopped at the snake pit. (This is a sunken enclosure with an island surrounded by a moat, and large Boa Constrictors and Anacondas on the island). It was feeding time for the snakes, and they were being fed live rabbits, and it made me feel so scared and horrible. The next morning was Easter, and I got a chocolate rabbit. I couldn't eat it, and I broke out with hives.

DME: That was a long time ago, and you know that you're not a snake, don't you? In fact, knowing what you know now about nature, that's how most creatures survive. Fish eat live shrimp, birds eat live insects, frogs catch live flies with their tongues, and big snakes eat live rabbits. A piece of chocolate is not even alive, and you would not have been a bad person if you had eaten it. It's understandable how a kindhearted little boy would feel sad for the rabbits, but that's in the long ago now. Can you picture yourself leaving that episode in the past, and just treating a piece of chocolate as a piece of chocolate?

IM: Yes.

DME: Then want it to happen, let it happen, and it will happen. [Then he was given alerting suggestions.]

The following week in class he raised his hand and said "I've been eating chocolate all week. It's the best thing I ever tasted."

The implications of this are significant. We know a lot about the immune system and antibodies. Their existence is a measurable biological fact. Did we suddenly eradicate the millions of antibodies of a true allergy, or was this just a psychic aversion that had persisted for 19 years? It seems more logical that it was a psychic aversion. But if so, shouldn't everyone with hives undergo a hypnotic review as part of the diagnostic workup before they are put on drugs and a restricted diet?

Warning: Since I didn't know if he had a true allergy or not, I carefully avoided giving him a suggestion that it would be all right to eat some chocolate. He did his testing on his own.

5. Identification

Identification occurs when there is a strong emotional attachment to another person who had or has the same symptom. Frequently, this person is dead or dying. It is as though keeping the symptom active also keeps the relationship alive. The other person may be a parent, grandparent, spouse, sibling, best friend, or hero.

When a parent dies of lung cancer, we would think it would be a wake-up call for their son or daughter to stop smoking. However, we have had a number of patients who continued to smoke after one of their parents (who smoked) died of lung cancer or some other smoking-related, fatal illness. For example:

A 37-year-old married wildlife artist, J., with a 2-pack a day smoking habit, consulted with BNE to stop smoking. I (BNE) employed waking state reframing and direct suggestion in hypnosis (DSIH) using the Zarren and Eimer (2002) Single Session Smoking Cessation protocol. J. called 12 days later and reported that he was smoking again. He had gone home feeling good after our afternoon session. However, late that evening, he received a phone call from his brother who had found their father dead in bed. J. stated that his father had "smoked like a fiend" all his life and "didn't take care of himself at all." As an adult, J. frequently smoked with his father. J. stated, "he smoked, I smoked. He was always around." When J. met his brother at their father's house that evening, there were cigarettes everywhere, and J. "started smoking again like a fiend."

Ideomotor analysis will bring up the identification and the state dependent subconscious reverie of this relationship. Smoking together may be in the patient's "feeling mind" a time of intimacy. People who smoke alone often do have reveries or daydreams of what they wish for.

The Treatment   *[handwritten: Recognize their identification then reframe]*

The treatment for this is to help the patient recognize the identification, and then to reframe the feeling that the other person is still there. The patient is a separate person who is not bound by the other's problems. Each of us is unique.

We also think of identification as modeling the other person to share a relationship and keep the relationship alive. The patient needs to recognize what is actually happening–that the root of the problem is that the symptom has been keeping the relationship alive in the patient's feeling mind. Once the patient recognizes this, the doorway is opened to helping the patient find a better solution to remembering the person and their special relationship. For example:

In the smoking recall session with J., I (BNE) hypnotized him, and set up IM signals. IM questioning revealed that, in his feeling mind, smoking did keep the relationship with his father alive. There was no guilt about his father's death as they had a great relationship. In trance, I (BNE) reframed the active Identification by asking J. to answer with his fingers if he felt that his father would want him to continue to smoke. The answer was "no." J's "feeling mind" readily recognized that there were healthier ways for him to positively remember his father and keep the relationship alive in his memory. Knowing this, J. answered with his feelings (fingers) that he was willing to give up smoking and get well; for himself, for his father, and for his wife. He stated that it was "time to move on." As of this writing, on 6-month follow-up, J. has remained a nonsmoker.

Earlier on in the history-taking, we ask the patient about who had the same or similar problem. If the answer included someone emotionally close, then we are alerted to this possibility. The ideomotor question is:

T: Do you sense, "yes" or "no" [stroke both fingers] that you are identifying with someone who had the same or a similar symptom?

IM: [If we get a "yes" answer to that,]

T: And the answer's yes. Is it all right to know who it is?

IM: [If we get a "yes"]

T: And the answer's yes. All right. When it comes to your mind, your yes finger will rise.

IM: [Yes finger rises]

T: Okay. Now with that person and the symptom in mind, would it be all right to go back to a particular time when this symptom was really important and then review it?

IM: [A "yes" to that leads to reviewing it. Say:]

T: When you start reviewing it your yes finger will rise, every time you come to something emotionally important, your no finger will rise, and when you've completed reviewing the episode, you'll signal with your thumb.

IM: [Be quiet until the thumb rises and at that point say:]

T: Would it be all right to review it again and tell me what's happening?

IM: Yes.

T: Yes. Okay. Go on now and review it and speak to me and tell me what's happening. [Notice that this is phrased in the present tense.]

[At some point, when appropriate, you can suggest the following:]

T: You can keep the relationship alive by keeping your happy memories of what you had and make that person proud of you for taking better care of yourself than he did. You are a different person than your [the person's name] was. You are not [your father, mother, etc.]. You do not have all the same genes, the same education, the same experiences, the same intellect, and so forth as your [father, mother, etc.]. You are an individual. Everyone is a separate individual responsible for their own behavior. You can stop [smoking or whatever] when you decide to do so. You are not helpless. Surely the person you care about would want you to keep your memories of the good times you had together and not to emulate harmful or self destructive habits of theirs.

Past Lives? Rarely, when the patient is asked to regress back to the first time they had this symptom, they come up with a "past life." It is not necessary for the therapist to believe in "past lives" to treat this. We think of this as just another example of Identification. After the IM review, and the patient bringing it up to verbal consciousness, you reframe by simply separating the life that happened to another body, at another time, in another place, from the present life.

T: Is there really any need to have this symptom in this new body, at this new time, in this new place?

P: The patient usually signals "No" and gets well.

Identification Case Example

Sometimes a person develops the same symptom as someone who was emotionally important in his life, particularly if that person is dying or dead. It's as though having the symptom keeps the relationship alive, even though the person is dead. It bears repeating that the treatment is to separate the identities. Everyone is unique.

A 45-year-old Hispanic man came to the emergency room with classic findings of acute appendicitis. I (DME) told him the diagnosis, and that he should have surgery without delay. The operation went smoothly, and the appendix came out easily through a small incision. It was not ruptured. On rounds the next morning his abdomen was fully distended with gas, and percussion of the abdomen sounded like a bass

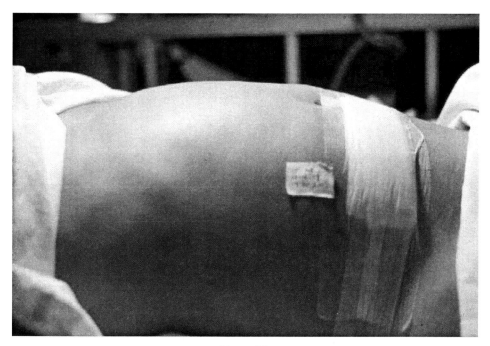

Figure 7.9

drum (see Figure 7.9). No bowel sounds could be heard. He had Paralytic Ileus (see Figure 7.10). This is a hypersympathetic paralysis of the bowel that can occur after extensive handling of the bowel (which did not happen), with generalized peritonitis (there was no sign of infection), or from sheer terror.

The diagnosis had been so easy that I had bypassed some of the history. His father had died of a ruptured appendix, leaving his mother destitute with eight children. When I found this out, I induced trance and set up ideomotor signals.

DME: Do you sense that you are identifying with your father's case of appendicitis?

IM: Yes.

DME: Have you been afraid you'll die?

IM: Yes.

DME: Have you thought about the fact that each person is different, that no illness is the same in different people, and medical science has progressed since your father's illness?

IM: No.

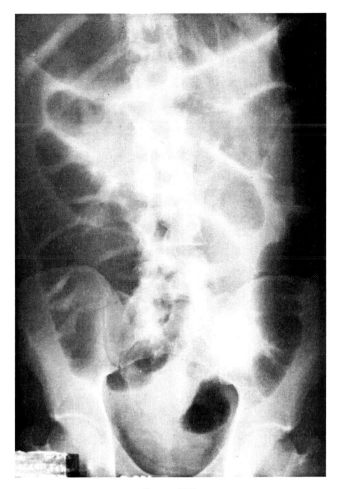

Figure 7.10

DME: Let me tell you some things that are different. Only half of your genes are from your father. His appendix was ruptured and complicated. Yours was not ruptured and was uncomplicated. We did not have antibiotics when your father was sick, but we have them now. At a deep feeling level, can you leave the past behind and realize that you are a separate person, in a modern hospital, with every reason to recover completely?

IM: (After some hesitation . . .) Yes.

DME: Good! Keep that thought in mind, and tell me what your favorite food is.

[Comment: With the identification separated, I still have to deal with the distention and paralysis. His colon is grossly distended, and I don't want him to blow out the stump of the appendix. The most powerful stimulant of natural peristalsis is savory food. Imaginary food works just as well. We all hear our stomachs growl when we walk past a bakery.]

Patient: Fajitas.

DME: Wouldn't it be nice to have a big serving of fajitas right now, just like Momma used to make?

IM: Yes.

DME: I wonder if you can close your eyes and picture all the fajitas you could possibly want. Notice the color that tells you they have been cooked to perfection. Can you smell that delicious aroma?

IM: Yes.

DME: As you bite into one, do you hear the crisp crunchy sound it makes?

IM: Yes.

DME: Can you notice the satisfying taste that you like so much?

IM: Yes.

DME: When it's just as though you are enjoying a comforting, delicious meal of fajitas, your YES finger will rise.

[Comment: It helps to get all the senses involved in this kind of visualization. Remember that a question is an indirect suggestion.]

IM: Yes (And a pleasant smile appeared on his face).

Within a half-hour he passed a large amount of gas, and his abdomen decompressed. He went on to a normal, uncomplicated recovery.

6. Self-Punishment

One of the things that causes symptoms is self-punishment. When we were children and got caught with our hands in the cookie jar, we got admonished or grounded and then it was over. As adults, we may hurt someone's feelings, or do something else we are not proud of, or think "bad thoughts," or fail to keep a promise, and no one punishes us. Something is missing and the subconscious mind can produce a symptom as a form of self-punishment. We tell this to the patient. Then we Ask ask:

,, .Then we Ask :

T: Do you sense that this symptom is a form of self punishment for real or imagined guilt? Yes or no?

IM: If you get a yes . . .

T: Would it be all right to know what you feel you shouldn't have done? Would it be all right to identify the offense?

IM: If we get a yes . . .

T: When it comes to your conscious mind so you can talk about it, your yes finger will rise. [Be quiet until the patient's yes finger rises.]

T: Speak to me and tell me what it is.

Depending on what it is, there are a number of approaches. If it is something that can be made up to somebody, then that may need to be done. If it is imagined guilt, then the patient may need to forgive himself. If the patient has been punished enough, he may need to realize this and let it go. If it is real guilt for something that the patient didn't do that he should have done, the question is: *Would the symptom go away if you did it?*

Self-punishment is often operative with persistent pain. The word *pain* derives from the Latin *poena* meaning "punishment." We have penalties, penitentiaries, and penal colonies to punish wrongdoers, and we have *pain* to punish ourselves. With persistent pain, one issue is the lack of an endpoint. If you were going to give yourself three lashes, it would be over after the third lash. So, one of the questions we frequently ask such a patient is: *Is it possible that you have already been punished enough?*

If the answer is "no," depending on the circumstances, we may ask: *Was it so bad that you deserve to suffer indefinitely?* Or, *Do you deserve the death penalty?* We sometimes find ourselves dealing with a patient who feels responsible for a loved one's death (e.g., If only I had been a better parent, my son wouldn't have died from an overdose). The statement, "if only" is a dead giveaway for imagined guilt. An imagined murder psychically calls for the death penalty just like the real thing. Smoking can be a slow death penalty.

In the case of imagined murder, it's imperative to get to the question of *intent*. Imagined murder is perceived with trance logic. The legal definition of murder requires intent to kill. The fact usually is that the patient is innocent of intent and wanted to protect the loved one. He continues to hurt because he cared. We need to keep at this until we can get an IM signal that the patient knows there was no evil intent and that he is innocent, and no longer deserves the symptom.

If the IM answer to the question, *Is it possible that you have already been punished enough?* is "yes," we ask the patient to answer with the fingers:

T: Then, would it be all right to let it go?
IM: If the IM answer is "yes" to that . . .
T: Is there anything to prevent you from letting it go right <u>now</u>?
IM: If that answer is "no" . . .
T: Great. Since this symptom has no more value, let it go right now. Say goodbye to the symptom.

If the answer is "yes," that there is a reason to keep the self-punishment, then we need to explore and find out what the reason is and resolve it using the IM questioning technique.

The subconscious mind treats imagined guilt as though it were real guilt. Anything that starts with "if only" is imagined guilt. For example, "If only I hadn't said that", "If I only hadn't made the phone call," "If only I had been there when Mother died," or "If only I hadn't missed that appointment," and so forth. We readily blame ourselves for catastrophes that we had no hand in causing and couldn't have prevented. A good reframe is:

> *We can only do the best we can with what we have at the time. Isn't that what you did?* [If you get an ideomotor "yes" to that, then ask:] *Would it be all right to forgive yourself by knowing and recognizing that you really would have done things differently if you had known* **then** *what you know* **now** *?* [If you get a "yes" to that, then ask:] *Would it be all right to let the symptom go?*

Only ethical people experience guilt, as opposed to sociopaths who have no conscience. So you are almost always dealing with people who have an ethos. Essentially, the idea you want to convey to the patient is that even if he did something wrong, he has been punished, and it's over now.

Religious feeling can be a powerful asset in treating these patients. The Bible says "Judge not, that ye be not judged," and these patients are judging themselves and prescribing punishment. This is violating the Commandment, "Thou shall have no other Gods before me." Humans are the accused, not the judges, and self-judgment is putting oneself in the seat of God. The God of Abraham tells us that he will forgive anyone who repents, and if you feel bad enough or feel guilty enough to punish yourself, it's because you are feeling remorseful and repentant.

The Treatment

If the patient is actually guilty and owes someone an apology, or has caused damage that needs to be recompensed, the right solution to that is obvious. They may need a lawyer instead of, or in addition to, a doctor or therapist. We treat imagined guilt, lawyers treat real guilt. The treatment for self-punishment is either, "Have you been punished enough?" or, "Find a way to forgive yourself."

Self-Punishment Case Example

When we're children and get caught doing something bad, we get punished, and the next day it's over. We learn that punishment ends the problem. As adults, we've developed a conscience with a sense of right and wrong. But we often neglect doing what we think is right, and since nobody else punishes us, we punish ourselves to fit with our world view. The subconscious feeling of guilt takes a toll, and can produce symptoms. This is particularly true in the case of chronic pain.

A 42-year-old widow consulted me (DME) about waking up every morning with temporomandibular headaches. She had been grinding her teeth at night (bruxing) for about a year and a half. Her dentist had made several bite blocks ("night guards") for her to wear at night, but she had chewed them up, and her lower teeth were worn and loose, and her gums were bleeding (see Figure 7.11. Her dentist had recommended pulling her teeth and making a prosthesis. At 42, she wanted to keep her own teeth.

Intake history revealed that shortly before the onset of symptoms a prominent male citizen had a heart attack, and died in her bed. She had to call 911, and there was a short report of the incident in the back pages of the newspaper. She was mortified, and felt embarrassed, angry, and guilty, and began to clench her jaw at night until it got so she'd wake up with bi-temporal headaches. She stopped going to church.

After intake and photographing the teeth, I induced trance with a rapid eye-roll induction, and set up ideomotor signals.

DME: Sometimes a discomforting symptom can seem necessary to compensate for a feeling of guilt. The subconscious mind dispenses this as a form of self-punishment. In your deepest subconscious feelings, do you sense that you have been bad, and that these headaches are a form of self-punishment?

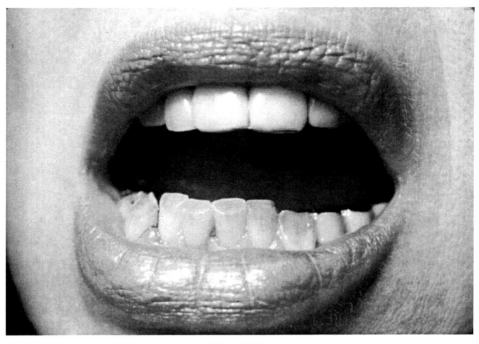

Figure 7.11

IM: Yes.

DME: Is it possible you have been punished enough?

IM: No.

DME: What happened that deserves such prolonged punishment?

Patient: It was M…'s death. It was so embarrassing, and the publicity. It was awful.

DME: Do you feel like it was unforgivable?

IM: Yes.

DME: Do you believe that God tells lies? (I can go to this because she's already told me she used to go to church, and she obviously has a faith-based conscience).

IM: No.

DME: Then do you believe his promise that he will forgive any sin of those who are contrite, and resolve to do better?

IM: (Short hesitation) Yes.

DME: Can you be contrite, and resolve to do better?

IM: Yes.

DME: Then we know God will forgive you, and it follows that you must forgive yourself. I'll be quiet right now while you get in

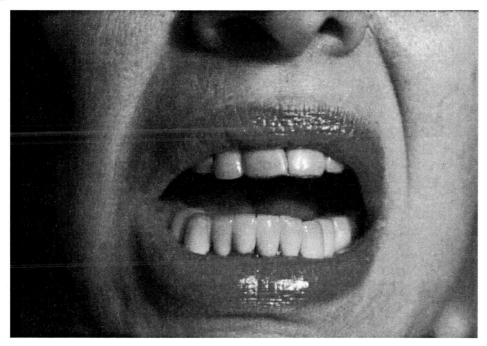

Figure 7.11

touch with your spiritual relationship with God, accept his blessing, forgive yourself, and let the past be past. When that is done, your YES finger will lift.

IM: (After 2–3 minutes) Yes (And I notice a faint smile appear on her face).

DME: Good. It's time to leave the past behind and get on with finding your joy and happiness. When you are alert again, I'm going to teach you a self-hypnosis exercise to help you stop grinding your teeth in your sleep.

After alerting, I taught her to induce self-hypnosis at bed time, and give herself the suggestion "All night long my jaws will be relaxed and comfortable, lips together, teeth apart." (Note: I violated my own rule that a suggestion should have ten words or less, but the extra four words added useful specificity).

Three days later she phoned to say that the headaches had ceased. I saw her two years later for follow-up photos (see Figure 7.12). Her teeth were firmly in place and her dentist had capped them to cover the ground-away surfaces. She was wearing lipstick, dating, and had her own teeth.

7. Suggestion

A suggestion is the imprint of a fixed idea that may be self-generated, or something that another person says at a time of emotional vulnerability. When you are vulnerable, what is said, even if not true or logical, seems true because trance logic is operating. It is responded to like a post-hypnotic suggestion—that is, it is carried out uncritically and automatically. Violating the idea causes anxiety. We introduce this problem to the patient as follows:

T: One of the things that causes symptoms is what we call a suggestion or imprint. It means that an idea has been accepted at a subconscious level. It is usually introduced at a highly emotional time and is from then on responded to automatically and uncritically. Answer with your fingers. Do you sense that you are being affected by a suggestion that some authoritative person gave you?

IM: If no, ask . . .

T: Do you sense that you are being affected by an idea that you gave yourself?

IM: If either of these is "yes," then ask . . .

T: Would it be all right to know when you got this idea?

IM: If "yes," ask . . .

T: Did it happen before you were age 20? [and work backwards until you get a "no"]

The Treatment

Since a suggestion can be put in, it can be removed if you know exactly what the suggestion or fixed idea is. It is often difficult for a person to verbalize this without carrying out multiple subconscious reviews. So, we revert to the retrograde search technique used above for Past Experience with multiple reviews.

When the time the suggestion was put in is identified, we do a regression to that time and ask what the suggestion is. Then we reframe it to whatever is needed to remove it. We either reword the suggestion or erase it.

Iatrogenic Suggestions. People tend to be emotionally focused when they go to the doctor. A common statement doctors make is "You have to learn to live with it." If the patient is frightened enough to be in an emotionally focused state, this type of statement can become imprinted in the patient's subconscious like a post-hypnotic suggestion.

Inadvertently, this fixes in place the symptom that the patient is seeking help for. This occurs because the patient's subconscious is alerted to pay close attention to the doctor's words and interprets them literally.

The result of this imprinting process is that the patient acquires a fixed idea. The fixed idea is dysfunctional. The patient doesn't get over the symptom. If the patient accepts the idea, "You have to learn to live with the pain," then the only way to get rid of it is to die. When this particular phrase is identified, it must be removed and reworded with such ideas as:

*You will be able to cope with this or, If you can live **with** it, you can also live **without** it.* Another pertinent reframe here is: *Just because we haven't got a cure for this YET, doesn't mean we won't ever have one.*

Birth Imprinting. An imprint can start at birth, particularly for an unwanted child. If the mother or father's comments around the newborn are rejecting, the infant senses that rejection on a sensorimotor feeling level. In hypnosis, that infant, now grown up, can paraphrase the statements that affected him on some level back then. Konrad Lorenz received the Nobel Prize in 1973 for his studies on birth imprinting in animals, and humans are part of the animal kingdom.

Suggestion Case Example

A common cause of symptoms is suggestion. Emile Coué (1922) said that suggestion has occurred when there is *subconscious acceptance* of an idea. The idea comes at a time of emotional vulnerability, and may be said by someone else, or may be self-generated. It becomes a fixed idea that is carried out compulsively, just like a post-hypnotic suggestion. The classic example of this is in the movie *Forrest Gump* when the other boys are throwing rocks at him, and he feels frightened and helpless. The little girl calls out "Run, Forrest, run," and he does so and escapes. From then on whenever he is stressed he runs, finally running all the way across the United States.

I (DME) was consulted by a prominent 68-year-old attorney who had been experiencing tinnitus for 6 years. It seriously interfered with his concentration. He had sought treatment at the Mayo Clinic, Cleveland Clinic, and Tulane Medical School without relief. He said that six years ago, he woke up with ringing in both ears, and the intensity had never abated. After intake, I induced trance, and set up ideomotor signals.

DME: Is it all right with your subconscious mind for me to help you with this problem?

IM: Yes.

DME: Before six years ago, have you ever experienced ringing in
           your ears? (Since he woke up with it, presumably from a
           dream, what memory was he dreaming about?)
IM: (Slow response) Yes.

[Initiate a retrograde search.]

DME: Was it before you were 50?
IM: Yes.
DME: 30?
IM: Yes.
DME: 10?
IM: No.
DME: 20?
IM: No.
DME: 21?
IM: Yes.
DME: So something happened at about age 20 that gave you tinnitus.
           Would it be all right to review it at a subconscious level?
IM: Yes.
DME: Each breath you take, go deeper and deeper, and when you
           start reviewing it your yes finger will rise, every time you come
           to something emotionally important, your no finger will rise,
           and when you have completed the review, you will signal with
           your thumb. (Stroking each finger as I mention it to give tac-
           tile feedback).
IM: He does the silent review with two No signals.
DME: Would it be all right to review it again, this time telling me
           what is happening, and letting your No finger signal each time
           there is something emotionally important?
IM: Yes.
DME: When you start the review your yes finger will rise, and you
           can speak to me.
Patient: Yes. I'm in the hospital, and they tell me I have malaria (No
           finger rises).
DME: Are your ears ringing?
Patient: Yes, they're treating me with quinine, and it makes my ears
           ring. It's springtime, and I'm on the track team going to the
           Olympics this summer.
DME: What happens next?

Patient: I'm worried, and I ask Dr. L… if I can run in the Olympics this summer.

DME: What does he say?

Patient: He says "If you ever run again you'll die." (no finger rises).

DME: So what happens?

Patient: I get well, quit the track team, and go on to Law School.

DME: I wonder if something related to all this happened the day before you woke up with tinnitus six years ago. (We know that a significant dream is usually triggered by something that happened the day before).

Patient: Nothing related to malaria. We had a party and my friends got me to agree to run for Governor (of Louisiana).

DME: So you agreed to RUN again! It's the duty of your subconscious mind to protect you, even from yourself. Do you sense that just like in the hospital at age 20, as long as you have tinnitus, you can't be dead yet?

IM: Yes.

DME: You didn't run very hard - in fact you lost, and you are not running now. I wonder if you still really need the tinnitus to prove you're still alive. Would it be all right with your subconscious mind to just turn it off, and leave it in the past?

IM: Yes.

DME: Then do it. Want it to happen, let it happen, and it will happen.

His tinnitus stopped, and at four-year follow up, he had no recurrence.

(**Comment:** Quinine is a general protoplasmic poison. It poisons every cell in the body, including the heart and all vital organs. The skill is in giving enough to kill the parasite without killing the patient. The ears are the most sensitive organ to quinine, and the onset of tinnitus is the sign that the maximum safe dose this patient can tolerate has been given. It takes almost that dose to kill the malaria parasite. I surmise that Dr. L. told the patient that it would be potentially fatal to engage in maximum exertion at the summer Olympics, and the patient has paraphrased what he heard as a dire threat.)

In the tropics, British troops were required to take a small daily "tonic" of quinine as a preventive against malaria, and with a little imagination they introduced us all to Gin and Tonic.

Chapter 8

IDEOMOTOR TECHNIQUE FOR RECALL OF SOUNDS HEARD UNDER GENERAL ANESTHESIA[1]

This chapter reviews: (1) the importance of the best hypnotic technique (i.e., ideomotor review) for recovering sounds heard under general anesthesia, (2) what information is available, and (3) how this can be used in the treatment of patients with persistent symptoms who have undergone surgery. Ideomotor signals are finger movements designated to nonverbally indicate a positive or "yes" feeling versus a negative or "no" feeling. These are analogous to nodding the head "yes" and shaking the head "no" in nonverbal response.

It has been demonstrated experimentally that under general anesthesia, animals can be conditioned to a sound (white noise) coupled with an electric shock (Weinberger et al., 1984). Later, hearing the sound caused aversive behavior. The injection of epinephrine simultaneously with the stimuli is what fixed the Pavlovian conditioning, for if saline was injected, there was no subsequent sign of the sound being heard. These investigators note that the effect is not due to a lessening of the depth of anesthesia by epinephrine, as theorized by Dubovsky and Trustman (1976).

In human studies of hearing under anesthesia, it is clear that aside from the rare instance where a patient has conscious recall of events heard under anesthesia (Breckinridge & Aitkenhead, 1983), unconscious memory traces often exist of sounds heard under general anesthesia. There is evidence that this is particularly true if what is heard

---

[1] Originally presented at the *First International Symposium on Memory and Awareness in Anesthesia*. University of Glasgow, Scotland, April 7, 1989.

could cause anxiety. No human studies have been done to our knowledge to see if the unconscious memories correlate with epinephrine release, as was suggested by the Weinberger study in rats.

Cheek (1959) was the first to demonstrate that by using hypnosis and ideomotor review, he could recover from the subconscious mind a recollection of meaningful sounds heard while under a surgical plane of anesthesia. The review involves raising the "yes" finger as the subconscious begins to review its perceptions about the surgery, raising the "no" finger every time something emotionally important to the patient occurs, and signaling with another finger when the review is complete.

These patients had no conscious recall at all until this technique was used, and in the first case, it required thirteen ideomotor subconscious reviews before the information could be brought to the verbal level. In addition, Cheek observed the regularity with which these patients fear and assume the worst (Cheek, 1980). This has been so unvarying in my (DME) experience, that I teach it to my students as a law which applies either awake, in trance states, or under anesthesia. The key word is *frightened.*

Cheek's Law of Pessimistic Interpretation

When a statement can be interpreted either optimistically or pessimistically, a *frightened* person will interpret it pessimistically (Cheek, 1981).

A good example of this was reported in the newspaper when President Reagan was shot through the lung. He was on oxygen and unable to talk. The news item reported that a member of the surgical team said "This is it," and the President "blanched (epinephrine?), grasped a pad and scribbled a note to a nearby nurse, 'What does he mean, this is it?'"

In his review of the literature, Cheek (1980) notes that Levinson (1965) did the only human experiment using a meaningful, anxiety-producing statement given by the anesthetist at an appropriate time during surgery. Ten patients had the operation stopped while the anesthetist said "Just a moment! I don't like the patient's color. Much too blue. His (or her) lips are very blue. I'm going to give a little more oxygen." The anesthetist then paused, hyperventilated the lungs and then after a moment or two, said, "There, that's better now. You can carry on with the operation."

Although none of the patients had any conscious recall, one month later under hypnotic regression to the surgery, four of the patients were able to repeat almost exactly the words used by the anesthetist. Four more remembered hearing something or somebody talking, and some identified the speaker as the anesthetist. Everyone in this last group displayed marked anxiety, and either spontaneously alerted from hypnosis, or blocked any further investigation.

The remaining two patients denied hearing anything. It is interesting that in hypnosis, it was possible to get this much recall with just a regression technique. Unfortunately, we will never know if the four who became anxious and discontinued the experiment would have produced specific recall with several ideomotor reviews and verbal reassurance that "it's just a memory, we know you got through it all right, you're safe now."

A number of very interesting controlled studies have been done that show statistically significant evidence of unconscious hearing under anesthesia. These include Bennett's (1985, 1987) suggestion to touch the ear during a post-operative interview (note that this is an ideomotor response, not a verbal one), and the studies of Goldmann and Levey (1986), and Goldmann (1988) on the recognition of cues given under anesthesia.

In their study with cardiac patients, Goldmann et al. (1987) noted that post-operative anxiety was a significant predictor ($p < 0.05$) of which patients reported recall. Goldmann (1986) had the ingenious idea to tell patients the blood pressure of an octopus during an operation under general anesthesia, and have them recognize it later when cued.

In all of the above studies, it is interesting that hypnosis did not enhance recall of bland and innocuous words (none of which would cause the release of epinephrine if heard). Bennett et al. (1985) reports using Hilgard's dissociation technique and got no recall.

Goldmann et al. (1987) report using Elman's (1970) induction, then asking the patient to reply to ten questions using ideomotor signalling. No ideomotor review was done before the questions were asked. Clarity suffers at this point because ideomotor signals only allow for "yes' or "no" answers, while six of the ten questions could not be answered in this way (e.g., What can you remember about the anesthetic room?).

Nonetheless, using this technique on the seventh to tenth day interview after cardiac surgery, seven patients (23%) recalled intraoperative events, five with the aid of hypnosis. Bonke et al. (1986) gave positive intraoperative suggestions to 91 patients having biliary tract surgery in a double-blind study and found that this protected those over 55 years against prolonged post-operative stays in the hospital. They do not report any attempt at hypnotic review.

There are no controlled studies where it is reported that the hypnotic review used Cheek's highly successful method of multiple ideomotor reviews prior to asking for recall. On the other hand, there are a number of uncontrolled studies of good meaningful suggestions under anesthesia associated with improved convalescence (Bensen, 1971; Daniels, 1962; Hutchings, 1961; Kolough, 1964), and there are anecdotal reports of physiological changes during surgery (Cheek, 1964; Clawson & Swade, 1975; Ewin, 1984).

I (DME) have had several clinical cases where post-operative review of anxiety producing sounds changed the clinical course, particularly in patients with chronic pain.

The Method of Ideomotor Review

Ideomotor signals (IM) are finger movements chosen to nonverbally indicate a positive or "yes" feeling by raising one finger, and a negative, or "no" feeling by raising another. These are analogous to nodding the head "yes" and shaking the head "no" in nonverbal response. The hypnotic subconscious review involves raising the "yes" finger as the subconscious mind begins to review its perceptions about the surgery, raising the "no" finger every time something emotionally important to the patient occurs, and signaling with another finger when the review is complete. After several subconscious reviews, the question is asked: *Would it be all right to bring this up to a conscious level so you can tell me what happened?*

When the answer is "yes," a standard regression with verbalizations of memories is done beginning with the last conscious memory before going into surgery.

Case Reports

Case #1. A 49-year-old male physician with a staghorn calculus in the right kidney required emergency nephrolithotomy under general anesthesia. The surgery was uncomplicated, no infection occurred, and wound healing proceeded normally. However, the post-operative course was complicated by severe, disabling, and unrelenting pain.

Seventeen days post-operatively, the patient was seen by Dr. David Cheek at this author's request. He was hypnotized and instructed to review the surgery at an unconscious level, signaling with his "yes" finger when he started the review, his "no" finger when he came to anything especially significant to him, and another finger when the review was completed. After a single ideomotor review (with some physiological signs of distress), another ideomotor signal answered "yes" to the question "Is it all right for you to bring this up to a conscious level and know what is happening?"

During the regression, the patient began to cry and said:

Patient: "I feel like I'm being cheated."
Cheek: "In what way?"
Patient: "My surgeon is not doing the surgery."
Cheek: "Who is doing it?"
Patient: "His partner."
Cheek: "Is he incompetent?"
Patient: "No."
Cheek: "Then perhaps there is more to it than that. Use finger signals. Did something happen before this to sensitize you?"
Ideomotor: Yes.
Cheek: "Did it happen before you were twenty?"
Ideomotor: No.
Cheek: "Before you were thirty?"
Ideomotor: Yes (etc. until age 24 was established).
Patient: "Nothing happened to me when I was 24. I have never had any surgery before." Then, the patient cried spontaneously again and said "My gosh, that's when my father died of a post-operative kidney shutdown."
Cheek: "That was sad then, but you are not your father, and having pain isn't going to keep anyone alive. You don't really need the pain any longer to reassure yourself that you're still alive, do you?"
Patient: "No."
Cheek: "Then why don't you just begin to experience all the comfort you need and let the past be past?"
Patient: "Okay."

Following this therapeutic session on a Saturday, the pain receded dramatically, and the physician returned to his regular working schedule on Monday, two days later. He has remained pain free for more than ten years. It was subsequently verified that the junior partner did the surgery and the reason was that the senior partner was leaving that evening for vacation. He simply said, "Since you'll have to follow him post-op, why don't you do the surgery?"

This case was reported in more detail to illustrate the technique. Subsequent cases will be summarized.

Case #2. J.M., a 31-year-old married white male, was in a three wheel, all-terrain vehicle accident and had an L4 disc removed with relief. Four years later, his automobile rolled over an embankment and he had five more operations on his low back. These included one at the L3 level, one at the L4 level, a rhizotomy, a meningocoele repair, and finally an L5-S1 discectomy. He reported having initial relief after the first surgery with gradual return of pain over several months. He was minimally helped by the second and third procedures, and the pain became constant and more severe after the fourth (meningocoelectomy). A meningocele is a cyst on the coverings of the spinal cord (meninges).

There was no change with the fifth surgery. He volunteered that he had had the fantasy after the fourth surgery that it might be better not to awaken from the anesthetic. He had spent two years essentially sitting in a reclining chair. He was admitted to the inpatient Pain Unit. Extensive workup including CAT scan and Electromyogram showed no impingement on the nerves, and radioactive Technetium body scan showed no active inflammatory process in the back. There was some facet arthritis at L4-5 and L5-S1. He had a negative attitude and did not improve in three weeks of intensive treatment with nerve blocks, TENS (transcutaneous electrical nerve stimulator) unit, physical therapy, group therapy, and relaxation therapy.

Using the hypnotic review technique described above, the fourth surgery was reviewed in trance. Three ideomotor reviews were done before he signaled that it was all right to do the regression. He reported that the surgeon found a meningocoele resulting from an error in technique at the previous surgery, and told the nurse "I'll fix him". This was misinterpreted as the pessimistic connotation of being "fixed" (i.e., a hostile *I'll fix him*), and he felt helpless. After rewording this to "I'll repair it," his attitude changed from self-pity to confidence, and he applied for the work-hardening program for rehabilitation, planning to get back into sales.

Although he still has pain, he has regained a sense of control, regards it as tolerable, and it is no longer constant. He has discontinued all pain medication and instructed his attorney to fix a date for trial or settlement of his case.

This case illustrates the powerful subconscious effect of hearing under anesthesia, and the Law of Pessimistic Interpretation.

Case #3. I (DME) was demonstrating trance phenomena in the course on hypnosis for junior medical students. The student volunteer had undergone a tonsillectomy at age four, and all he could remember was that he "hated the surgeon," After ideomotor review, he gave a deep sigh and signaled "yes" to my request for permission to regress him through the surgery.

He first heard a voice behind his head say "He's ready," then sighed again as he heard the surgeon say "This is an easy hundred bucks." There is no way to validate the accuracy of his perception, but the affect was appropriate. Subsequently, the student told me that he felt better about himself. In the past, whenever he had thought about the surgery, he had somehow felt that he had been injured in some way, and he was relieved to know that it was "just a dumb remark." Perhaps some future surgeons learned to be careful what they say.

Commentary

Many times in giving a history, a patient will say "Ever since my (T&A, gallbladder, hysterectomy, etc.) surgery, I've had (pain, anxiety, phobia, diarrhea etc.)." This should alert the therapist to be sure to do an ideomotor review of the operating room sounds as part of the treatment. At worst, it will be nonproductive. This clinical experience suggests that in doing experimental studies to test hearing under anesthesia, the best hypnotic technique to recover subconscious memories would be to do repeated ideomotor reviews until the patient will give a "yes" signal to a request to bring to a *verbal* level what he is experiencing at a *feeling* level. Then a hypnotic regression through the surgery should get recall. Note that if the "no" finger rises twice or more during the subconscious review, that too noxious events should be elicited in the regression and conscious review.

My (DME) experience with hypnotherapy of patients with symptoms attributable to hearing under anesthesia has agreed with Cheek (1980) that three factors are important in producing symptoms. Most important, the sound must be meaningful (i.e., capable of releasing epinephrine if heard in the waking state). Second, it is said by someone in authority (usually the surgeon or anesthetist). Third, and less important, it occurs at a time in the procedure that puts it into an appropriate context (e.g., in an exploratory procedure, one will ignore a reassurance given before the incision is made).

Summary

This chapter presented three cases where excessive post-operative pain or anxiety were caused by hearing sounds under anesthesia at an unconscious level, and the symptoms were relieved by ideomotor hypnotic review of the surgery, followed by verbal level regression through the procedure. The failure of others to recover this information is attributed to disregarding the ideomotor technique described by Cheek, who was the first to demonstrate that it could be done.

The "Law of Pessimistic Interpretation" is proffered. It is our belief that a study designed to test unconscious hearing under anesthesia should include a meaningful statement (or a simultaneous injection of epinephrine if allowed by the Committee on Human Experimentation) given by the voice of either the surgeon or the anesthesiologist in attendance (this could be prerecorded with a prerecorded null or bland statement in the same voice for a blind control) and at an appropriate time during surgery. Then it is hypothesized that the multiple ideomotor review technique would recover a convincing number of unconscious imprints.

Chapter 9

HYPNOTIC PREPARATION AND CARE
OF THE SURGICAL PATIENT

Anesthetized surgical patients tune in like radar to the voice of the surgeon and the anesthesiologist, the two people in whose hands their life resides. It is similar to how a mother tunes into the sounds of her baby even in her sleep.

With the increasing evidence that many patients hear and process sounds at an unconscious level during adequate general anesthesia, the protection of the patient from auditory harm becomes a new source of concern. This chapter will summarize our thoughts and experiences regarding the psychological preparation and care of the patient who must undergo surgery.

Preparation

Good preparation for surgery should promote confidence and relieve apprehension. The intent of the surgeon is to take the patient safely through surgery and on to a rapid return to health. This requires the patient's cooperation during diagnostic studies, removal of doubts and fears that cause stressful anesthetic responses, minimizing drug toxicity from chemoanesthesia, early ambulation, and freedom from post-operative complications. Much of this can be accomplished without hypnosis. However, employing trance and suggestion as tools achieves these desired results more efficiently and consistently.

As previously detailed by Ewin (1984), the best time to deal with physical and psychological post-operative complications is preoperatively. Good psychological preparation for surgery clarifies misunderstandings, explains what is to come, protects the patient from harmful

116

conversations in the operating room, and promotes the expectation of a rapid and a comfortable recovery.

Preparation Starts with the Referral

Preparation starts with the referral. The preoperative and prehypnotic suggestion given by a trusted person in the waking state sets the stage. Crile and Lower (1914), as detailed by Ewin (1984), observed that people fearing death from surgery sometimes die. When a patient expresses fears, a good screening technique is to use IM responses to have the patient visualize himself doing well several weeks after surgery. If the patient is unable to do this, then some analytic questioning should be done to determine the reason.

The Preoperative Release

In my (DME) hospital, the preoperative release that the patient must sign says:

> I understand and acknowledge that the following known risks are sometimes associated with this procedure and/or anesthesia: death; brain damage; disfiguring scars; paralysis; the loss of or loss of function of body organs; and the loss of or loss of function of any arm or leg.

My (DME) State law specifies that this meets all the requirements for informed consent.

I (DME) recently saw a male in his twenties who had been on crutches for six months following surgical repair (in another city) of a partial laceration of his Achilles tendon. The repair was solid, but he had a classic Reflex Sympathetic Dystrophy (RSD (now called Complex Regional Pain Syndrome or CRPS), with cyanosis, edema, hyperhidrosis, and severe pain that had not responded to medication or physical therapy.

When we reviewed the original injury in trance, he was relatively unconcerned about the procedure until the nurse handed him the release to sign, and he read the part about loss of function of a leg, which activated memories of a crippled uncle and visions of not being able to support his family. He did not see his doctor until he arrived in the operating room, and attempted to suppress his own fears.

The etiology of RSD or CRPS is unknown, but in an in-depth psychological study of 10 patients, Thali (1989) notes that, compared to controls, there is a "psychosomatic disposition." and "the behavior of the medical practitioner has a prophylactic effect."

In presenting the preoperative release, it seems important to keep the patient in his logical left brain, and away from right-brain pictures of these horrors coming true. The doctor is the one who can keep it impersonal and left brain, with something like:

> I can't guarantee the outcome of anyone's surgery, but I intend to protect you in every way possible from complications. You know that with surgery and anesthesia there have been reports of almost every problem you can name, including death ... etc., and I have to remind you of that. (pause) Before you sign this consent form, do you have any question you would like answered?

Properly handled, the consent form can be a means to increase trust without causing apprehension (Ewin, 1984).

The Preoperative Visit

The preoperative visit has been well described (Rodger, 1961; Cheek, 1962; Fredericks, 1980, 2001; & Ewin, 1984). David Cheek (Cheek, 1962, 1994) had many patients review their surgical experiences in trance which yielded information about common fears and reactions to sounds heard under general anesthesia and in the recovery room. His work provides a basis for developing a series of protective suggestions to be given to the presurgical patient.

A good preoperative preparation in the waking state should be given by all of the physicians that matter to the patient: the referring physician, the anesthesiologist, and the surgeon. It would be ideal if each important physician were trained to employ hypnosis. For example, as detailed by Ewin (1984):

Dr: [Touch the patient and take his pulse.] What do you like for your friends to call you?

P: <Name>.

Dr: May I call you that?

[**Comment:** It is assumed that the family physician is already calling the patient by his familiar name. However, for the consultants and the surgeon, this question implies that the doctor is asking for a more informal relationship in which the patient can safely confide his feelings without fear of ridicule or censure.]

P: Yes.

Dr: How do you feel about this operation?

P: Okay, I guess.

Extended Comment

One important clue to watch for is the reply "Okay, I guess." The "I guess" is a gratuitous afterthought, and comes from the subconscious, signifying that he would have told a lie if he had only said, "Okay." I (DME) would induce trance in this patient and do an age progression to six weeks post-op to visualize being well by then. If he can picture being well, then just suggesting that it will be that way suffices. If he is unable to imagine recovering, I (DME) use ideomotor signals to search for a cause, and either resolve it, or defer surgery until it is resolved. Famous surgeons, including William Halsted of Johns Hopkins, are on record as refusing to operate on patients who reported preoperatively their expectation of death (Finney, 1934), because of the experience that it often came true.

A few years ago I (DME) neglected this preparation in a case of acute appendicitis, and was greeted next morning with a complication of Paralytic Ileus. This is an acute distention of the entire bowel from paralysis due to overactivity of the sympathetic fibers (the ultimate *uptight*). Questioning revealed that when he was a child, his father had died of a ruptured appendicitis, leaving the family destitute. Disjoining this identification in trance, coupled with suggestions of the smell and taste of his favorite food restored normal peristalsis within the hour.

Cheek recommended a preoperative post-hypnotic suggestion to ignore any sound unless the patient's name is called first. Although he came to believe this was imperfect, though helpful, (personal communication), I (DME) still use it.

Dr: Has there been anything in your mind that you haven't mentioned, even if it seems silly?

Comment: Any answer should be taken seriously and dealt with fully. Often, it is a thought about something that happened to another person in surgery. It should be emphasized that each person is different, the doctors are different, and that everything possible will be done to prevent any such complication in this case, which is special. The good reputation and history of successes of the surgeon, anesthesiologist, anesthetists, and nurses in this hospital should also be emphasized.

Dr: Would you like for me to help you get relaxed to get a good night's sleep and to go easily through the surgery tomorrow (or whenever)?

P: [Universal] Yes.

Comment: Ideally, the key physicians and nurses should confer and be aware of each other's preoperative visits with the patient. If one doctor has taught the patient a self-hypnosis exercise, the other clinicians should reinforce and validate its employment by the patient.

Dr: If you could do anything else you wanted to tomorrow, where would you go for a laughing place?

Comment: Most patients will understand the question (but make sure of it!). It is expected that the patient will respond by relating what he does or likes to do for relaxation (e.g., fishing, boating, watching television, going to the beach), or for diversion. This can be used later for visualization. The patient's description of his laughing place should be clarified, and reinforced and validated by the clinician.

Checklist of Important Suggestions

Dr: [Induce trance using a rapid induction, then give suggestions such as the following:]

1. You will have an easy day tomorrow if you do what I say.
2. Tonight you should let yourself feel safe and comfortable, sleeping soundly, accepting the fact that you are turning this over to us now.
3. You can help your body heal best by having an attitude that nothing will bother you. Nothing will bother you.
4. In the morning, you won't want to eat or drink anything, so that all of your body functions will be at rest.
5. When you receive your preop injection here in your room, you should empty your bladder and let the sedative take effect while you relax and go to your laughing place.
6. From the time you leave your room until you return from the recovery room, you should simply enjoy your laughing place and completely ignore anything that people say <u>unless you are spoken to directly by name</u>. [Repeat]. <u>Completely ignore anything that people say unless you are spoken to directly by name.</u>

7. When your anesthesia is started, all pain sensation is blocked. Some people hear sounds during their operation, and if you do, you will ignore it because you will be feeling no pain and enjoying your laughing place.

8. You will get a constant supply of oxygen through a small tube in the back of your throat.

9. When the surgery is completed, you will be moved to a stretcher and taken to the recovery room. You will gradually awaken just as you do from natural sleep, relaxed and refreshed.

10. You will keep the arm that is getting IV fluids relaxed and still, and if there is an airway in your mouth when you awaken, simply push it out with your tongue, or remove it with your free hand since you don't need it when you are alert.

11. You will wake up remarkably comfortable, with a good appetite, and your normal bladder and bowel functions will resume quickly.

12. You will be up walking with help later in the day [if appropriate].

13. Whatever you need for comfort will be supplied, and your tissues will heal rapidly.

14. Now, I want you in your imagination just to picture all that I have just told you taking place, and then project ahead in time to when you feel healed and well and ready to leave the hospital. And when you do that, this finger will rise (touch index finger), and a date or the number of days will come into your mind so that you can tell me when it is.

P: Gives an IM and a verbal response.

Dr: [If the date is further into the future than expected, inquire about what seems to take so long, if it could be sooner than that. Work through any issues that need to be resolved or clarified.]

Dr: Now is the time for you to practice going to your laughing place and enjoying yourself, totally free of responsibility, just goofing off. Go to [visual imagery of the patient's laughing place], and [if true] I'll see you tomorrow.

Intraoperative Behavior

Building on the studies of Levinson (1967), Cheek (1980, 1994), Bennett et al. (1985), Goldmann (1988), and others showing that patients may unconsciously hear and process meaningful sounds under general anesthesia, the first International Conference On Hearing Under Anesthesia convened in Glasgow in April 1989, and the proceedings have been published (Ewin, 1989).

Patients under general anesthesia do hear <u>meaningful</u> sounds when given by the <u>person</u> to whom they are attuned (surgeon, anesthesiologist) at an <u>appropriate time</u> in the procedure. The surgical patient naturally has his attention fixed on possible danger. He is alert to anything threatening. Meaningless sounds are ignored. Any statement about his health or prognosis <u>is meaningful</u> and will be noted, just as an attentive mother may be able to sleep through a thunderstorm, but awake when her baby is crying. The <u>person</u> speaking is significant.

How can we protect these patients? Clearly, silence is golden, but regrettably it is next to impossible to attain. Why not ear plugs? This seems to be the simplest solution. However, it is clear in Levinson's (1967) case that there was an EEG alarm during the "meaningful silence" that preceded the planned noxious statement by the anesthetist. Might the patient misinterpret having ear plugs? Only studies will tell.

What about earphones with white noise or music? White noise has been rejected by Breckenridge and Aitkenhead (1983) as "a rather negative approach." Music is appealing, but only if the patient brings his own tapes! Music can have deep emotional associations with both joy and sadness, and only the patient knows his own associations.

Several years ago, I (DME) visited a friend in another state. He was scheduled to do a legal abortion the following morning, and as I had never seen one I asked to look in. He brought his radio to the operating room tuned to a music station. The patient was 17 years old and had a steady boyfriend she expected to marry, but he had abandoned her as soon as he found out she was pregnant. During the procedure (under local anesthesia) the radio played "Love and Marriage–go together like a horse and carriage" and the poor girl cried and cried.

Weinberger et al. reported in 1984 that injected epinephrine enabled Pavlovian conditioning of rats to a sound heard under general anesthesia. This fits with the clinical observation (Cheek, 1981, 1994; Ewin, 1989) that a frightened patient will assign a pessimistic interpretation to any statement that can be so construed, and that in hypnotic review, patients recall mainly comments that would cause fear or anger in the waking state.

With this as a working hypothesis, a few of many negatively interpretable remarks that I (DME) have encountered include, "Look at her heart out here flapping in the breeze" (Ewin, 1984, p. 219), "she'll never be the same after this" (Ewin, 1984, p. 220, Elman, 1970, p. 3), "I'll fix him" (Ewin, 1989).

Levinson (1967) reported a case of post-operative depression following surgery for a benign lesion. In hypnotic review, the patient recalled hearing the surgeon say that it might be cancer, and she recovered when disabused of this idea. Cheek (1965) reported about a 10-year-old boy with shortness of breath and a pulse rate exceeding 120 on exertion, whose patent ductus had been surgically ligated as an infant. At surgery, he was also found to have a small septal defect of no consequence. On hypnotic review, he reported hearing the surgeon say "not able to fix it" (referring to the septal defect). His cardiac evaluation was normal, and after hypnotic review with reassurance, his symptoms cleared.

Perhaps the best protection from conversation in the OR is to reorient ourselves to think as though every patient is under local anesthesia, and fully aware. Since surveys (Breckenridge & Aitkenhead, 1983) show that approximately two percent of patients under general anesthesia can consciously recall conversation (insufficient anesthetic?), and we cannot know when that will occur, this would be wise even if there were no evidence for unconscious hearing.

With this in mind, we recall Sir William Osler's (1904) admonition that ". . . in the surgeon no quality takes rank with imperturbability . . . coolness and presence of mind under all circumstances . . . and the physician who betrays indecision and worry, and who shows that he is flustered and flurried in ordinary emergencies, loses rapidly the confidence of his patients." We need to teach our staff how fragile a frightened patient can be on arriving in the OR.

I (DME) treated a lady whose pain was inappropriately prolonged after an operation by another surgeon. In trance, she said she'd never told anybody, but the only way she had been able to muster the courage to undergo the procedure was to get it into her mind that she would put her complete trust in the competence of her surgeon. She received her premedication and as she was being rolled into the operating room on a guerney, she saw a poster that said "How can I soar like an eagle when I have to work with all these turkeys?" and her heart sank.

As a speaker at a nurse's workshop on chronic pain, I (DME) was asked to do a demonstration. A nurse volunteered who had had a forearm fracture reduced under general anesthesia. It was painful and "never healed," although x-rays showed perfect alignment. During hypnotic review, she recalled that as her anesthesia was about to start, the nurse anesthetist noticed her name on the chart and said, "Oh, you're the nurse who got the job I wanted." In trance, she began to cry and said she felt unprotected, helpless, and frightened. She was given strong reassurance that nothing vengeful happened, and that it was time now to let it heal. She has been pain free for more than five years.

Conclusions

Humans respond to suggestions, both good and bad, at emotionally critical moments. Therefore, we must train ourselves to give our patients good suggestions. Knowing that patients hear under general as well as local anesthesia makes suggestion an important part of every surgical procedure. The patient is able to accept a suggestion at an appropriate time. While the patient is under general anesthesia, the appropriate time to give good suggestions for post-operative comfort is after the main procedure has been completed and while the skin is being closed.

Recovery Room

In Recovery, I (DME) have heard the nurse attempting to rouse a patient by saying "Wake up, Mr. X, it's all over." This can be pessimistically interpreted to imply "you're dead," and we think it is much better to be clearly optimistic and unambiguous. I (DME) prefer speaking into the patient's left ear (to access the right brain) something like this:

Mr. X, this is Dr. Ewin, the operation is completed and you're okay. You can feel comfortable and safe, knowing you're okay. When you wake up, you will be remarkably comfortable, with a good appetite, and all your normal body functions will resume quickly.

Technique for Recall of Sounds Heard Under General Anesthesia

Patients with persistent negative symptoms after surgery can be helped to get better using IM review and analysis. David Cheek (1981, 1994) pioneered and developed a reliable technique for bringing to a conscious level what was assimilated at an unconscious level during anesthesia or a concussion. In fact, it could do no harm to conduct such IM review on most post-surgery patients <u>when appropriate</u> as a way to screen whether everything turned out all right emotionally.

1. In trance, IM finger signals are set up so that one finger will rise to signal the beginning of an episode, another will rise to signal each time something upsetting occurs, and another will rise to indicate the end of the subconscious review.

2. The patient is instructed: *Let your deepest mind review the episode without trying to have any conscious thoughts.* In less than a minute, the patient's beginning finger (usually set up beforehand to be the "yes" finger) will rise.

3. If there's no movement of the "upset" finger before the "end" signal is given, all is well. Expect very little to be reported because what was heard under anesthesia was not meaningful enough to merit the patient's attention in a state in which his survival mechanisms were alert only to danger.

4. Typically, a patient will initially evince signs of distress (e.g., frowning, defensive posturing, rapid breathing), then the finger signal marking the beginning of the episode, followed by finger signals marking emotionally important occurrences, up through the end of the episode.

5. It typically takes several subconscious reviews before the memory of the experience can be brought to conscious awareness and talked about. The patient is asked to repeat his review at a subconscious level until he can say what he is reacting to. He is reassured that he got through it safely before, and it is all right to simply review the memory as many times as necessary and NOT repress it any longer. Usually two or three subconscious reviews suffice.

6. When signs of distress and upset manifest, <u>subconscious scanning should be repeated persistently</u>.

7. When the patient signals that he can bring the material to consciousness, he should be regressed to the episode and instructed to consciously review it while verbalizing what is happening. The number of negative events reported during the episode should correspond to the number of "upset" signals given during the subconscious review. Once brought to a conscious level, the negative

ideas that had been fixed in the patient's subconscious are reframed appropriately.

Summary

This chapter described our concept of ideal communication from the surgeon and other key physicians in the light of present day understandings of patients' reactions to both direct and indirect suggestions given before, during, and after surgery. The choices are illustrated with case examples and scientific references.

Chapter 10

TREATING THE COGNITIVE AND EMOTIONAL COMPONENTS OF PERSISTENT PAIN

Physicians only have partial success in helping patients with chronic pain obtain relief (Eimer, 2000, 2002; Eimer & Freeman, 1998). Pain relieving drugs have unpleasant side effects and often don't diminish the pain enough. Furthermore, the psychosocial ramifications of persistent pain are not amenable to a medical solution. However well meaning, the physician cannot repair the narcissistic wounds the patient sustains through loss of his social and vocational role status. Thus, the physician who must deal with such painful conditions as arthritis, fibromyalgia, chronic fatigue syndrome, low back problems, chronic headaches, reflex sympathetic dystrophy, thalamic pain syndrome, interstitial cystitis, post-herpetic neuralgia, idiopathic pelvic pain, and chronic dental pain, is sometimes at a loss as to how to lessen the suffering.

Pain AND Suffering

Study after study emphasizes the need to separate the word "pain" into two words—"pain," meaning the objective, measurable, neurophysiological signal, and "suffering," meaning the subjective, emotional, and evaluative response (Ewin, 1978, 1992). In fact, as far back as the 1960s, before Pain Medicine became a medical board specialty, Melzack and Wall (1965) posited a multidimensional system for classifying pain: the sensory-discriminative dimension, the motivational-emotional dimension, and the cognitive-evaluative dimension. These dimensions, or components, of the pain experience guided the development of Melzack and Wall's "Gate Control Model" of pain, and the development of Melzack's famous McGill Pain Questionnaire (Melzack, 1975).

The major motivational and emotional challenge that many people with chronic pain confront is coping with the permanence of their underlying physical injuries. Given the nature of pain as a survival-oriented, signaling system between body and brain, this permanence, and the emotional overlay, sets up a reverberating pain circuit between the brain and the rest of the body (Melzack, 1996; Melzack & Wall, 1982).

The Challenge

On one level, there is habituation. The patient adaptively learns to function amidst ongoing nociception. On another level however, there develops a hyper-sensitivity (and preoccupation with) to pain sensations (i.e., nociception), which is only adaptive if the pain changes, possibly indicating a worsening of the existing injury, or the emergence of a new one.

The net result, in many cases, is adaptive dysfunction and disability, which is often worsened by a system that frequently rewards suffering and dysfunction, and punishes getting well, through monetary incentives. The combination of the survival value of pain as a signal that something is physically and/or emotionally wrong, along with its psychosocial benefits, creates a formidable obstacle to getting well.

Despite the enormity of the challenges, there is a whole body of work in the psychological literature that has demonstrated that these obstacles can be removed, and that the motivated, persistent pain patient can be helped to obtain greater pain relief without more drugs (Eimer & Freeman, 1998; Gatchel, 2005; Turk, 2002).

Fear, dread, helplessness, and powerlessness are emotions commonly stirred by persistent pain, and these emotions color the patient's perceptions, very often increasing the patient's suffering immeasurably. However, the negative emotional and imaginative aspects of pain are often amenable to good hypnotherapy (Cheek, 1994; Cheek & LeCron, 1968; Crasilneck & Hall, 1975; Ewin, 1978, 1992; Hilgard & Hilgard, 1994; Zarren & Eimer, 2002).

Good hypnotherapy can relieve suffering because hypnosis deals with imagination, instincts, emotions, and value judgments. The insights cultivated from experience with hypnotherapy can provide valuable information for helping the patient cope with persistent pain.

The person who is disappointed when he sees his proverbial glass as half-empty can be elated by realizing that the glass is half-full.

Inducing Positive Feelings and Expectations

When anxiety and suffering are removed, it appears that pure pain does not hurt as much (Ewin, 1978). For example, when a needle pierces the skin to draw blood, the skin is being injured, the pain receptors are stimulated, and pure pain is produced. However, the patient may or may not suffer. Whether or not he does, is determined by how he feels about needles, drawing blood, white coats, the doctor's office, the circumstances for which blood is being drawn, and so forth. The same principle applies to visits to the dentist.

How many people dread going to a dentist who habitually either does not talk with his patients, or says, "Brace yourself, this will hurt"? On the other hand, the dentist who had made it a habit of talking with his patients and saying things like, "You are going to feel pressure [pure sensation absent the emotional and suffering component]. It will go away soon" [lack of permanence], probably has more comfortable and happier patients!

Hypnosis Is a Natural Remedy for Pain AND Suffering

These facts are what make hypnosis so effective for relieving persistent pain. Pain is involuntary. It comes without effort, and a good hypnotic state is also involuntary (achieved without effort). As with many things in life (e.g., falling asleep, swallowing, urinating, having an orgasm), effort is counterproductive when it comes to entering hypnosis. It is also counterproductive when it comes to coping with the experience of physical pain. Note that we are not referring to the necessary effort that needs to be put into rehabilitative endeavors, such as reversing deconditioning through a graded exercise program, improving endurance and so forth.

Pain is made worse by negative daydreams and the imagination. Hypnosis is a state of controlled positive daydreaming, and as Hilgard (1991) pointed out, "believed-in imagination."

Pain is made worse by negative attention and overpreoccupation with it as the focus of attention. Hypnosis involves the redirection of attention.

Pain is associated with tension and stress. Hypnosis is associated with relaxation and comfort, the emotional and physical opposites of the former.

Persistent pain is associated with feeling helpless and out of control. Hypnosis can give the patient a greater measure of control of his feelings and thoughts. This can translate into a different experience of the pain symptoms and a greater feeling of control over them–i.e., better coping.

In the hypnotic relationship, when the hypnotherapist asks the patient in trance, "Would it be all right for you to experience a small amount of pure pain as long as it is at a tolerable level?" he opens up a new doorway of possibility. Because of this, it is possible to hurt less. Nothing objective may have changed, but the patient who grants this permission feels he has regained some control in the moment. He can then be helped to extend that control over time to keeping the pain at a tolerable level.

No More Wild Imaginings

All human beings are capable of imagining the worst, and early in the evaluation of a pain problem, the clinician should comment on this universal human tendency and advise the patient of the harmful effects of harboring, nurturing, and hiding these fears. The more laboratory tests and consultations that are undertaken in search of "the cause" of the pain, the more time the patient has to wonder about himself and let his imagination and fears take over. Chronic fear of the unknown is a debilitating emotion, and unabated, it often leads to depression.

In a good trance, a patient will let down his defenses and be more open to dealing with his hidden fears. The patient's suffering is alleviated not only by removing his unreasonable fears but also by analyzing his problem (Remember the first intake question: "Tell me about your problem") and demonstrating how much suffering unbridled emotion can cause. Just making a diagnosis of emotional overlay and teaching the patient how to deal with his emotions takes away much of the mysteriousness of the condition, and gives the patient hope that, with practice, he can regain control of himself.

Conviction of Benefit Blocks Suffering

The conviction of benefit blocks harmful emotions and consequent suffering. Harold Beecher's (1946) often quoted battlefield studies illustrate his conclusion that "there is no simple direct relationship between the wound per se and the pain (suffering) experienced. The pain is in very large part determined by other factors, and of great importance here is the significance of the wound. . . . In the wounded soldier [the response to injury] was relief, thankfulness at his escape alive from the battlefield, even euphoria: to the civilian, his major surgery was a depressing, calamitous event."

Constant Pain

The *Constant Pain Syndrome* can be diagnosed readily, and may not be amenable to any treatment other than hypnoanalysis. The patient will say the pain is constant, NEVER goes away, and "I live with it." The therapist should show skepticism and challenge the patient with "What about when you're asleep?" If the patient insists that he falls asleep in spite of the pain, and is aware of it immediately on arising, he is asked, "Since this started, has there ever been any time when you were *completely* free of pain?" If the patient answers "NO" to this, it's unlikely that the pain is physical.

Physical pain is rarely, if ever, constant. Cancer pain can be completely relieved for several hours by opiates. Arthritis has remissions, or is relieved temporarily by treatment. Even the pain of a ruptured disc will relent for a short time by resting in certain positions.

"I live with it" implies that I cannot be alive without it, or more literally, the pain equates with life itself. No one can be without life for five minutes, and having this idea means that the patient cannot be without pain (i.e., life) for five minutes. The therapist who proposes to end this type of pain (life) is a threat to the patient, and the intuitive therapist can see that an attack on the pain with direct suggestions will be rejected even in deep trance. The patient needs hypnoanalysis.

The *constant pain syndrome* is characterized by the simultaneous occurrence of three things (Ewin's triad): (1) *mental disorientation* in which the patient may have had a concussion, a drug overdose, a stroke, an anesthetic, or even a lucent dream causing him to be unable to think clearly and respond in a normal way; (2) *fear of death* in which the experience is perceived as life threatening; and (3) *pain*.

Being mentally unable to deal with the perceived threat of death, the presence of pain is reassuring to the subconscious mind that he can't have died yet. When such a triad has occurred, and the patient has recovered normal waking mentation, the subconscious still clings tenaciously to the deeply imprinted idea that pain equals life. Therapy involves regression to the incident and accepting that it was a good idea at the time, but that it is no longer helpful.

Pain Reframe

We regress the patient to the time of the pain's onset and affirm the patient's perception that at the time when other signs of life were lacking, it WAS reassuring to feel the pain. We emphasize that this was only temporary. We suggest in trance, *that now that all the usual signs of life are present, and continue to be present, you can be alive without the pain rather than live with it. The pain had value at the time it began, but now there are all of the usual ways of knowing that you are alive. Wouldn't it be nice to experience a few minutes in trance of being pain-free and still alive?* An IM YES answer to this question is a point of entry in helping the patient relinquish unnecessary pain.

No Pain Lasts Forever

Patients who have persistent pain, especially if its cause is obscure, tend to ask themselves. "When will I ever get relief?" and "Can I stand it indefinitely?" With the patient in trance, it is helpful to give the simple direct suggestion that "no pain lasts forever." Repeating this suggestion at each visit plants the thought that the pain is NOT interminable, and this gradually becomes comforting for the motivated patient.

Other Negative Emotions Need To Be Let Go

If while in trance the patient reveals that guilt is a problem, the remark that *perhaps you have suffered enough to make up for the fault*, often will suffice as a start in terminating the self-punishment.

The cure for resentment and blame is an old one: FORGIVENESS. We point out to the patient that he is the one who is suffering, miserable and disabled, not the object of his anger. We may also take the strategy of assuming the role of spokesman for the patient's adversary, apologize for the physical injury and hurt feelings, and ask for forgiveness. Patients are often not ready to forgive immediately, but when they do, their suffering is greatly relieved and their ego is boosted. They feel that they are somehow a better person for it.

In sum, it is helpful to reframe pain as being a subjective experience consisting of two separate but interacting entities: the physical (nociceptive) pain sensations and the emotional suffering. The physical, anatomic, and electrochemical aspects of pain are treated as medically indicated by physical therapy, medicines, nerve blocks, electrical stimulators, and surgery. The suffering component involves the patient's (1) nonacceptance of the pain, (2) fear of the unknown, (3) pessimistic evaluation of the meaning of the pain, (4) feeling of no time limit on the suffering, and (5) often self-destructive feelings of guilt, resentment and anger. These emotions and imaginings are amenable to good hypnotherapy. When suffering is removed, pain tends to become tolerable, and it may even disappear.

Case Examples

A.G. was a 42-year-old white female, Ph.D. psychologist seen by DME. She complained of a constant headache "as long as I can remember." She had extensive medical work-ups and was diagnosed with "nervous headache." She had undergone psychoanalysis in seeking a cure. Both she and her analyst believed that there was significance in a recurring dream she had had since age four or five years, in which she is looking out the window watching her father bury something. She experienced anxiety just by talking about this dream. She admitted that somehow she felt that she was the thing that her father was burying. However, this insight did not yield a cure.

The patient went into trance easily and IMs were set up. She was first asked to review on a subconscious level her memories of what caused the headaches and what it meant to her, giving an IM signal with her thumb when she had completed this task. Questioning proceeded as follows:

DME: Would it be all right for you to go back and relive the experience again just as though you were there?

IM: No. [Comment: This is usual with a death experience as no one wants to go back and die again!]

DME: Would it be all right for your fingers to answer some questions about it?

IM: Yes.

DME: Yes. Okay. Did this happen before you were one-year-old?

IM: Yes.

DME: Yes. Did this happen after your birth experience?

IM: Yes.

[Comment: The retrograde search led to her tenth day of life, which was established as the date.]

DME: Does what is happening make your head hurt? [Comment: DME has shifted to the present tense.]

IM: Yes.

DME: Yes, it makes your head hurt. Are you sick?

IM: No.

DME: No, you are not sick. Have you been injured?

IM: Yes.

DME: Yes you have been injured. Are you afraid you are going to die?

IM: [No IM response.]

DME: Is your father there?

IM: Yes.

DME: Yes, your father is there. Does he say something that affects you?

IM: Yes.

DME: Yes, he does. Is it all right to know what he is saying?

IM: [Patient begins to cry.] "She is going to die . . .she is dead." [continues to cry and tremble.]

DME: But you survived. It is [date] and you are here, safe with us at this symposium. You got well. You are all right. Come back through the years, back to the present, to today [date] here with us. Safe. Now, you can look back through the years and know in the deepest part of your mind and being that you did NOT really die and you are quite intact and okay. You have earned an advanced degree, you are working regularly, you are successful, and you run a household. When you know this on a feeling level, your yes finger will lift.

IM: Yes.

DME: Yes. Good. When this happened, was the pain the only way you knew you were alive?

IM: Yes.

DME: Yes. At the deepest levels of your subconscious mind, does the headache give you a sense, some sense of reassurance that you have not died yet?

IM: Yes.

DME: Yes. Okay. Since the pain was the only way you knew then that you were alive, when it happened, it must have been very reassuring then.

IM: Yes.

DME: Okay. Yes. But do you really need it now that you have so many other ways to know that you are still alive?

IM: No.

DME: No. You no longer need it. That's wonderful! Since you don't need it any longer, why don't you just let it go?

IM: [None. Patient shows some agitation and spontaneously roused from her trance without answering. She then commented:]

P: This has been a very moving experience. [But she still had a headache.]

The foregoing took place at a pain symposium where the patient had volunteered for a demonstration of hypnoanalysis. Significantly, on the preceding day, she had watched a movie showing an African healer treating a native by incising the scalp and scraping the skull to let out the demons. The native patient in the movie was wide-awake in a trance-like state throughout the procedure and showed no signs of pain. The psychologist patient watching the film became so ill that she had to get up and leave the theater. The film somehow had stirred up her memory of the traumatic event that had happened on the tenth day of her life, that made her father say, "she is going to die."

On the evening of her first trance, the patient had an exacerbation of her head pain and she got very little sleep. Apparently, her instinctive sense of self-preservation could not lay aside a symptom that for so long functioned as a marker for life itself. The next day I (DME) hypnotized her privately.

In trance, I reassured her that there was no hurry and that even though she knew she did not need the headache any longer, no one could make her give it up until she was ready to do so. This was reassuring and reestablished her sense of control.

DME: Would it be all right with your feeling mind to be completely free of the pain for five minutes, knowing that you can resume it instantly if you choose to do so?

IM: Yes.

DME: Yes. Great. Your yes finger will lift when you are completely free of the pain.

IM: A few seconds later, her yes finger lifts, and she spontaneously smiles.

DME: Yes. Great. Now, <Name>, enjoy 5 minutes of complete comfort.

[Before the five minutes are up, DME continues . . .]

DME: Now <Name>, because you can be free of that pain for five minutes, I wonder if you can extend this relief to 10 minutes? Answer with your fingers.

IM: Yes.

DME: Yes, you can. That is great. Now enjoy a few more minutes of complete comfort.

[Silence . . . .]

DME: How do you feel? Speak to me.

P: Good.

DME: How comfortable are you now?

P: Very comfortable. I haven't felt this way, so relaxed in a long time.

DME: You haven't felt this relaxed in a long time. That's great. When you are in hypnosis and deeply relaxed, you cannot also be in discomfort or tense. That is because relaxation and those other negative feelings are physical and emotional opposites of each other. So, continue to remain in hypnosis and relaxation for a little while longer, and in a little while, when I rouse you up, some or all of that comfort will last after you are alert and back here in your waking state.

DME: I want you to relax daily and practice what we have done here together. Just take a few minutes when you can be by yourself and undisturbed, and rest back comfortably with your eyes closed and relax. If your mind wanders, that is okay. Hypnosis is just another way to daydream. Perhaps your mind will wander into a pleasant memory, or to your "laughing place," where you can enjoy yourself and not be bothered or disturbed by anyone or anything. And you can enjoy being in your laughing place for a little while until you are ready to rouse yourself up and come back to the present. Would that be all right with you? Let your feelings answer.

IM: Yes.

DME: At first, perhaps you can be comfortable in your laughing place for five minutes. Then, when you are ready, you can extend this comfort to 10 minutes. Eventually, you'll feel ready to extend your comfort and freedom from discomfort in your head to 20 minutes, and eventually, to one hour, one day, and eventually, when you are ready, extend that relief permanently. I'd like to ask your feeling mind if that feels all right, if that feels yes, agreeable. Answer with your fingers.

IM: [After about a minute and a half . . .] Yes.

The patient was alerted and they discussed the experience. Within three days, she reported that she was free of pain. Follow-up 11 months later revealed that she had been free of her headache since treatment (Ewin, 1992).

Handling "Slip-Backs"

As happened in the aforementioned case, very often, patients who experience significant relief from the pain in trance, experience an exacerbation, or "slip-back" of the pain later in the day or the next day. They typically have second and third thoughts about giving up a "life support system" they have relied on for months or years. This frequently results in their experiencing a paradoxical increase in the pain on the evening of the visit. If the patient calls in an anxious state, we see the patient that day as an emergency reassuring the patient on the telephone that his reaction is normal, and that he will feel much better by the end of the day. In the office:

P: What the hell did you do to me?

Therapist: So, you were able to make it worse?

P: I didn't make it worse! It just got worse.

Therapist: Your subconscious mind took control and made it worse. That's wonderful! It means that you've taken control of your pain. If you can make it worse, you can make it better whenever you choose.

P: Hmmmn.

Therapist: Would you like to cut it in half right now?

[**Comment:** The patient is in a win-win double bind because he just complained about the pain, so we put him right into trance and say:]

Therapist: When your pain is half as intense as it was on coming into my office, your yes finger will rise. (Wait for the finger signal.)

IM: Yes.

Therapist: Good. Would it be all right to have one minute of being completely free of pain again, realizing that it is better to be alive *without* pain than to be alive *with* pain?

IM: Yes.

Therapist: Yes. Good. Okay. When you are completely free of pain, your yes finger will rise.

IM: Yes.

Therapist: Good. Okay. Now, I am going to time one minute. (Time the minute.) Okay, it has been a minute. Has it been a surprisingly comfortable minute?

IM: Yes.

Therapist: Good. Now <Name>, because you can do it for one minute, then, whenever you're ready, you can do it for two minutes. Signal me when you are ready to do it, to be completely free of pain for two minutes.

[**Comment:** Keep suggesting increasing spans of time as is appropriate. For example, four, and then eight, and then twelve minutes, and then give the posthypnotic suggestion that *Eventually, you will feel ready to extend your comfort to 20 minutes, and eventually to . . .* and so on.]

Therapist: I'd like to ask your feeling mind if that feels all right, if that feels yes, agreeable. Answer with your fingers.

What about Secondary Gain from Pain?

Some patients have so much secondary gain involved from disability payments, pensions, liability litigation, family manipulation, etc., that a sudden and miraculous cure would be self-defeating and make them lose face. So, we mustn't overtreat to satisfy our own egos. These patients require a suggestion such as: "Knowing now that you can control your pain, whenever you are ready, you will be able to diminish your pain to a minimal and tolerable level, or turn it off completely at will."

Since pain is an emotional feeling and a sensation, pure pain without emotional overlay or conditioning is experimentally quite tolerable (Melzack & Wall, 1982). Other feelings that increase suffering require exploration, since they create overlay that can be moderated (Ewin, 1986).

Dealing with Nonacceptance

Nonacceptance is a problem because the patient didn't ask for the pain. It is involuntary. So, pain patients often ask the question almost like a mantra, "Why me?" This often stands as an obstacle to successful treatment as the patient refuses to move on until the question is answered. Since there is no satisfactory answer, we bypass it in trance and intersperse the suggestion that "pure pain doesn't really hurt that much." Later, we ask for an ideomotor answer to the question, "Would it be all right for you to experience a small amount of pure pain as long as it is at a tolerable level?" The patient who gives his permission feels that he has regained some control and will extend that control to keeping the pain "pure" and at a tolerable level (Eimer, 2000; Ewin, 1986).

Removing Negative Suggestions

A common and significant problem with many pain patients we have seen is the negative suggestion they have been given by doctors to the effect that "You have to learn to live with it." This is translated by the patient's subconscious to mean that the only way to get rid of it is to die! Obviously, this is not a good idea and it obstructs treatment. In trance, we remove this bad idea and replace it with something like, "You will find you can cope with it."

Glove Analgesia for Trance Ratification

When we feel we need to do trance ratification with a skeptical chronic pain patient, we'll do a rapid induction, set up ideomotor signals, and then proceed to induce glove analgesia in the hand being used for IM signaling. The cortical representation of the hand occupies approximately one-third of the sensory and motor strips in the contralateral hemisphere of the cerebral cortex (Penfield, 1974). We speculate that this may explain the well-known observation that glove analgesia is easier to induce than direct analgesia in other parts of the body.

Anesthesia is not feeling anything. Analgesia is not feeling pain. It's much easier to hypnotically produce the latter, so that's what we aim for. Glove analgesia involves suggestions of numbness in the hand and wrist, as might be experienced if the patient put on a thick glove. Once this sensory feeling is induced, further suggestions can be given for the patient to transfer (or displace, or rub, or send) the induced numbness and diminution of sensory feeling to any part of the body that hurts.

The patient can be directed to place the numbed hand directly on the painful body part, and then to rub that body part with the numbed hand, while visualizing the numbness flowing from the hand into the painful body part. If the patient cannot reach the painful body part, this is not a problem. The patient is told to place the numbed hand on an accessible body part, and it is suggested that the numbness will flow into the targeted painful area.

We induce glove analgesia in the hand that's doing IM signaling. The hand is positioned with the wrist flexed, forearm upright, and the elbow resting on the armrest of the chair, or the bent arm floating in the air.

T: Would it be all right with your subconscious mind for you to let your hand and wrist get numb and unfeeling?

IM: (Often) No.

T: Nothing happens for no reason. Speak to me and tell me why not?

P: Because I don't think I can do it. I'm hurting too much. (Translation: He's already tried as hard as he can and failed.)

T: It's true that you are hurting a lot, but I didn't ask if you COULD do it, I asked if you would give permission to let it happen. I'll tell you what to do. If you feel you would be interested in what can happen, your yes finger will rise.

IM: YES.

T: And we want to produce Glove Analgesia. So, the next question is, yes or no, are you willing at a deep subconscious level, to let this happen effortlessly without even trying? To just give it permission to happen?

IM: Yes.

T: Okay. That's good. Way, way, way down deep. Some part of your mind knows how to do this. To just let this entire wrist and hand begin to become numb. To begin to lose sensation so that I could pinch your skin and it wouldn't even bother you. . . . And <u>I don't know just how you'll do this</u>.

Some people picture themselves just wearing a magic numb glove over their whole hand and wrist. Some picture themselves wearing a big thick electrician's glove, so that nothing can bother it, nothing can hurt it.

Some make it cold and numb. People who have been in snow country know what it's like to go out and play in the snow until your hand gets so numb you'll hardly be aware of anything.

Some people have been on picnics where there's a big ice chest full of ice water, and a whole lot of different cans and drinks in there, and you reach and hunt and hunt for the one Budweiser® that you want, and by the time you find it, that hand is just as numb as if it had been in the snow.

Some people even visualize it as dissociated, just unhooked from the rest of the body, so that they don't feel anything in the hand.

I don't know how you'll do this. But you just gave it permission, and it'll begin to happen. This whole area will get more and more numb with each breath you take [Gently stroke the entire hand and wrist.] as you go deeper and deeper. And when it has become nice and numb, you'll let me know because your yes finger will rise.

[**Comment:** The therapist and patient must have patience.]

T: It happens without effort. Each breath you take, you go deeper and deeper. The deeper you go, the more numb it gets.

[**Comment:** As the therapist watches and waits, he gently validates and encourages the patient.]

T: That's right. . . . Deeper and deeper. . . . Hmmn. Hmmn. . . . All right. . . .

T: Something will change. More and more numb. Time for you to move on. All right. [If nothing happens after several minutes, stroke the yes and no finger and ask:] Is it still all right to let it happen?

IM: Yes finger rises.

T: Okay. There's no hurry. Take all the time that it takes to go as deep as you need to go.

[**Comment:** If appropriate, you can interweave the comment and question that "We tend to do it when we need it. Answer with your fingers. Yes or no, don't you really need to know how to do this?"]

IM: Yes.

T: Yes. More and more numb. Notice that something is really changing. . . . Now we got a "yes" signal. Keep it there. Keep it numb.

[**Comment:** For this kind of testing, we use a surgical instrument called an Allis clamp. This will grasp tightly but not penetrate the skin. It makes a measured, reproducible amount of pressure so that the patient can later compare the same pressure in the waking state. At this point, we take our Allis clamp and begin to gently and gradually pinch the skin tighter and tighter on the outer aspect of the wrist without setting the clamp at first. This is a form of gradual conditioning to the suggestion we are going to make. As long as the patient shows no signs of discomfort, we gradually squeeze the clamp tighter and tighter].

T: You may feel some pressure, but the more pressure you feel, the more comfortably relaxed you will become. [By using the word "pressure" we are telling the subconscious how to interpret any feeling that is there. A person doesn't mind "pressure" but doesn't want "pain"]. Now we set the clamp.

T: Now <Name>, stay deeply relaxed and open your eyes, and look at what you can accomplish.

P: Opens eyes and sees the clamp hanging from his wrist.

T: Now close your eyes and stay deeply relaxed and go twice as deep. (We remove the clamp as soon as the patient closes his eyes because seeing it may startle him enough to start left brain logical processing and lighten the trance.) I'm taking the clamp off and you'll be pleased with yourself and proud of yourself for what you're able to do. You never know when it may be useful to know that you can turn off discomfort.

[**Comment:** Be sure to remove the suggested sensations of analgesia before alerting the patient.]

T: Okay. Let your sensations all come back to normal. Let your whole wrist and hand come back to normal. (Then alert the patient.)

After alerting, we hand the clamp to the patient, and say: "Here, try this yourself in the waking state and see if you notice any difference." The difference is obvious. This ratifies to the patient that something new has happened. He has been in a trance and is capable of controlling his pain.

Case Example of Transfer of Glove Analgesia to Painful Body Part

Therapist: In your deepest mind, just visualize a change taking place in this hand and wrist (stroking the signaling hand and wrist). Just like in a daydream—I don't know how you will do it—some people remember getting the hand very cold and numb in the snow, or reaching into the ice chest for a cold drink. Some people can picture it like it had turned into a piece of wood. Some visualize wearing a magic numbing glove or a thick electrician's glove. Some even picture it for awhile as not even attached to the body, so no sensation can be felt. Whatever you choose to picture will work for you, and when it's numb enough so that I can pinch the skin without even bothering you, your yes finger will rise.

IM: (After 1 or 2 minutes) Yes.

Therapist: Okay. Keep that feeling. You may feel a little pressure now, and the more pressure you feel, the more deeply relaxed you will become. (Here we use a surgical instrument called an Allis clamp to squeeze the wrist skin gently at first, then to lock in place.) Stay deeply relaxed, open your eyes, and see what you can do. How does it feel?

Patient: Wow. I don't really feel very much at all in that hand.

Therapist: See what your mind can do? Now close your eyes. Experience how powerful your mind is, the power of the mind over the body. (Remove the clamp.) Now, make that hand twice as numb, and when you feel that the hand is twice as numb, your yes finger will rise.

IM: Yes.

Therapist: Yes. Good. Twice as numb. Twice as unfeeling. Twice as numb. Twice as unfeeling. Now take a deep, deep breath and go twice as deep.

IM: Patient takes a deep breath and then yes finger rises.

Therapist: Very good. Wasn't that easy?

IM: Yes.

Therapist: I'm only asking you to do the exact opposite of what you've invested so much energy into; that is, if something isn't working, you need to try harder and harder. The truth is that "bad ideas come without effort." So, how do you think good ideas need to come?

IM: Head nod . . . yes finger rises.

Therapist: That's right, without effort. Good. Now take that hand and place it on your abdomen, and I wonder if you can just imagine this; the numbness in this hand (stroke back of hand) flowing like cool running water through your abdomen and into your back. The numbness just flowing, like a trickle of Novacain to where it is most needed, in your back, making your back feel cool and numb, cool and numb, like it has been lying on ice. Like you're lying in the cold snow. Do you know what cold snow feels like?

IM: Yes.

Therapist: Good. It's just what your back needs now. It makes your back feel nice and numb. Without much feeling. Nice and numb and without much feeling at all. You might feel some touch sensations, but you want to have it like it doesn't feel any discomfort at all. Your yes finger will rise when your back feels nice and numb, nice and numb.

IM: Yes.

Therapist: Great. Now I want you to stay deeply relaxed and tell me how your back feels. Speak to me.

Patient: Nice and numb.

Therapist: Good. Your back is nice and numb. Now let your hand be normal again, and keep the numbness and the comfort and the protection in your back. It will last for several hours after I rouse you up.

A Direct Approach to Pain Reduction

We often have clinical success using the following direct approach with the patient in trance.

T: On a scale from 0 to 10, with 0 being "no pain" and 10 being "the worst you can imagine," tell me where it is now.

P: 6.

T: 6. Okay. Now, tell me what number would be tolerable. Possible to ignore.

P: Hmmmn. Uh, 2.

T: Okay. Two. Now you said that right now it's a 6. Is that so?

P: Yes.

T: Six. Okay. I wonder if you can make it an "8." Just for a minute. Make it an 8. And when you've gotten it up to an 8, your yes finger will rise.

IM: Yes.

P: I'm at an 8 now and I don't like it!

T: You made it an 8. Now, since you were able to increase it to an 8, you can decrease it back down to a 6, where it was a minute ago. Go ahead and do that now and let me know by lifting your yes finger when it's back at a 6.

IM: Yes.

T: Great. Okay. It's now a 6. So, <Name>, if you can turn it up to 8, then perhaps you have the ability to control it better than you knew. Since you now know you have some control, would it be all right to turn it down to a 5 right now? Answer with you fingers.

IM: Yes.

T: Yes. Turn it down to a 5 and your yes finger will rise when it's a 5.

IM: Yes finger rises.

The therapist works gradually over a period of visits to have the patient get it down to a tolerable number. If you go too fast, the patient may not be able to do it. You want to avoid another "try and fail." Every success leads to more success.

Indirect Approaches

Laughing Place Technique

[The therapist begins by stating the following:]

Laughter is a natural antidote to suffering. Everybody's got a place and a time where they feel like laughing. Where nothing can bother you and nothing can disturb you.

T: Would it be all right with your feeling mind for you to find your laughing place now?

IM: Yes.

T: Yes. Good. Go ahead and find your laughing place and when you are there, your yes finger will rise.

IM: Yes.

T: Good. You are there. Would it be all right with your feeling mind to bring it up to a conscious level and tell me all about it?

IM: Yes.

T: Yes. Good. Go ahead and tell me about your laughing place.

P: [Tells therapist about his laughing place.]

T: Would it be all right for you to enjoy being there for a little while, experiencing it with all five senses, consciously and subconsciously, just as if you are really there?

IM: Yes.

T: Yes. Good. Enjoy it with all five senses. What you see. What you hear. What you smell. What you taste. And what you touch. Get into being there, and when you feel it and enjoy being there with all five senses, your yes finger will rise.

IM: Yes.

T: When you know that you are feeling more comfortable, your yes finger will rise.

IM: Yes.

T: Everyone experiences pain on both a subconscious and conscious level. Sometimes, pain is just subconscious, beneath our awareness. We may be unaware of what happened to make the pain break through into conscious awareness. When we are in our laughing place, and the subconscious pain goes away, we may not even be aware of it. That's because it's subconscious.

T: <Name>, when you know that the subconscious element of the pain is totally gone, your yes finger will rise.

IM: Yes.

T: Great. Now <Name>, would it be all right with your feeling mind to make some of that subconscious relief conscious? Answer with your fingers.

IM: Yes.

T: Yes. Good. Go ahead then, and when you know that your conscious pain is diminished by 25 percent, your yes finger will rise.

IM: Yes.

[**Comment:** The therapist keeps on helping the patient chip away as much pain as possible until he gets a NO, or an objection, which then needs to be addressed. At the end of the procedure, say:]

T: Take a mental snapshot of your Laughing Place so that at any time, while we're doing therapy, we can shift to that instantly no matter what else is going on. When you learn self- hypnosis, you can also find your laughing place is a very pleasant daydream to drive out stress and pain, because it doesn't hurt at your laughing place.

Rossi and Cheek's "Body Lights" Imagery

I (BNE) often employ Rossi and Cheek's (1988) rapid hypnoanalytic imagery technique for helping patients experience relief from pain. Cheek (1994) classified this method as an "indirect" approach to ideomotor search for causal events. After inducing trance and setting up IM signals:

Therapist: Imagine you are standing in front of a full-length mirror. Look at yourself in the mirror and see tiny colored lights in different parts of your body. These colored lights represent different physical sensations. There is a different color for every sensation including pain. In fact, there are even different colors for different types of pain. The more intense the sensation is, the more intense, the brighter, the color is. When you see the total picture, your yes finger will slowly lift.

IM: Yes finger eventually lifts.

Therapist: Now that you see the total picture, would it be all right with your feeling mind for you to scan the entire picture and tell me what sensations the colors of each light represent?

IM: Wait for a yes.

Therapist: Would it be all right with your feeling mind to choose the least uncomfortable part of the body to do some therapeutic work? Answer with your fingers.

IM: Wait for a yes.

Therapist: Yes. Let your feeling mind go back to a time when that body light stood for some other comfortable sensation. Your yes finger will lift when you are back at that time.

IM: Wait for yes finger to lift.

Therapist: Now, orient forward in time to the first moment when that body light that now stands for discomfort took the place of the light that stood for comfort. Your yes finger will lift when you arrive at that moment. When you are there, please tell me your age and what is going on.

IM: Wait for yes finger signal and for the patient to verbally respond.

Therapist: Yes. You are . . . years old and [repeat in the present tense the when, what, where and with whom of what the patient relates].

Therapist: Is there any good reason now, why you have to continue having discomfort in that body part?

IM: Wait for an IM or verbal response.

Therapist: [If the patient answers "yes," it is important to explore the patient's felt reasons. If the patient answers "no," ask:] Now that you are aware of what is happening, is your feeling mind willing to let you turn off that discomfort and continue the healing process so that you can get well?

IM: Wait for a response. If the response is no . . .

Therapist: [The therapist should explore with the patient's permission the factors that stand in the way of turning off the discomfort. The therapist should also ask:] Answer with your fingers. Is your feeling mind willing to let you turn down the dial on that discomfort so that you can continue to heal?

IM: Wait for a response. If the response is yes . . .

Therapist: Yes. Okay good. Now I'd like you to imagine a future time when you will no longer be suffering from discomfort in that body part. When it feels more comfortable. When you are there, your YES finger will lift and you will see the month, day, and year as though written on a chalkboard right in front of you.

IM: Wait for a response.

Therapist: Okay. Great! Tell me what you see.

IM: Wait for a verbal response.

Therapist: Thank you. Now lock in on that with every cell in your mind, and body and feelings. Want it to happen, let it happen, and it will happen.

It is suggested that the patient practice orienting to that future time and rehearse imagining the associated more comfortable sensations. The above steps are repeated for other more painful body parts so that the patient gradually works his or her way up a hierarchy of increasingly painful body parts.

Cheek and LeCron's Method

I (BNE) have been using Cheek and LeCron's (1968) ideomotor analysis protocol for years with good success. Their protocol is employed as illustrated in the following case:

A 48-year-old single, white male college professor (R.) consulted BNE for hypnosis for pain management after being referred by his HMO primary care physician. He said that his doctor told him that I (BNE) helped people manage their pain better using hypnosis. Although skeptical, he made the call and booked an appointment. An hour and a half was devoted to the intake.

I learned that R. was diagnosed with spinal stenosis, fibromyalgia and chronic fatigue syndrome, and that he had undergone back surgery three years previously, which entailed laminectomies at L3-4, L4-5, and L5-S1 vertebral levels. The surgery had eliminated his leg pain, but his symptoms of fibromyalgia and chronic fatigue worsened after the surgery. At this point, he was thinking of taking early retirement on long-term disability.

At the end of the first visit, after the intake and history-taking, he was hypnotized using a rapid trance induction, and ideomotor signals were established. He was seen for a second visit three days later. The second visit lasted about one hour and ideomotor analysis was conducted. The following is a summary of that session:

T: Is it all right for me to help you with this problem?
IM: Yes.
T: Would it be all right to let your subconscious mind orient back in
Permission time to the first moment in your life when pain of this sort first became important to you?
IM: Yes.
T: Yes. Okay. Let the subconscious part of your mind orient back in
Direction time to the first moment in your life when pain of this sort first became important to you. When you're there, your "Yes" finger will lift. As it lifts, please bring these memories up to a level where you can tell about them.
IM: Yes.
permit *T:* Is it all right to tell me what's come to your mind?
IM: Yes.
T: Yes. Tell me what's come to your mind.
IM: I remember being in my apartment and realizing that I had this "yuppie disease," this chronic fatigue syndrome they'd been talking about.
T: Tell me what the date is.
P: It's December of 1992.

T: It's December 1992 and you realize you have this "yuppie disease." What leads you to realize this?

P: I'm not getting better.

T: You're not getting better. Does anything happen, or does anyone say something to you that makes the pain and fatigue you're having seem very important?

P: Hmmm. Yeh. This chiropractor said he cannot do anything for me, and that my back is like that of a 70-year-old.

T: (Repeats P's last statement.) Did anything happen before this, at an earlier time, which made what the chiropractor said seem very important?

P: Huh hmm. I kept having like these flues and back attacks. And after each flu, I'd be drained and washed out for weeks.

T: Answer with your fingers, yes or no. Did what that chiropractor said make you feel that you could not get well?

IM: Yes.

T: Knowing what you know today, on Tuesday, October 6th, 1998, yes or no, answer with your feelings, is it possible that the chiropractor was not very knowledgeable about pain and rehabilitation?

IM: Yes.

T: Sure. That chiropractor was not very knowledgeable about how to get people with your problem well. Yes or no, didn't you see another doctor who had a better treatment plan?

IM: Yes.

T: Sure you did. And tell me what he said.

P: He said I don't need surgery. He said I need physical therapy.

T: Uh huh. He was a respected neurosurgeon and he said you need physical therapy. Did you go for the physical therapy?

IM: No.

T: No. You didn't go for it. Tell me why you didn't go for it.

P: Because I was depressed.

T: So you didn't follow that doctor's advice because you were depressed. Okay. You were depressed then. And eventually you needed to have surgery, and it was a successful operation, wasn't it?

IM: Yes.

T: Now, here you are today, on Tuesday, October 6th, 1998. Knowing what you know now, answer with your fingers, yes or no, does your inner mind feel willing to let me help you get well?

IM: Yes.

T: Yes. Great! Okay. Project forward to the time when you are completely over this trouble and are no longer afraid of it recurring.
When you're there, your "yes" finger will slowly rise, and tell me
the date that pops into your mind.

IM: Yes.

P: It's Saturday, December 26th, 1998.

T: (Repeats date.) Okay. Yes or no. Is there anything else we need to
know before we start working toward this goal?

IM: No.

T: Would you like to learn self-hypnosis?

IM: Yes.

I (BNE) taught the patient a brief self-hypnosis exercise. I instructed
him to practice it for two to three minute periods ten times a day. We
rehearsed it to make sure he got it and could do it. We then rehearsed
turning the pain ON and OFF, and making it WORSE and then BET-
TER as described earlier.

The patient called the following day and complained that his pain
and fatigue had somehow gotten worse. I saw the patient that evening
as an emergency. IM analysis revealed that the patient had dreamt
about conversations he'd had with his mother who was a very anxious
woman and very overprotective. We uncovered the fixed idea (that he
had gotten from her) that he worked too hard and didn't relax enough
(this was not so.). As a result of this fixed idea, he believed that he was
a very fragile person and vulnerable to getting sick if he overexerted
himself, mentally or physically. In trance, I removed this suggestion.

We also practiced turning the pain ON and OFF, and making it
WORSE and then BETTER, first on a subconscious level, and then on
a conscious level. I also reframed and removed the fixed idea that HE
had caused all of his physical problems through careless weight lifting
several years before his pain problem started.

IM signaling revealed that, on a feeling level, he felt that now that he
knew these things, he could get better. The patient was seen for one
more visit two weeks later. He reported that he was practicing his self-
hypnosis, and that he was feeling hopeful, and had more energy.

The patient came back for another visit in January of 1999, after his
visualized recovery date. He was dating someone and feared that his
medical problems would scare the woman off. In both waking and hypnotic states, these fears were reframed in light of the overall improve-

ment in his functionality, improved energy level, diminished medication use, and overall greater comfort.

THE "WHITE LIGHT"

This is a guided imagery technique for helping a patient finish some "unfinished business" with a deceased loved one. It's also useful for helping a patient gain self-esteem. It is a useful tool in grief or bereavement therapy as well as in pain management psychotherapy (Eimer & Freeman, 1998).

Summary

We begin by seeding in the waking state, that the White Light is part of the near-death experience for us all, no matter what our religion (even for atheists). We suggest that it is possible to safely visit the White Light to make contact with an important person who has passed, and communicate with that person.

We start by agreeing to go together to the White Light. Trance is induced and IM signals are set up. If it's appropriate, with the patient's permission, we either hold hands, or we put our hand on the patient's. We then begin by setting the scene—that it's twilight, and way off in the distance we can see a little twinkling light like a small star, pure white and brilliant, even though it's so far away.

Together, we, and the patient, start walking towards it, and we notice that it is coming towards us, getting larger and brighter all the time. Soon we become aware that it has no form—it's not a mist, it's not a cloud, it's not a person, but there is an awesome energy, warm and bright, and as it envelopes us, we realize that it IS energy, and that energy is LOVE. We can inhale it, and feel it spread through every cell in our bodies, making us know that we're precious—not perfect, but precious.

And the White Light brings with it an important person who has gone before, and we suggest that the patient can have a private conversation with that person to clarify any unfinished business. This is a time when one can ask for forgiveness, give forgiveness, share love, and reassure each other. We state that we'll be quiet while the patient takes all the time he needs to complete his conversation, and that when he feels content, he can just nod his head to let us know (5 to 10 minutes of silence, perhaps some tears).

After the nod, we suggest that it's time now for us to say goodbye and return to our office, but we take with us the reassurance that we experienced that all of us are precious—not perfect, but precious. We turn away and know that the White Light is going back, getting smaller and smaller, until it's just like a little, twinkly star that disappears, and we come back to TODAY. . . . (We state the exact day, and date, because "today" may still be a regression back to the day the patient's loved one died).

Case Example

The journey is begun with the patient in trance, and after IM signals have been set up. The case of one patient who had long-standing, ongoing issues with his stern father (who was now deceased), went like this:

T: Do you know what the "White Light" is?

IM: Yes.

T: Yes. Raymond Moody wrote a book called *Life After Life*. He interviewed people who had "near-death experiences" and had recovered and come back alive. No matter who he interviewed, or what religion they had, if they had a "near-death experience," they all saw the "White Light." It's an energy concept. Light is a form of energy and the energy they reported in the White Light was love. But it didn't have to be deserved, or earned. It was love that was given because it was needed. It engulfed them. They experienced an awesome love, and it was so wonderful that when they came back, they didn't care about whether or not they actually died! Almost universally, they said "There's something important I have to do before I can go back. I have to love more here, and be a better person, because I want to go back and experience the White Light again." A lot of them said that the White Light brought somebody with it. In particular somebody they had unfinished business with.

Now, I'm going to ask you <Name>, "yes" or "no," if I go with you, would you like to go visit the White Light right now?

IM: Yes.

T: Yes. I wonder if the White Light will bring your father. Maybe he has something to say to you and you have something to say to him. But let's just see ourselves in the twilight. Walking together. Maybe holding hands. And way off in the distance, we see a bright pinpoint of light, like a twinkling star. It's coming toward us, and as it does, it gets bigger and brighter, and brighter and bigger. Pure, brilliant white light. It has no form, no shape. It's not a mist, it's not a cloud, but we experience it as a warm loving energy as we bask in its comfort. It makes us feel precious, absolutely precious.

And your father has gone before you. . . . Look around and see, "yes" or "no," does he know you're here?

IM: Yes.

T: Does he come back? Does he have something to say to you?

IM: Yes.

T: Does he think you're precious too, now that he's experienced the White Light?

IM: Yes.

T: Oh, I think that he needs to pass this on to you. In spite of his toughness, he's followed you all this time. And he's very proud that a part of him is still here, helping people, teaching, growing. I'll be quiet while you and he communicate in this atmosphere of comfort. When you have completed saying what's really important, your "yes" finger will rise (silence for 2 or 3 minutes).

IM: Yes.

T: Does he ask you to forgive him for letting you feel so bad for so long?

IM: Yes.

T: Does the White Light communicate to you that all of God's children are precious and they're entitled to feel lovable, just because they've been made, and you're one of God's children?

IM: Yes.

T: We all ought to do the best we can with what we've got, but we don't have to prove we're lovable, because that comes with the territory. It's a freebie. We may not act lovable all the time, or even feel loving all the time. But the issue is whether or not we're willing to accept love when it knocks. When the White Light comes and it engulfs us, are we going to hold our breath and NOT inhale it? Yes or no?

IM: No.

T: That would be our stubbornness.

T: This gift is a special kind of love we know as charitable love. It doesn't ask for payback. It's what the White Light brings, and when someone says "I don't accept charity," they're rejecting feeling precious. Perhaps your dad didn't think that he was precious until he got to the White Light. But he knows now, and he knows that he was precious, and that you are precious. You wanted to please him. Didn't you?

IM: Yes.

T: And has he just told you that you really do please him?

IM: Yes.

T: Each breath you take, feel this energy. Feel this unconditional love. Just loving <Patient's Name> because he's <Name>. Breathe it in. Let it go through your lungs and into your bloodstream. Circulate it through your heart and to your brain. Your liver, your muscles, your skin. And if you can accept a gift, a gift of love, that makes you vulnerable, but it also makes you stronger. Can you feel it making you stronger?

IM: Yes.

T: You will be able to continue to process this. I wonder if your father is there in your presence, if you are aware of a message from him in the form of the White Light?

IM: Yes.

T: It's been there all along. All you have to do is inhale it. You're just as precious to your father, your mother, your wife and your children. And your peers. It's all there for you. Accept it.

IM: Yes.

T: Now it's time for us to come on back. The White Light begins to move away and get smaller and smaller and smaller, and we can look way off in the distance and finally it's like a tiny blinking star, and it goes out. And we look around and here we are back in . . . on [Date: Month/Day/Year]. And when you're ready, just open your eyes and come back, fully alert, sound in mind, sound in body, and in control of your feelings.

Comment. Later this patient reported that he felt a decrease in tension, and more satisfaction and self-esteem since his visit to the White Light.

Chapter 11

SELF-HYPNOSIS

The reason for teaching a patient self-hypnosis is to continue the process of positive change. Self-hypnosis can be used for relaxation and stress reduction, for reinforcement and further imprinting of self-suggestions, and for ideomotor self-analysis. Cheek and LeCron (1968) pointed out that "the easiest way for one to learn to hypnotize himself is first to be induced by someone else and be given posthypnotic suggestions for induction. There should be some definite formula to follow, stated in detail. By going through this formula, the subject enters hypnosis".

After we've done hypnoanalysis, and gotten closure on a problem, we suggest to the patient while in trance, that from now on, anytime he wants to use self-hypnosis [posthypnotic suggestion], he can get just as deep or even deeper than he is now by simply getting comfortable, closing his eyes, rolling his eyes up, and taking a deep breath and holding it for a count of three (i.e., rapid eye-roll self-induction), and as he EXHALES, go immediately into a pleasant, comfortable hypnotic trance [this is the formula]. He can use this method to reinforce his determination to accomplish his current goal.

Relaxation and Stress Reduction

If the patient is under situational stress (e.g., starting an examination, beginning a project), it's a good time to make it a practice of having relaxing moments of self-hypnosis and going to his laughing place. Just 30 seconds of this will significantly reduce situational stress.

When regular self-hypnosis sessions are indicated, something like the following can be suggested to the patient: *You can practice your own self-*

hypnosis twice a day for about ten minutes each session. When you do your self-hypnosis in the morning, it helps you start the day off right, and when you do your self-hypnosis in the late afternoon, after work, it helps you leave the pressures of work at work. Each time you do your own self-hypnosis, it reinforces and strengthens the positive things I say to you when we are working together.

Further Imprinting of Self-Suggestions

With habit issues like smoking and weight reduction and nail biting, the self-suggestion we typically use is: "I live in the most precious body in the world. And I reject . . . because it hurts me." These are in effect two separate suggestions, neither of which has more than 10 words. Having those two suggestions sink in is a good time to reward himself with a short visit to his laughing place to feel so good, and then self-alert.

Self-Hypnosis Tape

When we've done a significant hypnoanalysis, on our last or next to last visit with the patient, we will often make a personal self-hypnosis tape. The tape can:

1. Summarize what insights we've had.
2. Reinforce our reframes.
3. Give ego-strengthening suggestions to develop new solutions and continue to overcome the problem.
4. As we discuss below, guide the patient in conducting his own self-analysis session.

Chronic Pain

For chronic pain patients, we make a self-hypnosis tape that includes whichever of the following suggestions may seem most appropriate for that particular patient. Add others as is appropriate.

1. No pain lasts forever.
2. I can have all the comfort I need.
3. I'm just as good as anybody else, and I don't have to prove that to anyone.

4. It's all right to have some mild discomfort as long as it's tolerable.
5. Pure pain doesn't really hurt that much.
6. I can numb my hand and pass the numbness to where it hurts.
7. I can take a vacation and go to my "laughing place."
8. I can temporarily turn off the pain.

Studying

For students who are having trouble concentrating on their studies, we like for one word to be the title under a picture to be used in self-hypnosis. I (DME) teach my medical students to write down the following as their picture:

> "CONCENTRATE means: From now on when I want to study, I'll get comfortable, with a good light, and ignoring all distractions, focus on what I'm reading, understand it, store it in memory, and recall it at will."

Before beginning his study time, the student is to read this three times, go into self-hypnosis, and simply let the word CONCENTRATE be the title under the picture in the daydream of what CONCENTRATE means as specified in the written self-suggestion. After a short trance, the student re-alerts and starts to study. Every 20 minutes, he should take a short break, and repeat the above.

Test Anxiety

I (DME) had to take a course in differential equations (advanced calculus) to get into medical school. I was used to making A's, but somehow felt that this was too complicated for me to understand. In the window of a bookstore, I saw a book titled *Calculus Made Easy* and bought it. The blurb on the inside jacket said, "Any fool can calculate. You're surrounded by fools who calculate. What one fool can do, another can." That's all I read in the book because somehow, in my mind, I knew I could calculate and had never equated calculus with calculating. The next day, I went to class and looked around at all the fools around me who were calculating and I decided I could do it too. I raised my grade to a B. It was too late to make an A.

I tell this story to my patients who are having test anxiety. They know the information, but they are not getting it onto their test answer sheet. I suggest that they lay aside their books the night before the examination, get a good night's sleep, go to the test, and look around at all the fools who are going to pass, do a momentary self-hypnosis with the title, "What one fool can do, another can," self-alert, and then take the test. When confronted with uncertainty about which of two answers is best in a multiple choice, I suggest, "Trust your guts (read right brain), not your intellect (read left brain)."

If the student has the fixed idea that he has to make a perfect score, we remove that suggestion by pointing out that the passing grade is (whatever it is), and the object is to pass. There's nothing wrong with making 100, but it is not the goal. This also works with doctoral students who are stuck in getting their dissertations done. They are helped to understand that they just have to get it done. It doesn't have to be the best dissertation ever written, or Nobel Prize material.

The only people who come for hypnosis are people who have been failing examinations in spite of the fact that they have the intellectual capacity to have passed. They are desperate for help. There is often a disabling level of embarrassment or shame associated with having had to take a board or licensing exam multiple times. The patient feels as if his career is threatened by failing the examination which adds to his anxiety level.

"What One Fool Can Do Another Can"

The treatment should include hypnoanalysis. We set up the IM signals in trance.

T: In order to get into (medical school, law school, etc.), a student has made outstanding grades through college and now he is flunking. For you, there is something different about being a medical student, law student, bar candidate, etc. than being an undergraduate, graduate student, etc. The subconscious message is that I have a duty to other people, and if I don't do this right, somebody else will suffer. Nothing happens for no reason at all. There is a reason that you're used to making high grades and now you're failing. <Name>, is it all right for you to know what feeling has changed?

IM: Yes.

T: All right. In your subconscious, review what feels so different and when you know at a conscious level, your YES finger will rise.

IM: Yes rises.

T: Tell me what crossed your mind.

P: If people's lives are going to depend on me, I can't afford to make a mistake.

T: In other words you should be perfect? You should make a 100 on the test?

IM: Yes.

T: But the passing grade is 70 (or whatever). Nobody's perfect. All through medical school (or law school, etc.), your teachers repeat and repeat the basic things you need to know, and you learn how to use the library and the internet as resources to find specific information on diagnoses, drug reactions, (in the case of law students, case law, legal precedents, and so on). Even after you get out of school, you are supervised as an intern and on through your residency. [In the case of practicing doctors or attorneys: You have access to colleagues for consultation.] The goal right now is to simply pass and get your degree. There's nothing wrong with making a 100 on a test, as long as you remember that the goal is to pass, and the passing grade is 70 (or whatever it is).

T: Would it be all right to turn off the idea that you'll get anxious if you don't get a perfect score?

IM: (After a moment, there is usually a big sigh.) Yes.

T: [At this point, we tell the story of what one fool can do another can, and suggest to the student to begin the test taking by looking around at all the other fools who are going to pass. This usually suffices.]

Being a professor, I (DME) treat this problem as a teacher-student consultation rather than as therapy. Therefore, I (DME) do not monetarily charge my medical students who have this problem. I do tell them they owe me, and when they ask me what, I say "You owe me an invitation to your graduation" (an indirect suggestion that they will succeed).

I (BNE) am in private practice and I do charge a fee. Even so, my patients often will say to me, "I will be eternally grateful (or indebted) if you help me pass the exam." I typically respond: "The only thing you'll owe me is to call me when you are notified that you've passed, and to continue to be the best (doctor, lawyer, judge) you can be." (another indirect suggestion that he will pass).

Self-Hypnosis for Self-Analysis

When we want to do self-analysis of a symptom (headache, cough, unexplained fatigue, an itch, pain, etc.), or uncover the origins of a self-defeating emotional overreaction (e.g., defensive anger or hot temper when "hot buttons" are pushed), we go into self-hypnosis and set up our own ideomotor signals. We then go through the seven common causes as noted in Chapter 7.

If it's a Conflict, we know we must make a decision. If it's Organ Language, we must reword it. If it's Motivation, we know we must find a better solution. If it's a Past Experience, we need to repeatedly regress and reframe. If it's an Identification, we must separate the identities. If it's Self-Punishment, we identify what caused the feeling of guilt, and either remediate it, or forgive ourselves. And, if it's a Suggestion, we identify the idea and remove it.

We can teach this self-analysis method to the patient in trance. However, it should not be taught prematurely. First the patient must have been taught self-hypnosis. Second, he must be practicing self-hypnosis in between sessions. Then, after we've conducted a significant hypno-analysis, the motivated patient can learn to use self-analysis to continue the process of change, deal with recurrences of the symptom, and better understand the origins of self-defeating emotional overreactions.

After IM signals have been set up in trance, a dialogue such as the following takes place:

T: Yes or no, would you like to learn how to use self-hypnosis and your fingers to do your own self-analysis?

IM: Yes.

T: When you want to do self-analysis of a symptom, or understand the origins of a self-defeating emotional overreaction, such as when your "hot buttons" are pushed, you enter self-hypnosis, and then you set up your finger signals. You think to yourself, "If I ask myself a 'yes' or 'no' question and the answer is 'yes,' my yes finger will slowly rise to signal that I agree." Then you ask yourself a question that you know is "yes," and your yes finger will rise. Next, you think to yourself, "If I ask myself a 'yes' or 'no' question and the answer is 'no,' my no finger will slowly rise to signal that I disagree." Then you ask yourself a question that you know is "no," and your no finger will rise. Then, you think to yourself, "If I ask myself a 'yes' or 'no' question and the answer is 'I don't know,' or

'I'm not ready to answer yet,' I will raise my thumb." Now, answer with your fingers, yes or no, does that feel all right?

IM: Yes.

T: Yes. Okay. And each time your fingers answer a question, you go deeper and deeper into self-hypnosis, and get more in touch with your deepest and most heartfelt feelings. Then, you ask yourself, you think to yourself, "'Yes' or 'no,' is it all right for me to better understand this problem I have with [whatever the problem is] so that I can feel better?" You wait for your fingers to answer.

T: If the answer is yes, you continue to ask your feeling mind questions. If the answer is NO, respect that answer, and come out of your self-hypnosis when you are ready to re-alert. Now answer with your fingers, yes or no, does that feel all right?

IM: Yes.

[**Comment:** Deal with any objections or questions the patient raises.]

T: You can begin your self-analysis of the problem by asking your feeling mind a direct question such as, "Is it all right to subconsciously review the cause of this problem?" If you get a "yes," go ahead and review it on a feeling level. Think to yourself, "My 'Yes' finger will rise as I begin to review it, my 'no' finger will rise each time I review something emotionally important, and I will raise my thumb after I've completed my review."

T: Next, you ask your feeling mind, "Yes or no, is it all right to bring this cause to a conscious level, so I can consciously know what it is?" If you get a 'yes,' go ahead and review it with your fingers on a conscious level. If you get a 'no,' that's all right. Just leave it for another time. Now answer with your fingers, yes or no, does this feel all right?

IM: Yes.

T: Yes. Then when you have reviewed enough and you are ready to stop your self-analysis and exit self-hypnosis, you count to three and at three, blink your eyes and alert yourself, and you'll feel wide awake, alert, refreshed, relaxed, sound in mind, sound in body and in control of your feelings.

T: Answer with your fingers. Yes or no, is it all right for you to rehearse doing self-analysis right now?

IM: Yes.

T: Yes. Good. Orient your mind to a problem you want to solve, or a symptom you want to be free of, and use your fingers to analyze the problem. For example (with a "weight loss" patient), if you find yourself overeating again, ask your inner mind, yes or no, if it's all right to know the reason you are overeating. If it feels "yes," scan the reason on a subconscious level. Your "yes" finger will rise as your subconscious begins to scan, your "no" finger will rise each time your subconscious reviews something emotionally important, and your thumb will lift when you've completed your subconscious review. Go ahead and rehearse this now, and when you have completed your rehearsal, signal with your thumb.

IM: Thumb rises.

T: Good. Okay. Now answer with your fingers and your feelings. Yes or no, is it all right to know the reason on a conscious level?

IM: Yes.

T: Yes. Okay. Bring the reason up to a conscious level and when a thought comes to mind, your "yes" finger will lift.

IM: Yes.

T: Yes. Good. Now ask your inner mind, and answer with your feelings, "Yes or no, now that I know this, is it all right to stop overeating and find another way to deal with the reason I overate?"

IM: Yes.

T: Yes. And when another better way comes to mind, your "yes" finger will rise.

IM: Yes.

T: Great. Now you know how to do your own self-analysis. When you are ready to re-alert yourself, just as you'll be doing on your own, count to three, and at three, blink your eyes and come back awake, alert, refreshed, sound in mind, sound in body and in control of your feelings.

A personalized self-analysis tape can also be made to guide the patient through this process.

Weight Loss

I (BNE) see numerous patients in my practice for weight loss. In most cases, the problem that has to be addressed is overeating. While the reasons vary, some common causes are: an identification with one or both parents, a learned (or conditioned) association of eating with comfort, a motivation to be overweight for its secondary benefit (e.g., to avoid being sexually attractive, or the opposite motive of substituting stomach gratification for sexual gratification), a compulsive desire for sweets, low blood sugar, guilt feelings and self-punishment, and conflicts over body image, being healthy, or sex. Investigation with ideomotor signaling will bring out the emotional causes, and regression and reframing with ideomotor analysis can help the patient find a better alternative.

Weight loss patients are typically experts at dieting, and more of the same is not the answer. It often helps to tell the patient that he can forget about diets and calories, and instead focus on making some changes in his eating habits. The kinds of foods eaten, and how often and how much, are more important than calories and grams of fat. The patient must be helped to transform eating from a compulsion into a conscious choice.

The first visit is devoted to the psychodynamic intake and giving the patient his first experience of hypnosis. Direct suggestions in hypnosis (DSIH) are administered based on the information gathered in the intake.

At the second visit, trance is induced, IM signals are set up, and the patient is taught self-hypnosis for relaxation, stress reduction, and for reinforcement and continued imprinting of individualized self-suggestions. Hypnoanalysis is initiated.

Based on the data obtained in the first two visits, a 15-minute self-hypnosis tape is made before the third session, and given to the patient at that third visit. First, four to five direct therapeutic suggestions are recorded. Each suggestion is repeated three times. These suggestions are followed by a rapid self-hypnosis trance induction. Each of the suggestions is then repeated three times, followed by a suggestion for exiting self-hypnosis such as:

> When you're ready to alert yourself and come out of hypnosis, count to three, and at three, blink your eyes and then open them, and come back fully alert, awake, refreshed, sound in mind, sound in body and in control of your feelings. If you're listening to this tape before going to sleep, count backwards from three, and at one, continue to relax and drift into a comfortable and peaceful sleep state. When you awake, you'll feel rested and refreshed. Your deepest mind will continue to process the things we're working on, and reinforce the helpful suggestions.

Direct therapeutic suggestions such as the following are recorded on the tape:

• You live in the most precious body in the world, and when it gets sick, you get sick with it. And when it finally dies, you'll die with it.

- Your body is innocent. It has to take what you give it.
- Only you can take care of this body.
- It's all right to walk around a little bit hungry to remind yourself that you are doing something for your own health.
- Fat hurts you.
- Cookies, candy, etc. hurt you and you refuse to be tempted.
- For you, but more so for your body, junk food is poison.
- For you, and for your body, overeating is like poison.
- Half of your food feeds your body. The rest is garbage.
- You are not a garbage can.
- You will be able to avoid sweet, sugary foods easily.
- You will also be aware that sweet foods no longer taste as good as they did.
- You will be eating slowly and filling up quickly in a comfortable way.
- You will eat less and enjoy your food more.

Hypnoanalysis is conducted during the third and subsequent visits. By the end of the third visit, ideomotor signaling has been employed for questioning the patient as to the causes of his problems with weight and overeating. Typical questions include (adapted from Cheek & LeCron, 1968):

1. Is there some emotional or subconscious cause for you to be over-weight? To overeat?
2. Is your feeling mind willing for you to know the reasons for your overeating? For your being overweight?
3. Are you identifying with someone, perhaps a parent, who over-ate, or was overweight?
4. Do you think of food when you are emotionally upset?
5. Do you overeat when you feel frustrated? Nervous? Guilty? Ashamed? Angry? Sad? Needy? Bored? Rejected? Insecure?
6. Is one of the causes that as a child, you felt better when you were fed?
7. Does food serve as a reward for you?
8. Do you like your appearance now?
9. Do you tend to dislike yourself as to your body image?
10. Do you tend to dislike yourself in other ways?
11. Are you punishing yourself by being overweight?
12. Are you unconsciously trying to harm yourself by being over-weight?

13. Do you substitute food for sexual appetite?
14. Is there some conflict in your inner mind over sex that leads you to overeat or be overweight?
15. Are you carrying out some fixed idea implanted in your mind as a child about eating, such as about not wasting food, having to clean your plate, eating a lot is good for you, or any other similar ideas?
16. Are you using your overweight condition for some purpose, possibly as an alibi of some kind?
17. Are you trying to make yourself unattractive to avoid sex or members of the opposite sex?
18. Are you possibly using this condition as a way of being a rebel, to be contrary to yourself or others?
19. Are there any other reasons or motives for your overeating? For your being overweight?

Other questions are formulated depending on the individual case. Answers to these questions are subjected to ideomotor analysis. With a motivated patient, by the end of the treatment, symptom self-analysis is also taught.

PART III
ANNOTATED CLINICAL SESSION TRANSCRIPTS

Cognitive Hypnosis Protocol
  Education
  Waking State Reframing
  Trance
  Direct Suggestion

Chapter 12

ILLUSTRATION OF THE TECHNIQUE WITH A COMPLEX SMOKING CESSATION PATIENT

The following transcript of an entire hypnosis session illustrates the technique: rapid trance induction, set-up of ideomotor (IM) signals, and rapid hypnoanalysis employing ideomotor (IM) search and review methods. The patient, whom we shall call M., is a 38-year-old, 10 weeks pregnant, asthmatic, married white female, who came to see BNE for help to stop smoking. She had had two previous miscarriages. The transcript illustrates how IM analysis can be employed to help a patient stop a self-destructive habit. The patient is helped to develop empathy and communication with her "younger self" (a.k.a. the "inner child"), as well as with her unborn baby.

Background

M. was initially seen by BNE for a one-visit smoking cessation session. The Zarren and Eimer (2002) brief cognitive hypnosis protocol was employed, featuring education, waking state reframing, trance induction, and direct suggestion in hypnosis (DSIH).

The following day, the patient called BNE and reported that she had smoked several cigarettes after becoming annoyed. An appointment was made for a no-charge follow-up visit, as is my (BNE) usual practice within the first two weeks after seeing a smoking cessation patient who calls and says she has started smoking again.

Given that DME was coming to stay with me (BNE) to finish this book, it was agreed on the telephone that the patient would see both of us at my (BNE) office. The patient provided her informed consent for the session to be videotaped. She was introduced to DME, and DME

169

conducted the hypnoanalysis session while I (BNE) operated the video cam recorder.

M. felt that the problem was that she was "addicted" to cigarettes. She said that she was smoking three-quarters of a pack to a pack a day. She started smoking when she was 17.

The problem started when she became pregnant for the third time after having had two previous miscarriages since getting married.

M. described herself as rebellious and very independent. However, she didn't work and stayed at home. Her husband of 2 ? years (her first marriage) made the living, and she described her husband as "good to me."

History taking revealed that M. had been "always" sick as a child, and that it was "normal" for her to be in and out of the hospital for asthma attacks.

She reported that she smoked more when she was "stressed," "aggravated" or "annoyed" and that she was "a big worrier" and got angry a lot. She reported that she smoked to relieve nervousness. Her first wish was "Not to ever smoke."

Her answer to what she would do that she could not do now if she was "cured" of the habit was: "I probably wouldn't worry about my health as much," and that she wouldn't be "so dependent" on her asthma medications and inhalers.

Interestingly, her answer to the question of the worst thing that ever happened to her was a motor vehicle accident seven years previously, and not the two miscarriages. The most frightened she'd ever been was when she had a bad asthma attack coupled with pneumonia a few months previously that landed her in the hospital for seven days.

The session involves IM exploration of the patient's feelings about her own birth and her little self (a.k.a., "inner child").

Trance Induction and IM Set-Up

[Trance was induced with the Ewin Rapid Eye Roll Induction and IM signals were then set up.]

T: Get comfortable. Close your eyes and keeping your eyelids closed just as thought they're glued together, roll your eyeballs up as though you're looking at the top of your forehead, looking way way up. . . . And take a deep breath, the deepest breath you've ever taken, deep breath, and hold it, hold it, . . . and as you let it alllllll out, just like a balloon collapsing, just draining all the tension out of every nerve and fiber in your body.

Your eyes relaxed . . . jaws unclenched . . . shoulders droopy . . . shifting into daydream type thinking. We all daydream best when we're relaxed . . . and feel how comfortable that feels. . . . shoulders droopy . . . arms limp and floppy and your abdomen soft.

Each breath you take as you exhale, just picture yourself just blowing stress and tension out into the atmosphere never to return. . . .

Take another deep breath and blow out fear, just blow it out, let it go and replace it with your strength and courage that got you through so much for all these years. . . .

And another deep breath and blow out anger . . . just blow out anger, it uses up so much energy. Blow it out and replace it with love . . . That's obviously the part of you that you really like. You're bringing it to life more now, you're into a happy marriage, you value your health more, and all that anger and rebelliousness that went on for so long . . . let it go. . . . Another deep breath and now blow out guilt including imaginary guilt. Just let it go and replace it with innocence and forgiveness because the past is past. . . .

Your legs are all loose and limp and lazy-like, and your mind as relaxed as your body, feeling calm . . . and safe . . . you're safe in here M., nothing can happen to you and its all right to go as deep as you need to go to solve this problem and to go inside and find that part of you that knows that you're precious. Even little baby M. when she was first born was precious and she still is, and sometimes it's easy to forget.

Now we're going to set up a way for you to signal to me how you feel without even talking.

T: If I ask you a question and it *feels yes,* it feels okay, this finger will just slowly rise to signal that yes, it feels okay, that's right. (stroke designated yes finger, gently lift it and then lower it.) Do you like for your friends to call you M.?

IM: Yes.

T: (Stroke finger) Okay. Of course, you already told me that. Every time your feelings answer a question, you'll notice a wave of relaxation go over your entire body as you go deeper and deeper in touch with your deepest most heartfelt feelings . . . about yourself, your feelings about life, about happiness. . . . Way, way down deep.

T: If I ask you a question and *you disagree,* something's wrong with that, you have a *no feeling* about it, this finger will slowly rise to (stroke, lift and lower designated No finger) signal nah uh, that's not right, you don't even have to know why, it just doesn't feel right. Is today Christmas?

IM: No.

T: (Stroke finger) No. Of course not. This isn't Christmas. This is the 14th of May, 2005.

T: If I should ask a question that *you're not ready to answer yet,* or *don't want to answer,* (lift thumb), you just signal with your thumb and that's all right.

T: And if something crosses your mind, you want to talk to me or ask a question, just raise your whole hand and we'll talk. (raise and lower hand)

T: And my first question to your feeling mind, your deepest mind, is, is it all right for me to help you with this problem?

IM: Yes.

T: Okay. Good. Fine. Way, way, way down deep. Calm and safe.

[**Comment:** DME first tries the "Direct Approach" to IM search (see Chapter 4). The patient is uncomfortable with this.]

T: Would it be all right with your feeling mind to go back to the very beginning? You told me "always, always," you used that word. I was always sick as a child, "always" starts when you're born. Would it be all right, yes or no, to go back at a feeling level and review your own birth experience?

IM: "No" finger lifts. Then the thumb lifts, and then, her no finger lifts again.

T: No. Okay. That's all right, you don't have to do that. . . . Is it all right for your fingers to answer a few questions about your birth? (Strokes yes and no fingers.)

[**Comment:** DME validates that it's okay, and asks if she's willing to explore it from a safer distance.]

IM: Yes.

T: Okay. Because we get imprints. We have little bits of knowledge in there. Does your feeling mind feel like it is a good experience to be born?

IM: Yes.

T: Good. Did you feel wanted?

IM: Yes.

T: Okay. Huh hmm. Did something happen to make it difficult for you to breathe?

IM: Yes.

T: Okay. Huh hmm. Did you sense perhaps the cord was around your neck?

IM: No.

T: No. Okay. Sometimes you're a very long labor. It can be very difficult for the baby to get enough oxygen. Was it a very long labor? Were you being squeezed to the point where you had difficulty getting air?

IM: Faint thumb signal, followed by faint "yes," followed by a NO.

T: No. Okay. You know sometimes just getting a baby born, the baby's been living off the mother's oxygen in the womb all this time from the placenta, and there comes a time when they cut the cord and you have to fill your lungs with air, and sometimes this can be kind of difficult. Do you sense, yes or no, that you had some difficulty with your first breath? . . . When you fill your lungs for the first time? Was that your introduction to life? Having difficulty breathing?

IM: No.

T: No. Okay. Did this start after you were actually born?

IM: Yes.

[**Comment:** DME next tries the "Chronological Search" method (see Chapter 4). She is also uncomfortable with this. M. is blocking on something.]

T: Yes. Okay. Let's go forward to the first time that breathing became too important (repeats and strokes yes finger). And when you find it, your "yes" finger will rise.

IM: No signal at all.

T: Huh hmm. Go ahead and find it and then signal with your "yes." Pay attention to it.

IM: No signal at all.

[**Comment:** DME next tries the "Retrograde Search" method (see Chapter 4). The patient responds to this.]

T: (Strokes yes and no fingers) Does this happen before you were born M.? That's your first time that breathing becomes too important?

IM: No.

T:　Okay. Was it before you were two years old?

IM: Yes.

T:　Okay. So it's between one and two. Do you catch a cold?

IM: Yes.

T:　Ah Hah. Is that when they first diagnosed your asthma?

IM: No.

T:　No. They don't even pick it up then. They just think it's a cold. Do you go to the hospital with this where you got sick?

IM: Yes.

T:　Huh hmm. Very sick little girl about one, maybe one and a half years old. Bad cold . . . something's going on. Does it feel like you are not going to get enough breath?

IM: I don't want to answer.

[**Comment:** The patient is blocking.]

T:　That's all right. But we know you're going to get enough breath. Would it be all right to review this episode, to review it at a feeling level . . . just the significant imprints of that? Would it be all right to review it? This little girl is a little bit less than two years old. She's very sick and she lying in the hospital, and they say she's got a bad bad cold. Would it be all right to review this like you have a cold as a little girl?

IM: No.

T:　No. Is that because it's so frightening that you're afraid you might die? And is this what little girls do. It's so frightening that she can't even review it?

IM: Yes.

T:　Ah hah. She's afraid she might die. Huh hmm . . . .Way, way, way down deep. . . . You know when a person has asthma, they can breathe in, but they hold it like it's the last breath they're ever going to get. And they 'hoo, hoo, hoo' going out. It's a problem in exhalation, not inhalation.

T:　And while your thoughts and feelings are back on this frightened little girl, who is just under two years old, in the hospital scared she's going to die, what's she going to do? Yes or no, do you begin to hold your breath like this is the last breath I'm going to get? I know I'm going to hold on to this? Is that what your subconscious mind is feeling? Like you're under water. You take a breath and you go down under the water?

IM: Yes.

T: Yeh. Get it and hold on to it. You know, just like the whales do and the dolphins. They never blow any breath out under the water. They come to the surface, blow it out, and then they get a new breath and go back under. Would it be all right to practice breathing with me, knowing that it is safe to blow it out? Because were surrounded by air. There's plenty of air. We can get all the breaths we want. Knowing that, would it be all right for us to practice blowing out breaths?

IM: Thumb rises (I'm not ready to answer signal)

[**Comment:** We are wondering why the patient is "resisting." What is she afraid of?]

T: All right. Would it be all right to take three deep breaths? And blow them all out and feel how good that feels? Because this is something you can teach that little two-year-old.

IM: No IM response.

T: It's safe. I won't let anything happen to you. We can tell little baby M., we're going to teach your subconscious mind that it's all right to let the breath go, because it's not the last breath you're going to get. You're surrounded by air. Take a nice deep breath and blow it alllll out, every bit of it, just blow it out. It's all right to let it go because there's plenty more air.

IM: M. follows deep breathing instructions.

[**Comment:** It seems that M's rebelliousness and obstinacy is at play.]

T: And another nice deep breath in, and blow it allll out when you've gotten it. Blow it allll out.

IM: M. continues to follow deep breathing instructions.

T: That's it. Let it go. Let it go. Let it go. And another deep breath. Deep breath. All the way. All the way. Fill your lungs up. Another deep breath and then blow it allll the way out

IM: M. continues the deep breaths.

T: How good that feels. . . . . And grown up M. can tell little baby M. that there's plenty of air. It only seemed like she'd get so sick she'd die, but we know she didn't. That she won't . . .

T: I'm going to be quiet for a little (strokes IM signaling fingers) while little baby two year old M., really gets that message, that it was a cold and it may have seemed like you were so sick you were going to die, BUT it doesn't happen, there's plenty of air that you're going to be able to breathe. When she gets that message and knows that its safe to blow it out, your yes finger will slowly rise.

T: [Waiting on the finger . . .] Huh hmmm. Each breath, you go deeper and deeper and it gets easier and easier to blow all that breath out and realize that there's plenty of air for another breath.

IM: Tentative Yes.

T: Huh hmm. Good clear signal. Way, way, way down deep. Let it come up. She got the message [strokes yes and no fingers]. Now "yes" or "no," does anything happen BEFORE this to sensitize you to it? Maybe even while you're in your mother's womb, maybe she catches a cold, and she has trouble breathing. . . . Did anything happen before this episode in the hospital so that breathing gets too important?

IM: No.

T: No. Okay (strokes No finger). Very very good.

[**Comment:** Searching for a previous sensitizing experience]

T: Now there are things we know about people and children with asthma, being afraid that they can't breathe. And there's been some good psychological research to the effect that just hearing themselves wheeze is reassuring. Somehow they know that they can blow the air out and that they are breathing. That this isn't their last breath, that they can get another breath. Now, sometimes smoking is reassuring. You've got to be breathing if you can blow it out and see all that smoke.

T: I want to ask you, yes or no, do you sense that somehow smoking has been reassuring to you about your asthma . . . that you can blow the smoke out and see it?

IM: Yes.

[**Comment:** Is this a rationalization that she can buy? DME continues, and reframes her feelings and beliefs about breathing.]

T: Yeh. Isn't that interesting. So you can. But you don't have to see air! And you don't have to be reassured if you're aware of the deep feeling that you can breathe. Not only breathe it in, but breathe it out. Little M was a frightened little baby, going in and out of the hospital with ordinary little colds because it would make her anxious about her breathing. But the past is past and grown up M has got good reasons to be happy and to be healthy. . . . And as time goes on, you leave all that behind.

T: I wonder if you can imagine, picture it, feel it, see it, visualize it, . . . grown-up M, knowing what you know now, taking that little baby, two-year-old M in your arms and telling her, you're going to know that it only *seemed* like she couldn't breathe when she had a cold . . . that you know she's going to make it, and that she's safe, she's well loved, she's wanted, she's precious, and she can be strong and not afraid.

In your mind, when grown-up M can take little baby M and tell her what she needs to know, your yes finger's going to rise, and after you've told her everything and you know that she knows it, you'll signal with your thumb. . . .

IM: No response.

T: Taking little baby M in your arms . . . you may even want to practice with her. Taking a few deep breaths, and show her that she can blow it out. . . . And you can make her feel safe and strong . . . and unafraid. . . .

IM: No response yet.

T: When you have her in your arms, and you're talking to her, your yes finger will rise.

IM: Yes rises ever so slowly.

T: Huh hmmm. Huh Hmm. All right . . . Huh hmm. Hmmm. . . . Boy, it just feels so good to just blow it out and RELAX. . . . With each breath going deeper and deeper . . . And when little baby M. knows that it's going to be okay, you'll signal with your thumb.

IM: Thumb rises.

T: Good. Okay. She knows that now. And bringing that forward to today, today May the 14th 2005, to grown-up M. Grown-up M can tell whether or not she can breathe and blow her air out. When grown-up M knows that she doesn't have to see her breath, that she doesn't have to smoke to know that she can breathe, when grown up M knows that, your yes finger will rise (strokes yes finger). The smoking has no value for helping you see your breath, for helping you know that you can breathe. When you know that, your yes finger will rise.

IM: YES

[**Comment:** The reframing continues and utilizes her need to be independent, and her stated desire to be less dependent on medicine.]

T: Huh hmm. Yeh, that's really kind of a kid's idea almost, because you're not really dependent any more. You're independent and one of the results that'll happen when you're cured of the smoking habit, is that you'll be less dependent, more independent, of your medicines.

T: Does your deepest mind know that if you stop smoking, and you know you can blow your breath out, does it know that you don't need as much medicine? Yes or no? That you can be more and more independent of your medicine?

IM: Yes.

T: Hmmm–Isn't that good?

IM: Yes.

T: Lock that in your mind, and in every cell in your mind and your body and your feelings, for you are an independent person, and you can be strong and unafraid . . . because that's really where anger comes from often, from when we're frightened. . . . Most of us in high school learn about the fight or flight response, that if we're frightened, we have two choices–we can run or we can fight. So, if something is frightening, like you might have a cold coming on, and all those other past things are gone now, when all those memories and thoughts come up–it's frightening. And you found out, yes or no, that you can use cigarettes for rebellion, haven't you? You can blow smoke in their face.

IM: Yes.

T: Go ffffff feh. (exhaling) Yeh. And it relieves some of that tension. You told me I feel like I need it to relieve the tension and anxiety. Well, if a person can't breathe, and you blow out some smoke, you can see you are breathing. Unh huh. Does that make some sense?

IM: Yes.

T: Yeh, but you don't need that anymore. If you catch a cold, we've got much better medicines now than when you were a child. And if you keep yourself in good health, you'll hardly ever catch a cold. You can exercise and eat right. You can walk and ride a bicycle, and so on. And if you're in good shape, yes or no, you also know that's got to be good for your baby, don't you?

IM: Yes.

[**Comment:** Reframing the idea of "addiction."]

T: Sure. Your baby needs you breathing in your oxygen. And sometimes, we'll do something for somebody else what we won't do for ourselves. Now I wonder, if you can just blow away the idea of being an addict? You're not an addict. It only seems like that because you have feelings of wanting to relieve the anxiety. That doesn't make you an addict. You can dump that idea. Can you dedicate this to your new baby, that you're going to stop smoking comfortably?

IM: Yes.

T: Yeh. Because once that baby is born, you still don't want any second-hand smoke around, do you?

IM: No.

T: No. Of course not.

[**Comment:** Ego strengthening.]

T: As far as you're concerned, you live in the most precious body in the world, don't you?

IM: Yes.

T: Yeh. Can you take care of this body easily and comfortably and be pleased with yourself and proud of yourself to stop smoking comfortably now?

IM: Yes.

T: Good. This is a long-standing habit. So, feelings of gosh darn it, I feel like I want to smoke will come up during the first few days . . . but that's when you make a decision, a conscious choice. . . . Look, I'm doing this for me and my baby, and for my lungs, these are precious lungs. . . . And the choice is, the positive choice is that I reject this stuff, it's poison. . . . And every time you make a good decision, you have a psychological law helping you. It's called the Extinction Phenomenon. It says that every time you make a good decision, it gets easier and easier to make the same decision until the issue is extinguished. It doesn't even come up. It doesn't even cross your mind, that "it's time to smoke" or "I feel like smoking," even when I'm angry. A lot of times when I'm angry, I'm scared. And I'm going to find out what I'm scared of and deal with it directly and not by hurting myself. Yesterday you made 13 good decisions. And that's the beginning of extinguishing the idea that you want to put smoke in these precious lungs and have it circulate through your body.

T: Picture yourself stopping smoking proudly and comfortably, pleased with yourself and proud of yourself, and when you picture that happening, your yes finger will rise.

IM: Yes.

[**Comment:** Dave Elman's (1970) suggestion for "locking in."]

T: (Holds yes finger) <u>Lock</u> in on that. <u>Want</u> it to happen. <u>Let</u> it happen. And it <u>will</u> happen. Before you come awake, is there anything else that you feel we need to clear up, anything that could block you in any way from making your wish come true? You had one wish that you would stop smoking, and you can stop smoking comfortably. Is there anything in your subconscious mind that could block you in some way from accomplishing this?

IM: No.

T: Great. (stroke no finger). Nothing in there now. Okay. There's nothing to block it. <u>Want</u> it to happen. <u>Let</u> it happen. And it <u>will</u> happen. And you can be surprised at how easily you can do it. For the first few days, maybe the first week, if you get the old sensations you used to deal with by smoking, just deal with it by taking several deep breaths and see if you can deal with it by blowing out the feeling, blowing out the guilt, and be pleased with yourself. You're independent, strong and not afraid.

[**Comment:** Utilizing a therapeutic double-bind for alerting.]

T: When your deepest mind knows you can do this, you'll blink your eyes, open them and come back fully alert, sound in mind, sound in body and in control of your feelings.

IM: After about 35 seconds, the patient opens her eyes and smiles.

T: How do you feel?

P: (Shrugs shoulders). Okay. (Smiles) Very relaxed.

[**Comment:** The patient has no other comment. She appears not totally convinced.]

T: Will it be easy to let it out and take that big deep breath?

P: Yes.

T: Won't that be nice.

T: Now of course take the medicine that you need. You can tell if you need it or not. But on the other hand, there's nothing wrong with tapering it down so you don't need as much. If you're feeling good, there is nothing wrong if you see what happens if you take a little less medicine. Any additional thoughts?

P: No. Not really.

Comments and Lessons

This case illustrates several realities about hypnosis in general and the ideomotor technique of hypnoanalysis in particular, some of which were discussed in Chapter 5:

1. It illustrates that for clinical hypnosis and hypnotherapy to be effective, there must be a collaborative teacher-student relationship. The subject must be willing. He must <u>want</u> it to happen, <u>let</u> it happen, and it <u>will</u> happen. This wasn't totally the case here.
2. No one can be made to do something against their will, that they do not want to do, <u>with</u> or <u>without</u> hypnosis as a therapeutic change tool.
3. A person in hypnosis is NOT a zombie. He hears everything that you are saying and is aware of everything going on.
4. Hypnosis is NOT a truth serum.
5. The subconscious is protective. When a hypnotized patient is not ready to visit certain issues, he retains the ability to say NO, I'm not ready to do this yet.
6. The patient with a hidden agenda will do whatever he feels is necessary to realize his agenda. We cannot make the patient tell us his hidden agenda. He has to be willing.
7. If a patient needs to retain <u>conscious</u> control over his experience, he will.

Unfortunately, we were not successful in helping this patient stop smoking, given the above realities. A telephone follow-up one week after the session revealed that she started smoking again the evening after the session. There were indications during the session (see comments above) that M. was not a full participant or collaborator in the treatment process. We hypothesize that there were issues and memories that she chose not to share, and she may have had a hidden agenda.

This case transcript, while clearly illustrating the technique, provides a clear example of the fact that the patient retains control of herself and where the session is permitted to go. M. did not stop smoking after a session of DSIH. However, she entered hypnosis (she was "relaxed"). M. did not stop smoking after hypnoanalytic exploration. Although, she entered hypnosis, and got relaxed, she did not allow exploration of key issues. As far as we were able to determine, M. continued to smoke throughout her pregnancy.

Chapter 13

A SIMPLE SMOKING RECALL SESSION

C. was a 57 year-old married white female who was seen by BNE. C. was seen for a one visit stop smoking session a week earlier, when BNE used Brief Cognitive Hypnosis consisting of the intake, waking state reframing, a brief trance induction, and DSIH. She stopped smoking for two days and then called the office on a Friday after she started smoking again. BNE worked with her on the telephone using DSIH. Then she called again on the following Tuesday afternoon and reported that she had started smoking again. BNE saw her for a smoking recall session in the office as part of their contract, at no charge, on Tuesday evening.

The first thing BNE did was to ask C. to "tell me about your problem." She stated that on Sunday, her husband had some old friends come over. They called to say they were going to be in the neighborhood. She related that her husband met his first wife through them and that he's still friendly with their family. She stated that his ex-wife had accused her of horrible things, and that she had always been extremely uncomfortable around her and them. So, after they said they were going to come over, she stated that she told her husband, Bob, that she needed a cigarette. She gave in to her urge and went to the store and bought a pack. She had about 10 cigarettes, and then threw the rest of the pack away. That was Sunday night.

On Monday night, the day before our recall session, she stated that her husband bought her a pack without her asking for it, and she was up almost all night drinking coffee and smoking; fighting with herself. She stated that she even put them in the garage, and kept going out to the garage to smoke and that "I should have called you last night."

182

BNE hypnotized C. and after setting up the IM signals, and beginning the scan of the seven keys, we got a strong yes to the first key, Conflict. In summary:

[T. is the therapist. P. is the patient.]

T: One of the things that causes symptoms is what we call *conflict*. A conflict occurs when a person wants to do one thing and feels he ought to do the opposite. When you are being pulled in two directions. Answer with your fingers. Do you sense that you are being affected by a conflict?

P: YES finger rises.

T: Would it be all right for you to bring this conflict up to a conscious level?

P: Yes finger rises.

T: I'll be quiet while you bring it to mind, and when you are aware of the conflict, your YES finger will rise.

P: Yes finger rises.

T: Would it be all right to tell me about it?

P: Yes rises.

T: Speak to me and tell me about it.

P: For my health, I have to quit. But for my enjoyment, I don't want to quit. There's also the rebel in me that hates Society as a whole making smokers bad people. You get excluded from restaurants. I rebel against nonsmoking signs. I smoke to get a point across that everybody should be free to do what they want. I want to control me. I don't want other people controlling me. So, the more they say you've got to quit, the more I rebel. But I want to quit. The cheating I did was a mistake. My coughing returned, and other things; I felt tired, and had trouble breathing. Different things. The days I didn't smoke, I felt much better. My coughing disappeared. I could lay in bed without coughing!

T: C. You are being pulled in two directions and you are suffering from a problem in indecision. You need to decide which choice to make, abandon the thoughts about the opposite choice, and get on with your life. Which choice you make has to be your own. But having made one, I can help you feel comfortable carrying it out. Answer with your fingers. Are you ready to make a choice?

P: Yes finger rises.

T: Yes, you are ready to make a choice. That's great.

T: Answer with your fingers. Now, that you know this, are you ready to refuse to smoke and get well?

P: Yes finger rises.

T: Yes, you are ready to refuse to smoke, to be a nonsmoker for good, and get well. When you have stopped, your cough will clear, your taste will improve, you'll have more money, you'll feel better, you'll live longer. You'll be pleased with yourself. And, you'll be in charge of you. No one else will be. You'll be in control of you.

T: Would it be all right for you to subconsciously review everything that you felt and did related to this issue from Sunday through the present?

P: Yes finger rises.

T: OK then. When you begin your review, your yes finger will rise. When you have finished your review, raise your thumb.

P: [Patient raises thumb and says:] I need to quit. I want to quit.

T: Would it be all right for you to review it all again, and then when you have finished reviewing it again, tell me what you learned?

P: Yes finger rises.

T: OK then. When you begin your review, your yes finger will rise. When you have finished your review, raise your thumb, and tell me what you've learned; what's on your mind.

P: I really want to quit. This time it's for good.

T: [Repeats what patient said]

T: What changes will occur in your life when you stop for good?

P: I'll feel better about myself. I'll breathe better. Stop coughing and sleep through the night. I'll eat better, and taste better.

T: Is there anything else you think I should know about your problem?

P: No finger rises.

T: No. As a nonsmoker, from now on, you'll control your appetite. You'll taste your food better and enjoy your food more. And you'll make better food choices. And since you'll enjoy your food more, you'll need to eat less. Smoking is slow suicide. From now on, as a nonsmoker, you'll feel more in control because you'll accept responsibility of being in charge of you. You'll feel better as you treat yourself and your body with more respect and dignity.

P: Yes finger rises.

T: Yes, you will treat yourself with more respect. From now on, whenever you feel an urge to smoke, or have thoughts about smoking, or are about to put a cigarette in your mouth, it will come strongly into your conscious mind that you have a free choice—either to go ahead and poison your lungs and your body, or to be normal and healthy and proud of yourself.

P: I choose to stop for good.

T: You choose to stop for good. Because you are important and you will continue to be pleased and proud of your decision to refuse to smoke and get well.

I roused the patient out of hypnosis. We talked briefly. The patient mentioned that this was for good. That the primary thing we hit was that this was all about the "control business," and that she had been looking at the issue "ass backwards." That "It had still been controlling me." That it had to be from now on "for me, by me, rather than for me, by everybody else."

Follow-up: After six months, the patient is still not smoking.

Chapter 14

ONE VISIT CURE OF A
HYPERSENSITIVE SCAR

The following annotated transcript of a "one visit cure of a sensitive scar" illustrates the application of the rapid hypnoanalysis technique. The essential cause of the subject's psychosomatic symptom was discovered to be a suggestion that had been imprinted in her subconscious at the time of origin of her symptom. The subject was a third-year medical student who volunteered to be a demonstration subject during a class taught by Dr. Ewin.

[The Intake]

Dr. Ewin: Let's get her to come sit down right here, Elizabeth. And can you show them your scar, maybe stand up, stand up and turn. (There's laughter and Dr. Ewin says to the students:) Listen, this is professional, now, we're going to act professional. She's offering to help us look at this scar on her leg. (to Elizabeth now) And you can run all you want to, you played. . . .

Elizabeth: I played soccer. I play, I can play all sports.

Dr. Ewin: You don't limp?

Elizabeth: And I don't limp.

Dr. Ewin: It's not hurting you right now?

Elizabeth: It doesn't hurt me.

Dr. Ewin: And you can bend it and it doesn't hurt?

Elizabeth: No problem. It doesn't hurt.

Dr. Ewin: All right.

Elizabeth: Doesn't hurt.

Dr. Ewin: When does it bother you?

Elizabeth: It bothers me if somebody comes up and goes to like give me a Charlie horse or something. You know, do the grab your knee. If somebody puts their hand in there, it, that's excruciating, I mean, I'm near. . . .

Dr. Ewin: It's excruciating *pain?*

Elizabeth: Yeah, I mean, I can nearly pass out from that. If I'm carrying a suitcase and it hits me there, you know, again that's just like stop dead in your tracks no matter how much it's, you know, drop the suitcase. If I'm running or if I'm walking and I hit the side of a table and it hits me right in there it's the same. And it's just, it starts about right there (pointing to the uppermost tip of her scar), and it goes to right here (pointing to a point on her scar about an inch from its lower tip). This whole area.

Dr. Ewin: But you can . . .

Elizabeth: I can put my hand down flat (demonstrates placing flat hand over scar) on it. But, I can't, like for me to run my finger along that (she demonstrates by running her finger through the air above her scar) no way.

Dr. Ewin: Have a seat (she sits) and tell me what you know about the origin of this.

[Assessing the patient's conscious understanding.]

Elizabeth: Ok, I was born with congenital hip dysplasia which they didn't catch until I was walking. So I was about, well, actually well into when I was walking. I started walking about ten months and some of my parents friends were like, "She's walking but she walks with a limp." And my parents were like, "It's not a limp, it's a baby waddle." (laughs) You know, finally like they had about three friends who said, "No, she has a limp." So the next time my mother took me to the pediatrician. She said, "Measure her legs, everybody's telling me that she's walking with a limp," and he measured my legs and sure enough one was shorter than the other. And then, I guess I was about a year old then, and they went and they tried to put me in traction and I guess they did that for about a month, and that didn't work very well. And then they did some... I'm not, I've never, I keep meaning to get the hospital records, but I don't know what it is and my parents aren't really sure. They did hip surgery. I've got the scar that comes from here to here (dragging her finger from the inside of the top of her right thigh, across the top of her leg in a horizontal line) where they relocated the hip and then they did something to the knee. And I'm not sure if it was just because things had formed with me walking on it or what, but they had to do, they had to realign some of the ligaments or something on the knee, I'm not sure what. . . .

Dr. Ewin: And when you recovered from the surgery you were walking within a few months, pretty, pretty straight?

Elizabeth: Yeah, uh-huh, I was, I was in a body cast in the hospital for like nine months. During that whole time and then when, you know, when I came back home, you know, I had to relearn walking, relearn everything else you learn between when you start to walk and then. Essentially it was like being a year old again as far as walking and all that.

Dr. Ewin: Nine months in a body cast at age two.

Elizabeth: Right.

Dr. Ewin: What do you think that has to do with you deciding to be a doctor?

Elizabeth: Oh. (laughing) I think that has just about everything in the world to do with me being a doctor!

Dr. Ewin: There's a reason for everything. Nothing happens for no reason. A perfectly good reason, but. . . .

[Seeding the idea of subconscious causes of symptoms.]

Elizabeth: Yeah, I don't think there are many four year olds that say "What do you want to be when you grow up?" I want to be a surgeon. (laughs)

Dr. Ewin: We think protectively in the right brain. You know, if I just knew everything about it, I could keep this from happening and it's very protective. Uh, is there anything else you think I ought to know?

[Seeding the idea of subconscious processing.]

Elizabeth: Um, there's one thing. Actually I was thinking about it the other day. And I know at one point I was home and that, you know, there was, I had a pin there. (pointing to scar) And the pin fell out once, eh, while I was in the crib. And my mother came over, and she tells this story, and she was freaking out about it and came and was like "Oh my god. The pin." and she managed to, she just like took it, and just stuck it back in. And then like the next day went to the doctor. And the doctor was like "Oh the pin's in fine." But I know this was something that really super traumatized her. So I'm not, I'm wondering if she was like don't put your hand near there or don't touch that or something like that because she, it's something that. . . .

Dr. Ewin: How long after you were out, or you were still in the cast when this. . . .

Elizabeth: I think I was still in the cast when that happened because there was like a hole right there for the pin. (pointing to her scar)

Dr. Ewin: Ok, holding the cast?

Elizabeth: (nodding) Holding the cast, right, with a pin. Because she said she really couldn't see but she just kind of stuck it back in there. (moving her arm in the air as if sticking a pin through something)

Dr. Ewin: How clever. All right, just get comfortable and. . . .

Elizabeth: A comfortable slouch. (she reclines in chair)

[Formal trance induction and setting up ideomotor signals. Note: Underlines and italics indicate emphasis.]

Dr. Ewin: As comfortable as you want to be. That's fine. (lights dim) Close your eyes. Roll your eyeballs up and take a deep, deep, deep breath, and hold it, hold it, Elizabeth, and as you let it allllllllll out. Just like a balloon collapsing. Just draining all the tension out of every nerve and fiber in you body. Your eyes relaxed. Jaws unclenched. Shoulders droopy. Very quickly going down deeper, deeper relaxed than you've ever been.

I'm going to touch your left index finger. Let this be your "yes" finger. If I ask you a question, and it feels yes, you agree with it. That's ok. This finger will slowly rise to signal that you have a yes feeling about it. *[Yes finger.]*

Dr. Ewin: Are we at Tulane? Are we at Tulane? (finger rises) Of course we're at Tulane. Every time your feelings answer a question you'll go inside a little bit deeper and get more in touch with your own inner feelings. *[Deepening suggestion.]*

If I ask a question that you have a "no" feeling about, you disagree, *you don't even have to know why*, without even talking, this finger will just (Dr. Ewin slowly lifts her middle finger) slowly rise to signal that you disagree and have a no feeling about it.

Dr. Ewin: Is today the fourth of July? (finger rises) Of course not. This isn't the fourth of July. This is the tenth of June 1993.

Dr. Ewin: If I should ask a question that your subconscious mind is not ready to answer <u>yet</u> or doesn't want to answer, just signal with your thumb and that's okay. And if something crosses your mind, you want to talk to me or ask a question, just raise your whole hand and we'll talk.

Dr. Ewin: The first question is, is it all right with your subconscious mind for me to help you with this? And the answer's yes. Ok, great. Way, way, way, down deep. . . .

[Obtaining permission.]

Dr. Ewin: I'm going to ask you to let your mind regress, back through time, back through time. Just as though you're there. To the *most* significant incident that's related to the continued sensitivity of this scar on your leg, and review it at a feeling level. Just the way it came to a little girl, just the way it came to a little girl. And when you've finished reviewing it, your yes finger will rise.

[Suggestion for symptom regression and direct search for an important memory, with suggestions for subconscious review and re-vivification upon locating it. Suggestion of "yes" finger lifting as a marker of completing the subconscious review. DME pauses while he waits for the subject's finger to rise. Note that this is an abbreviated symptom regression without asking for a "no" signal at each emotional point in the review.]

Dr. Ewin: That's good. I won't let anything happen to you. *[Reassurance of safety.]*

Dr. Ewin: Your mind is protected with the fact that this is 1993. You're safe here at Tulane. So, take your time. That's good. When you're safely through it your "yes" finger's going to rise. That's good.

Dr. Ewin: Now, let's go back through it again in more detail. And so, you just went through it and sort of read the headlines. This time the fine print. Who's there? Where you are? What's being said? What the emotion is? Whether you're afraid or not? Whether you're angry? Whether you're in pain? What's happening to the important people and what are they saying about it? And when you've reviewed it again in detail and you're safely through it, your "yes" finger will rise. Give me a clear signal.

[Second subconscious review to pick up more information.]

Dr. Ewin: Give me a good clear signal. It's twitching.

Dr. Ewin: That's good. Very good. Would it be all right to bring it up to a conscious level so you can talk about everything just like you're there? Seeing everything, hearing everything, feeling everything, back through time. When you get there, your yes finger's going to rise. Everything that's important about it, everything that's important about it, who's there, what's being said, how you feel, what you're thinking. There it is. Speak to me. Speak out loud. What's happening? How old are you?

[Asking patient's permission to consciously process and relate the experience.]

Elizabeth: Two.

Dr. Ewin: Are you at home?

Elizabeth: Yeah.

Dr. Ewin: Huh?

Elizabeth: Yes.

Dr. Ewin: You're at home. All right. Are you in the cast?

Elizabeth: (nods yes) My mother's yelling.

[Note the use of the present tense.]

Dr. Ewin: Your mother's what?

Elizabeth: Yelling.

Dr. Ewin: What's she saying? Listen to her. She's not yelling for no reason. Why is she yelling?

Elizabeth: SPANISH. SPANISH.

Dr. Ewin: What?

Elizabeth: SPANISH. SPANISH.

Audience: Que pasa?

Elizabeth: The pin.

Dr. Ewin: The pin? What's happened to the pin?

Elizabeth: It fell out.

Dr. Ewin: It fell out. How are you feeling? Are you even aware that the pin has fallen out?

Elizabeth: No.

Dr. Ewin: No. A pin like that doesn't have any pain. You're not aware of it even. It's in place, but you know, you know when she sees it. Don't you? Ok, what does she say?

[Note the use of the present tense.]

Elizabeth: What is she going to do?

Dr. Ewin: What is she going to do?

Elizabeth: It fell out.

Dr. Ewin: Uh huh. Is she very upset?

Elizabeth: Yes.

Dr. Ewin: Does she cry?

Elizabeth: No.

Dr. Ewin: Is she angry?

Elizabeth: No.

Dr. Ewin: She's just scared?

Elizabeth: She's scared.

Dr. Ewin: Let your feelings answer this. The fact that she's so scared, does that make you scared? (yes nod) Sure. You're bonded with mother. There must be something very awful wrong. Huh?

Elizabeth: Yes.

Dr. Ewin: Go ahead now. What's happening?

Elizabeth: She's, she's got the side of the crib down, and she's. . . .

Dr. Ewin: She's got the side of the crib down. And what?

Elizabeth: And she's trying to come look in and see what . . . and see if she can see anything in there.

Dr. Ewin: She's trying to look through the hole in the cast?

Elizabeth: Yeah. And I don't know if she, she has a flashlight or what.

Dr. Ewin: You don't know if she has a flashlight or not, but she's trying to look inside the cast.

Elizabeth: And no one else is home.

Dr. Ewin: No one else is around.

Elizabeth: And my father's not home from work yet.

Dr. Ewin: And your father's not there. Ok. She's got to do something. Is she talking out loud?

Elizabeth: Yes.

Dr. Ewin: Are you picking up what she's thinking, and feeling, and saying?

Elizabeth: I think my sister and my brother are there.

Dr. Ewin: You think your sister or brother. . . .

Elizabeth: I think they're both there.

Dr. Ewin: They're both there. Ok.

Elizabeth: My brother, I think he's in his school clothes, so he must have just gotten home.

Dr. Ewin: Your brother's in his school clothes so he must have just gotten home. (Elizabeth smiles) Something's funny. What?

[Note how Dr. Ewin repeats, or reflects, the patient's verbal and nonverbal responses as a sort of human biofeedback machine and for clarification. The patient in deep trance may not know that she is talking, and may not know what she is saying.]

Elizabeth: (laughter) I think my mother just told them to leave her alone.

Dr. Ewin: Your mother just told them to leave her alone. Huh. Ok. Get out of here. Got a real problem.

Elizabeth: I think they're sticking their heads in her way.

Dr. Ewin: They're sticking their heads in the way. They want to see it too. Huh?

Elizabeth: Yeah.

Dr. Ewin: Well, you've been kind of the center of attention around there for awhile. Haven't you?

Elizabeth: Yeah.

Dr. Ewin: Yeah. Ok. Now what's happening?

Elizabeth: I think she's, she's trying to fix the pin. She's trying to figure out if she should put it in right now.

Dr. Ewin: She's trying to figure out whether she should put it back in or not?

Elizabeth: Yeah.

Dr. Ewin: All right.

Elizabeth: She figures it can't hurt.

Dr. Ewin: She figures it can't hurt. So what does she do?

Elizabeth: She stuck it in there.

Dr. Ewin: Just sticks it right back in through the hole. **[Note that she changes to the past tense and he brings her back to the present tense.]**

Elizabeth: Yeah.

Dr. Ewin: Does it bother you when she does that?

Elizabeth: No.

Dr. Ewin: No. This thing's perfectly smooth and you've already got a track in there. It just slips right back in. Something else is important now, though. Lets come to it. **[Note present tense.]**

Elizabeth: I don't know, I can't tell if she's talking to me or if she's talking to herself.

Dr. Ewin: You can't tell if she's talking to you or talking to herself.

Elizabeth: Out loud.

Dr. Ewin: She's talking out loud. What's she saying?

Elizabeth: She's saying that we have to keep the, stay away from the pin, so it doesn't fall out.

Dr. Ewin: She's saying you have to stay away from where the pin is so it doesn't fall out again. Does she put some tape over it? Something to hold it in?

Elizabeth: I can't tell if she, if she wraps something around it.

Dr. Ewin: That would make some sense. Wouldn't it? **[Reframe.]**

Elizabeth: Yeah.

Dr. Ewin: Yeah. Because if it falls out, I would think that would make some sense.

Elizabeth: I think she wraps something around.

Dr. Ewin: Mhmm.

Elizabeth: I don't know what. I think she puts a paper cloth over it and then wraps it in tape.

Dr. Ewin: Now let's go on from there. The next day she takes you to the doctor? When do you get to the doctor?

Elizabeth: I think a couple days later.

Dr. Ewin: In a couple of days. They just pick you up with the cast and all and take you to the doctor?

Elizabeth: Mhmm.

Dr. Ewin: So let's get into the doctors office. Your mother tells him what happens?

Elizabeth: Uhuh.

Dr. Ewin: Now pay attention. What's his reaction to that?

Elizabeth: He tells her to talk slower because he can't understand her.

Dr. Ewin: He tells her to talk slower so he can understand her. She's excited again. Isn't she?

Elizabeth: Yeah and he. . .

Dr. Ewin: There's a reason. **[Attempted reframe.]**

Elizabeth: He doesn't speak Spanish.

Dr. Ewin: He doesn't speak Spanish.

Elizabeth: I think that the pin in the leg. . . .

Dr. Ewin: What about the pin?

Elizabeth: She put it back in.

Dr. Ewin: She tells him she put it back in. What's his reaction to that?

Elizabeth: That that was good.

Dr. Ewin: He says that's good?

Elizabeth: Mhmm and he looks at my leg.

Dr. Ewin: Does he take the cast off and look at your leg?

Elizabeth: No.

Dr. Ewin: How can he look at it with a cast on?

Elizabeth: Mhmm. . . . I'm in that room again.

Dr. Ewin: You're in that room again. Uhuh. All right.

Elizabeth: They put me on the table.

Dr. Ewin: They put you on the table.

Elizabeth: And everybody leaves.

Dr. Ewin: And everybody leaves.

Elizabeth: They all move and there's a sound, then they come back.

Dr. Ewin: There's a sound. Then they come back. What's it sound like?

Elizabeth: It's zzzuut.

Dr. Ewin: It's zzzuut.

Elizabeth: And then they come back. It sounds like they took an x-ray.

Dr. Ewin: It sounds like they took an x-ray. Yeah. Mhmm. Now pay attention. What does the doctor say now?

Elizabeth: That the pin looks fine.

Dr. Ewin: He says the pin looks fine.

Elizabeth: He says she did a good job.

Dr. Ewin: That she did a good job.

Elizabeth: She should have been an orthopedist.

Dr. Ewin: She should have been an orthopedist.

Dr. Ewin: Let your feelings answer this. Does he say something about what might have happened if you'd gotten an osteomyelitis or an infection? I'll be more specific. Do you sense that you're carrying out a suggestion or an idea that something's going to be wrong with this? Wrong where the pin went in on a long-term basis.

Elizabeth: Yes finger rises.

Dr. Ewin: Is this something your mother says?

Elizabeth: Yes finger rises.

Dr. Ewin: Yes. Good clear signal.

Dr. Ewin: Is your mother the one who said it?

Elizabeth: No finger rises.

Dr. Ewin: No. Okay. Is it the doctor?

Elizabeth: No finger rises.

Dr. Ewin: No. Is it your father?

Elizabeth: Yes finger rises.

Dr. Ewin: Yes. Let's go find that. Is this something perhaps that when your father came home after your mother put the pin back in and she told him, that he said "My gosh"? Does he object to what she did?

Elizabeth: No finger rises.

Dr. Ewin: No. When does he say this? Does he say this after you get out of the cast?

Elizabeth: No response.

Dr. Ewin: There's something missing. We'll be quiet for a moment. Go find what's going on. When it is. Review your father saying something about the thing being painful or tender or something going wrong with it on a long-term basis. Something that sticks with you. That has meaning to you. That frightens you. Go find it and when you've reviewed it, you'll let me know because your yes finger will rise.

Elizabeth: Yes finger rises.

Dr. Ewin: Okay there it is. Speak to me. Tell me what's happening.

Elizabeth: I don't know when it is.

Dr. Ewin: You don't when it is. That doesn't matter. Tell me what's happening.

Elizabeth: He says be careful. I think the cast is off.

Dr. Ewin: You think the cast is off and he's saying be careful. [Staying in the present.]

Elizabeth: Be careful. With the scar.

Dr. Ewin: Be careful with the scar. Is there any infection in it? Is there any pus? Anything that's any complication that's taken place?

Elizabeth: No.

Dr. Ewin: He just says be careful with the scar. Isn't that an interesting thing to take literally? Be careful with the scar. He doesn't say anything about being careful with the leg. Does he?

Elizabeth: No.

Dr. Ewin: It's all right to run and play and play soccer and everything else. Huh? Just be careful with the scar. Do you realize you've been carrying this suggestion out all this time? You've been very careful with the scar. You won't let anybody touch it. You won't even touch it yourself! That's got to be hard when the scar's fresh. Maybe that idea has outlived its usefulness now.

[Reframing the fixed idea, "Be careful with the scar", with the idea that the original suggestion has outlived its usefulness.]

Dr. Ewin: Since it's a perfectly healed scar and the internal ligaments and mechanics of the knee are obviously normal and intact, would it be all right with your subconscious mind to realize that dad was being very protective at the time and it was a good idea at the time but that that idea's outlived its usefulness now? **[Asking Elizabeth's subconscious permission to let go of the outdated fixed idea.]**

Dr. Ewin: Ask your feeling mind if there's any reason that it has to keep on being so protective of that scar. People have had scars. People get appendectomy scars and gallbladder scars and all kind of scars and they heal up in a few weeks and then they're perfectly all right. All these football players have had their knees operated on and they keep right on playing. Is there any reason in your subconscious mind for you to keep this any longer? **[Checking for subconscious objections to giving up that fixed idea.]**

Elizabeth: Yes finger rises.

Dr. Ewin: And the answer's yes. **[There is an objection.]**

Dr. Ewin: Would it be all right to bring it up to a conscious level so we can talk about it?

Elizabeth: Yes finger rises.

Dr. Ewin: And the answer's yes. Speak to me. Why would you need to keep being so careful about the scar?

Elizabeth: 'Cause I feel like throwing up when someone touches it.

Dr. Ewin: You feel like throwing up when someone touches it. That's the way you used to feel. Would it be all right to stop feeling that way? **[Reframe.]**

Elizabeth: Yes finger lifts.

Dr. Ewin: And the answer's yes. You're just plain old excessively frightened. You know lots of people who get very frightened and get sick?

Elizabeth: Yes finger lifts.

Dr. Ewin: The answer's yes. But if you're not frightened of it anymore there wouldn't be any reason for you to feel like throwing up?

Elizabeth: Yes finger lifts.

Dr. Ewin: No. Okay. And if it weren't sensitive, let me ask you this, would it be all right to, you know, we already know that you can make this part numb and I'm not going to test your scar, but in your mind think about it. Would it be all right for you to make that scar just as numb and insensitive as you were able to make your hand? Would it be all right to do that?

[Dr. Ewin had previously induced hypno-anesthetic numbness in Elizabeth's hand and taught her how to do it herself.]

Elizabeth: Yes.

Dr. Ewin: Yeah. In fact, it would be very nice wouldn't it?

Elizabeth: Yes finger lifts along with a verbal yes.

Dr. Ewin: Ok. I'm going to be quiet. Send it a message. Tell it that's the way you want it to be. You own your own mind and you own your own body. You own your own feelings. They have to do what you tell them to do. Take all the time you need and make it numb. Then when it's nice and numb and it's going to stay that way so that nothing can bother, nothing can disturb, your yes finger will rise.

[Direct suggestion in hypnosis (DSIH) for healing.]

Elizabeth: Yes finger lifts.

Dr. Ewin: Good clear signal, good clear signal. Now lock in on that with every cell in your mind and your body and your feelings and keep it that way. 'Cause the past is past and what was helpful at a time in the past no longer has any value to you. You'll be much more pleasant and comfortable.

[DSIH for locking the healing feelings in place and for imprinting the reframe in Elizabeth's subconscious. Suggestions for ego strengthening and benefits of getting well.]

Dr. Ewin: Have that area along the scar nice and numb so that if you inadvertently hit it or touch it, it won't be any different than hitting the side of the other leg, and you'll be pleased with yourself and proud of yourself that you've done this.

[Post-hypnotic suggestion for subject to have a different feeling response along with ego strengthening suggestion.]

Dr. Ewin: Before I rouse you up is there anything that you want to ask or anything that you want to say?

Elizabeth: No finger lifts.

Dr. Ewin: No. Okay. Then, in a moment, I'm going to count to three and when I say three blink your eyes tightly and open them wide and rouse up wide awake, fresh, alert, comfortable. Comfortable, sure of yourself, confident, sound in mind, sound in body, and in control of your feelings. One. Rousing up slowly now. Two. Three.

[Subject alerted.]

Elizabeth: My neck hurts.

Dr. Ewin: You didn't lean far enough. We needed a reclining chair.

Dr. Ewin: Any thoughts? See what happens if you put your finger on the scar. Is it any different?

[Testing.]

Elizabeth: (runs finger along scar) That's really weird.

Dr. Ewin: You can do it?

Elizabeth: Yeah. Really strange.

Dr. Ewin: Would it be all right if I do it?

Elizabeth: Yeah.

Dr. Ewin: Now I'll be gentle, but what you said what you couldn't do was run a finger along the scar.

Elizabeth: Right.

Dr. Ewin: Now I'm going to be, I'm going to do this very lightly (running finger along scar) Does that bother?

Elizabeth: No.

Dr. Ewin: I'm going to do it a little more. Was that a little bit?

Elizabeth: No.

Dr. Ewin: You realize that you've got X number of years here of sort of Pavlonian conditioning but you can decondition. Every success leads to more success. You're going to be all right.

[Post-trance reframing.]

Dr. Ewin to Class: When I heard this story, suppose you were referred this patient. She can walk perfectly well. No limp. She can run with her knee, she can play soccer, and yet can't touch this scar. Are you going to give her some medicine? What kind of medicine will you give her? Xanax? Valium? They're not going to do anything. Darvon? Pain killer? Not going to do anything. You going to prescribe a psychoanalysis? She doesn't need analysis. She's acting on a post-hypnotic suggestion, "Be careful with the scar," but it's never been removed. It's done at a time of high emotion, when she's frightened, when they're taking that cast off. I've listened to enough of these things so that when she gave me the waking history I just, I felt confident that we would come to something.

And you remember my closing question was, "Is there anything else you think we ought to know?", and that's when you told us about the pin falling out. I immediately, you know, thought My gosh. They're going to be scared you're going to get an osteomyelitis because not too many years ago that was a very, very crippling disorder in a child and antibiotics wouldn't control it very well. I mean you could just fall down from a scrape.

Elizabeth: That's crazy.

Dr. Ewin to Subject and Class: But, and I expected that the doctor was going to, you know, say my gosh and chew your mother out and upset you and say you're going to get osteomyelitis. See it's not what the doctor, what I think, you have to listen to the patient. And when I didn't get something with some emotion in it, I kept on going until we got a closure. It had to be something else that had some power in it. Your mother didn't say anything bad, when she, the power was there.

Dr. Ewin to Subject and Class: Did you see her (indicates heaving chest and heavy breathing) emotional response? The power was there, but mother said good things. Then the doctor came out and he's very important. He said good things. It had to be something else. So you keep going and then I think you can feel that something is different now. Can't you?

Elizabeth: Yeah. I mean I usually don't really pay much attention unless someone touches it. Otherwise it doesn't feel like anything.

Dr. Ewin: It doesn't bother you, but you can push it pretty hard?

Elizabeth: (pressing on scar) Yeah.

[Closure on making the point how a suggestion given at a highly emotional time or at a young impressionable age can imprint a fixed idea in the patient's subconscious that stays frozen in time and outlives its original usefulness, and causes symptoms.]

Chapter 15

WORKSHOP DEMONSTRATION SESSION WITH AN ASTHMA PATIENT

The patient is the son of a workshop attendee. Dr. Ewin begins by conducting an intake interview.

DME: Tell us how old you are.

P: 19.

DME: 19.

DME: When is your birthday?

P: Dec the 2nd.

DME: Dec 2, okay. Mine is the 7th, my birthday will live in infamy. Are you familiar with FDR's statement about Pearl Harbor, December the 7th? He said "the day that would live in infamy."

DME: <Patient Name> tell me about your problem.

P: Well, I have had asthma ever since I can remember, and I would like to be free of medication. But um–I have tried cutting down and it doesn't seem–I mean I have cut down some and it doesn't seem to fully go away.

DME: You would like to be free of medication . . . what medicines are you on?

P: Right now I am taking Proventil. Um . . . . Ventolin, it's a generic . . . and Asmacort. And actually I am supposed to be taking another one but like I said I am only taking two a day.

DME: How much Asmacort do you take?

P: Four puffs two times a day. And then the Ventolin is as needed.

DME: What do you remember about the first time you had an episode?

P: Actually I cannot remember the first time. I mean, I have early memories, but I don't–

DME: What is your earliest memory?

P: Um, my earliest memory is I think . . . what I think would probably be chronologically my earliest is—I had a very bad asthma attack once, and the hospital was down the street from where I lived. And my mom didn't know that we would park at the emergency room, so I ended up having to walk in the Chicago winter to the emergency room with an asthma attack. I think that is my earliest memory.

DME: About how old were you?

P: I would guess maybe—somewhere between 7 and 9. But I know I had asthma before that.

DME: Your mother didn't know she can park there, huh?

P: No.

DME: Were you very frightened, do you remember that?

P: I actually-actually I don't ever remember being too frightened. Maybe once in awhile, but I've had it for so long that I knew there was help for it. I mean I was never afraid of dying or anything. Just of being uncomfortable.

DME: Is there a time you're aware of—when it's better, or when it's worse. When are you most likely to have a problem?

P: I think I'm most likely to have a problem: first when I am exercising, playing soccer or anything like that. . . . And second, when I am anxious. When I'm anxious, my asthma gets a lot worse also.

DME: What kind of things make you anxious?

P: Well, I think I'm a very naturally high-strung person. But, um, actually I don't know—I couldn't really cite—you know—instances. Um . . .

DME: When is it better?

P: When I'm not exercising and not anxious.

DME: (Laughing) OK, if you're not exercising, or not anxious.

P: Yeah, it's usually pretty good the rest of the time.

DME: That's good.

P: And actually—I suppose, I've been thinking about it, I should also add seasonal. It is seasonal. During the winter, it's worse, and—uh—different times of year.

DME: Do you have any other medical problems? Like sinusitis, or chronic infections? Do you tend to get infections easily? Or colds? Or flu? Or anything like that?

P: I think I'm pretty normal with those. But . . . but I do have a post-nasal drip on and off. That and just other allergies. You know, I've tried allergy medication things in the past.

DME: Do they seem to help?

P: Um, they do. I guess. I don't really like the sprays but. . . I tried Claritin® for a while when it was really bad. And it worked. And when it got better, I went off it and I haven't had to go back on since. This is about a year ago.

DME: If you were cured, what would you do that you can't do now?

P: Well I think I would just be more confident, because there is always a feeling that I always have to have my inhaler with me. That I always have to worry. If I'm going camping or something, you know. Or, if I am doing something very rigorous, I always have to be worried about if I am going to be coming down with asthma, if I am pushing too hard or something. So I think if I, like I said, I would just feel more confident, and . . . I am actually doing some traveling next semester, and I am hoping do that kind of thing as much as I can. So that would be good for me.

DME: Can you tell us where you are going to travel?

P: Yeah, actually, I am going to Chile to visit my sister, who lives there. And then I think we are going to Europe for a while . . . and just sort of traveling around and backpacking.

DME: Do you like wine?

P: Actually I don't drink anymore.

DME: Oh, okay, because they make very good wine in Chile. What do you like for your friends to call you?

P: I go by <Name>.

DME: <Name>?

P: Yeah, it was the name that I was raised with, for the most part.

DME: (Repeats name.) May I call you that?

P: Definitely. It is more natural than <his formal name>.

DME: We're teaching. (to audience) I bring this up at this point in the history. . . . And there is an indirect suggestion. I am asking "What would you like for your friends to call you?" Sometimes your friends don't call you what you would like. You know, I have a patient who is impotent and his friends call him "Snake" and he doesn't like being called "Snake." . . . So, it's not "What do your friends call you", but "What do you <u>like</u> for your friends to call you?" And having gotten an answer, the request "May I call you that" which is an indirect suggestion that I would like the patient to feel that I would like to be his friend.

DME: In any event <Name>, that's a nice name . . . <Name> in your entire life, what's the worst thing that ever happened to you?

P: Um, I think it was probably when my parents split up when I was young that was probably the hardest thing, the worst thing.

DME: How old were you?

P: Two years old.

DME: What made it hard?

P: Well, I was too young to really know what was going on. And I think it was a lot of feelings without–um–necessarily knowing what was going on. And it's taken me a long time of going back through that. . . .

DME: Who did you go with when they split?

P: I lived with my mom more than with my dad on the weekends.

DME: Ok. <Name>, in your entire life, what is the worst thing you ever did?

P: Um–very bad . . . well, honestly as much as I hate to admit it there was a time when I was young and I was really in a lot of anger. And there was a time I pushed my mom. . . . Like um, I would never hit her, but I did push her, and I felt really bad about it.

DME: Ok, it made you feel guilty?

P: Yeah, definitely. Very guilty.

DME: Have you made up with her over that?

P: Yeah, yeah. I made amends for all of that.

DME: Ok. <Name>, in your entire life, what is the most frightened you've ever been?

P: Well, just to be brutally honest, I used to do a lot of drugs when I was younger. I cleaned up three years ago. But, one morning . . . one time when I was doing drugs, I seriously thought I had lost it. I thought I had flipped out. And um, that was the most afraid I have ever been in my life.

DME: About how old were you?

P: I was 17 at the time.

DME: And you said flipped out, in what way?

P: I thought I had just gone crazy. Like the war stories–the stories that you hear of people just losing it from taking too much acid or too many drugs . . . and I thought that had happened to me.

DME: Was this acid?

P: Um, actually I was only, I was smoking pot, but I had done a lot of acid and I thought I was having a flashback.

DME: Um-hum. Okay. <Name>, in your entire life, what's the most angry you have ever been? Really in a rage?

P: Um–that, I'm honestly not sure. I've done a lot of raging in my life, throughout the years.

DME: First thought?

P: I think maybe, once about 3 to 4 years ago with my brother. We were talking about our lives when we were younger, and just really disagreeing . . . and I really lost it that time. Yeah. . . .

DME: What was it over?

P: Um.

DME: Was it your younger brother?

P: Yeah, he is my younger brother. He is two years younger. And we were talking about the situation with our parents. And he–I mean he was saying that he had felt really vulnerable in a lot of ways, and like no one had tried to help him. And I felt like I had definitely tried to shield him a lot, and my older sister had. There was a disagreement over that issue.

DME: Ok. <Name>, in your entire life, what was the best thing that ever happened to you?

P: I actually think a blessing in disguise–was getting clean from drugs. And it was that experience I related earlier.

DME: Good. About taking charge of your own life.

P: Yeah, definitely.

DME: <Name>, if I had a magic wand, and one wish would come true, what would you wish?

P: Um, aside from the wishing for more wishes? Um, I guess I have a selfish wish, and a philanthropic wish and I don't know which I would go with.

DME: Let's go with both.

P: The selfish wish is really just to feel good. You know, to feel good with myself, and others and God, or whatever the greater thing is that um–and actually I suppose it could just coincide with the second which would just be for everyone to feel like that. For everybody to feel um, good about themselves and to be . . . sort of, I almost want to say protected. To be fed, and clothed, etc.

DME: Third wish, real good magic wand. Third wish, what would it be?

P: Um—I think I would wish to be more in touch with what actually exists beyond this material plane. I would like to know what is out there in a bigger sense; I think that would be my last wish.

DME: <Name>, how many wishes would I have to give you to be free of asthma?

P: Honestly, it wouldn't be in the top ten for sure.

DME: It wouldn't be in the top ten?

P: No, just because it isn't something that bothers me everyday you know . . . so much. And I think I would have in line the things that really bother me in my life on a more regular basis.

DME: Good, do you think it would help you though in reaching your other goals? About feeling good about yourself, and others?

P: Absolutely. I definitely do; and I think you hit a very good point when you said um "Taking control." I would like to take control of that issue in my life, and feel that I had that mastered, or that it wasn't an issue anymore.

DME: Ok, I need your attention to this particular problem, which is why I am asking you this. I want to make a way to move this up into the list. <Name>, is there anything else you think I ought to know?

P: Um—I guess only that I do try to live my life in the spirit of self-improvement. So, along the line of doing this, you know. Um. Constant self-improvement. So, although that might not be so high on the actual list, it goes right in line with how I am trying to live my life. But other than that I don't think so.

DME: What do you know about your early childhood? Any illnesses? Did you ever have any whooping cough, or surgery?

P: Actually the only thing I know is that I got a cold when I was really young, like the first couple months of my life. A really bad cold, which was always sort of assumed turned into the asthma that we are discussing right now. Besides that I do not really know about any childhood physical illnesses.

DME: And you must have heard people talk about this, the really bad cold. Was there concern that you were really seriously ill? I mean, you're calling it a cold. We don't think of a cold as something really serious. But here is a little baby, just a couple months old. . . . Were they concerned that you weren't going to come out of it? Why do they think you went into asthma?

P: Um. Well, actually I don't really know. I guess I should say that it was quite a bad cold, bad enough that people were worried and there was medical attention, as I understand it.

DME: Was it pneumonia?

P: No, it wasn't pneumonia. It was a cough. And uhm–I don't know.

DME: The doctor came?

P: Right, or I may have still been in the hospital. I'm not sure of the time frame. But um, I do get the feeling that they were worried and it did um. Doctors have always said since that day that it could very well have been one of the early causes.

DME: The doctors said that?

P: I mean, the doctors said that prompted by my family's suggestion. I don't know, uh-.

DME: Have you had any episodes where you couldn't breathe? Where you were drowning, or had plastic over your head? Or anything that uh–that you know of that made it difficult to breath aside from your asthma?

P: Actually, no. Um, I don't think I have ever experienced that. But it has always been a fear in me, of not being able to breathe. Even in other regards like what you are saying, so, uhm–yeah.

DME: Do you swim?

P: Yeah, I do swim. I mean, not regularly. But I love to swim when I do.

DME: Ok. What do you know about your birth?

[**Comment:** DME is inducing a regressing state of mind.]

P: Um, I actually don't know very much. I was born in Wales, which is my mom's home country. I guess I really only know about the hospital and the circumstances around it.

DME: Obviously you have been told. Were you 9 month, full-term? As far as you know?

P: As I understand it, yeah.

DME: Was it a Cesarean?

P: No, it wasn't.

DME: Any kind of emergency that you've heard of? Did your mother do all right after?

P: Yeah, she did.

DME: Did she get sick?

P: No, not that I know of.

DME: Nothing that you know of. And you were a second child?

P: Yeah.

DME: Had your mother ever lost any pregnancies before that, to your knowledge?

P: I think so, actually. I'm not sure, but I think she did.

DME: Where do you think that happened? Before your older sister, or between the two of you?

P: Actually I don't know. . . . I think she mentioned it happening a couple different times.

DME: She mentioned miscarriage?

P: Right, so, uh, I think it–honestly it could have been both. You know, I really don't know. It could have been before my sister was born, and then between us. Or it could have been some-where further down the line after. I'm not sure.

DME: Just somewhere in there. You didn't have a twin.

P: No, I didn't.

DME: Nothing, as far as you know, it was just a healthy, normal. . . .

P: Yeah.

DME: Uh, do you mind answering some other questions? We are all professionals here, and your privacy will be respected.

P: No, not at all.

DME: [To audience] Does anyone have any questions that they think would be helpful to get answers to?

Aud: I'm not clear as to when asthma became a problem for you as far as you're concerned.

DME: The question is when did the asthma become a problem as far as he is concerned.

P: Well, um, I guess it coincides with my earliest memories, is when I started becoming concerned about it. I was probably, like I said, somewhere between seven and nine. Right in there.

Aud: Where were you living at–when you were between seven and nine?

P: I was living in Chicago. I came over–I said I was born in Wales, but I was raised in Chicago.

DME: Did your mother come back to Chicago after you were born in Wales?

P: I think she waited a couple months. And actually, I was just thinking, I was there visiting. . . . I try to help her out all the time. . . . When you were asking if my mom got sick, I don't think she did–but this may be relevant. I think she said she was depressed for a couple months after, and stayed in Wales for a while, and then came back.

Aud: In school, did you have an asthma attack at school?

DME: Did you ever have an asthma attack at school?

P: Um, all the time. Actually, I was a local hero in school because I would leave gym class and puff on my inhaler and then come back. And I was one of the most athletic kids in the class, so even now my old Gym teacher still tells the next grades of kids about me. It's crazy! (laughing)

Aud: So, did they make an occasion out of it?

P: No, not at all. I think because I was one of the most athletic, and I was one of the best in sports. I guess when I was younger I didn't feel as comfortable using my inhaler in front of other people, but no one ever did make fun of me for it. That I can remember.

DME: Somebody had another question?

Aud: Going back to the seven to nine, what grade were you in at that time?

DME: What grade were you in?

P: I honestly don't know, I mean I can guess as good as you can, you know.

Aud: Did you move?

P: No, I lived in the same house with my mom the whole time. And the same school.

Aud: You were very good, had a natural ability at your sports. Did you hold yourself at a high expectation? Did you feel pressure to continue to excel?

DME: Did ya'll hear that question? Did he feel pressure to excel in sports?

P: Well, to the first part of your question, did I hold myself to a high standard; I definitely feel I did that. But I never felt pressured to excel at all. Um, definitely not by my parents, neither of them which were very athletic. So, anything I was doing was great as far as they were concerned. And, I do think I held myself–and I do think–I hung out with the other athletes and within ourselves there was a high level of competition, and merits.

DME: Let me ask you, in that regard, did you think that you had to prove that you could do that in spite of your asthma?

P: Well, maybe. I don't think that was a conscious thought on my part.

DME: All right, this looks like this is a good time- we are a little early. Why don't we go ahead and eat lunch.

[CLASS BREAKS FOR LUNCH AND THEN RETURNS.]

After lunch now, I (DME) skip the recap and start recording again. <Name> has returned to the stage.

DME: <Name> Hi, come have a seat. Any thoughts or any questions before we start?

P: No.

DME: You're all set?

P: Yup. (Nods)

DME: Ok. Are you ready to do some hypnosis?

P: Yup.

DME: Do you know what the one thing is that you are most likely to do that will interfere with this?

P: What?

DME: It is trying too hard. If you start trying to be the best patient I've ever had, or wondering if you are doing it right. You know you have to be out of trance to test whether you are in. So, I want you to not give a hoot whether you do this right or not. Just do what I ask you to do, and let it happen.

P: Okay.

[THE TRANCE INDUCTION]

DME: Get comfortable, and close your eyes. And keeping your eyelids closed, just as though they are glued together, roll your eyeballs up as if you are looking at the top of your forehead. Looking way, way up and take the deepest breath you have ever taken. Deep breath, deep breath, deep breath <Name>. Deep, hold it, hold it, feel it pressing against your chest. And as you let it allllllllll out, just like a balloon collapsing, just draining all the tension out of every nerve and fiber in your body.

Your eyes relaxed, jaws unclenched, shoulders droopy, arms limp and floppy. It's all right to smile, the more you smile the deeper relaxed you will be. It's a nice way to be.

[Utilizing the fact that the P. is smiling.]

Abdomen soft. With each breath you take as you exhale, just imagine that you're blowing out stress and tension into the atmosphere, never to return.

Take a nice deep breath, and blow fear out. And replace it with your courage, and your strength.

Take another deep breath, and blow anger out. Let it go, and replace it with your love and your warmth and your kindness.

Take another deep breath, and blow guilt out, even imagined guilt. And replace it with forgiveness, and innocence.

Your legs all loose, limp, and lazy-like. And your mind as relaxed as your body.

Feeling calm, and safe, and precious. It's very easy for us to forget that we're precious. But your feelings matter, and you can be strong and unafraid.

I'm going to see if I can pull this table up a little bit. I'm going to ask you to put your hand up, your elbow up, on the table just like that, let your hand be relaxed. You'll find it's more comfortable in this position, and hold it right there.

[Preparing to set up IM signals.]

Now I want to teach you a way to signal how you feel without even talking. So if I ask you a question and it feels "yes, "it feels agreeable, it sounds right, this finger will just slowly rise to signal that that's agreeable, that it feels okay. Do you like to be called <Name>?

P: Raises "yes" finger.

DME: Yes, you already told me that. Every time your feelings answer a question, you notice a wave of relaxation go over your entire body, as you go a little deeper relaxed, and become more in touch with your deepest, most heartfelt feelings.

If I ask you a question and you disagree, you have a "no" feeling about it, this finger will slowly rise to signal. You don't even have to know why. If it just does not feel right, if there's something wrong with it. Is today the fourth of July?

P: Raises "no" finger.

DME: No, of course not, this is NOT the fourth of July. It's the eleventh of November. Every time you smile [utilization of the patient's behavioral manifestation of an internal response or BMIR], every time your feelings answer a question, you go just a little bit deeper, and more comfortable. More into daydream-type thinking.

DME: If I should ask a question that you're not ready to answer yet, or you don't want to answer, that's all right. You just signal with your thumb. Way, way, way down deep.

DME: And if something crosses your mind, you want to ask a question or talk to me, just raise your hand and we'll talk. Way way way down deep.

DME: And my first question to your feeling mind, "Is it all right for me to help you with this?"

P: Raises yes finger.

[Next, DME guides P. to find his "laughing place".]

DME: All right. Good. Way, way, way down deep. The first thing that I would like to do is to ask you to find your laughing place. You're down in the South now, down South in Br'er Rabbit country. Everybody's got a laughing place. And Br'er Rabbit had his briar patch where no one could bother him, where no one could disturb him. Nobody goes into the briar patch and bothers you there.

But also, people's laughing places are very pleasant places. Sometimes, it's just an old swing in the backyard, or at the beach during a picnic. Or with your first love, or sometimes it's just a fantasy. But, I'm going to be quiet for awhile, and ask you to find your laughing place. The scene that goes with it; the colors, the shapes and the sounds. When you find the place where nothing can bother, where nothing can disturb, you will let me know because your yes finger will rise.

P: Raises yes finger.

DME: That's good. Is this something you'd like to share with me?

P: Sure.

DME: Speak to me, tell me. What is your laughing place like?

P: Actually, it's um . . . it's in an AA meeting.

DME: Ok, and you feel good in there? You feel safe in there?

P: Yeah, definitely.

DME: And you've got friends in there?

P: Hmmn.

[Laughing place rationale explained.]

DME: Okay, well great. Way, way, way down deep. I want you to kind of get a snapshot of that, because any time we get into anything, or even later on, if things may not seem to be going well for you, it's nice to have a little spot to retreat to. You can find a little privacy, and just take a moment, and go to your laughing place. It's kind of like a mini-vacation from what Shakespeare calls "the slings and arrows of outrageous fortune."

DME: Now, let's get back to the things you told me earlier. When I asked you to tell me about your problem, you said "I've had asthma ever since I can remember, I'd like to be free of medicines." I get a sense that you feel like your asthma is controlled pretty well, and that it's not as much of a problem as it is just having to worry about medicine. Is that correct?

P: Raises yes finger.

DME: Having to look after it, and wondering where it is, knowing that it is in your pocket and available to you. Is the medicine that's the main problem that you want to get rid of? That might not be a fair question. Obviously if you get rid of asthma, you don't need the medicine. Right?

P: Raises yes finger.

DME: Okay, but, obviously also you couldn't get rid of the medicine unless you got some control. But if you–let's pass on that. [It's OK to correct what you are asking or saying in midstream!] Would it be all right for you to go back through time, back to the very first time, that breathing was too important to you? To the very first subconscious memory. I won't let anything happen to you <Name>. You're not going to be alone.

P: Raises yes finger.

DME: May I have your permission to put my hand on your shoulder to let you know that you're not alone?

P: Raises yes finger.

DME: [DME puts hand on P's shoulder briefly.] <Name>, you are never going to lose touch with the fact that this is 1999, and you are here in New Orleans. Even though we are talking about a little electrochemical thing we call a memory. We don't even know what a memory is, it might be in your big toe. But, would it be all right to go find the first feeling, the first time it got super important to get another breath?

P: Raises yes finger.

[DME begins a "retrograde search."]

DME: Ok, way, way, way down deep. Did this happen before you were 10 years old?

P: Raises yes finger.

DME: Uhuh, that's right. Did it happen before you were five years old? Every time your feelings answer a question you get more in touch with your deepest, most heartfelt feelings. [Deepening.]

P: Raises hand to speak.

DME: Speak to me.

P: If I don't know consciously the answer, should I just go with–

DME: Yeah, go with what you feel.

P: Okay.

DME: Yeah, <Name>, do you feel like if it was before you were five years old?

P: Raises yes finger.

DME: Ok, good way, way, way down deep. [To audience:] Now see how valuable it is to have a speaking question. And you notice he didn't initiate that without first raising his hand.

DME: <Name>, did it happen before you were four years old?

P: Raises yes finger.

DME: Uhuh. Okay. Before you were three years old?

P: Raises yes finger.

DME: Uhuh. Way, way, way down deep. And before you were two years old?

P: Raises yes finger.

DME: Uhuh, way, way, way down deep. Would it be all right to go back and review it at a feeling level, just at a feeling level, would it be all right? Knowing that you got through it all right, no matter how bad it seemed, you survived it. Would it be all right to review it at a feeling level?

P: Raises yes finger.

[DME's asking for P. to do his first subconscious review.]

DME: All right, I have my hand on your shoulder, I won't let anything happen to you. Just let your mind have permission to review that very first time that you seemed sort of desperate to get another breath. And when you start reviewing it, your yes finger will rise. Every time you come to something emotionally important to you, your no finger will rise, and when you have completed reviewing it, you will signal with your thumb.

OVERANALYTICAL or DOUBTS

[**Comment:** What follows illustrates how we handle a patient's doubts about the process, and the tendency to overanalyze and stay in "left-brain thinking".]

P: Raises hand.

DME: Speak to me.

P: I feel like I cannot get into a conscious memory.

DME: You do not need to get into a conscious memory. Just give your mind permission to find what that feeling is, the very first time. The feeling. . . . Nothing happens for no reason at all. Your deepest mind knows where it got its ideas. What it feels like to be having difficulty breathing, feeling that you need to get some air.

P: Raises yes finger.

DME: It's all right, I won't let anything happen to you. You're going to make it all right.

P: Raises whole hand.

DME: Speak to me. Asks for verbal response

P: I feel like I cannot shut off my analytical mind to get to the feelings.

DME: All right. It just feels like that, you can get to that. Go back as far as you were, you gave me a yes signal. Find that. And, yes or no, would it be all right to let your fingers answer some questions about it?

P: Raises yes finger.

DME: Yeah, okay. Does it feel like . . . you can't get a breath, or does it feel like—I am going to ask you two questions. First one is; does it feel like you can't get a breath? Second question is; Does it feel like you better not let go of it when you've got it? First question: Does it feel like you can't get a breath?

P: Raises yes finger.

DME: Uhuh, second question: Does it feel like, having gotten a breath, does it feel like I better hang onto it? I might not get another one?

P: Raises yes finger.

DME: Yeah, okay. Does your deepest mind know that no matter how bad it was, you did get a breath and you did survive it?

P: Raises yes finger.

DME: Okay. Do you sense that we've, that what you're dealing with is the cold . . . is the respiratory illness that you had right after you were born? Do you sense that this was the first time this was a real problem? In the room in Wales, where it is cold, and you're sick?

P: Raises hand.

DME: Speak to me. You don't know?

P: I don't know.

DME: That's okay. You don't have to know.

P: What does the . . . what does the thumb represent?

DME: Thumb is the "I'm not ready to answer yet, I don't want to answer." You don't have to answer any questions. It's a free country. Some part of you knows what you just reviewed though. Do you sense that you might not survive it? Is it that bad?

P: Raises yes finger.

DME: Is there a lot of emotion in it? Not only from you, but from other people. Is there a real sense of danger?

P: Raises no finger.

DME: No? Okay. Would it be all right for us, right now, to take three deep breaths, and realize that the past is past. That that is all over. That there is plenty of air now, breath it in and blow it all out. Let it all go, cause it is okay to let it all go because there is plenty air for another breath. Another nice deep breath, and blow it all out. And another nice deep breath, deep breath, and blow it all out. Oh blow, blow, blow, let it all go. Cause why? There is plenty more air. Take another deep breath, and let it all out. Because that was a long time ago, under very different circumstances. And now you've grown up, and now you are in charge of your own breathing. Feel how good it feels to take a nice deep breath. Feel that air caressing your vocal cords, going down through your windpipe, and out into the little air sacs in the edge of your lungs, and let it go. Very, very relaxed and safe.

[**Comment:** DME is reframing the problem of not feeling like he can breathe. That was in the past and it's over. Now, in the present, the situation is different. He is in charge of his body and his breath, and no longer needs to fear not being able to breathe. Dr. Ewin has him experience the proof of the validity of this reframe by gathering evidence or data so to speak, through slow deep breathing. He then goes on:]

DME: Do you sense that if you were at your laughing place you could control your breathing at any time?

P: Raises no finger.

DME: No, you don't? Okay. Does it feel good to take a deep breath, and then to blow it allll out?

P: Raises yes finger.

DME: That feels good? Okay.

[**Comment:** Note how Dr. Ewin repeats the patient's responses to give him feedback. In a deep trance, patients are often unaware of what they are saying or what their fingers are doing until they are reminded.]

DME: Would it be all right with your feeling mind for you to go back and subconsciously review that first experience you told me about earlier?

IM: Yes.

[**Comment:** Note how Dr. Ewin keeps at it, keeps focusing and refocusing the patient on the significant early memory.]

DME: It's cold, and you have to walk. I want you to find the important things about that episode and review them at a feeling level. When you start reviewing, your yes finger will rise, every time you come to something emotionally important, your no finger, and when you finish reviewing it, you will signal with your thumb.

IMs: Yes, no, no . . . thumb.

DME: That's all right, that was good. Let's just imagine you sort of went over that just reading the headlines. Now let's go over it again in more detail, like you're reading the fine print. Go through the same episode. When you start reviewing your "yes" finger will rise. Every time you come to something emotionally important your "no" finger will rise, and when you finish reviewing it, you will signal with your thumb. More detail, who is there, what are they saying, how you feel, what's good about it, what's bad about it.

IMs: Yes, no, thumb.

DME: Would it be all right to bring it up to a conscious level? So you can tell me about it?

P: Raises yes finger.

DME: All right, go back to the start, when you're feeling all right, and then something happens, and just speak to me, and tell me what's happening.

P: Well, I think I, I feel like the story starts when I am already breathing sort of badly. I am upstairs with my mother, grand-mother, brother and sister. And my mom is getting ready to take me to the hospital. And there is sort of a feeling there, that in a way it's a show, and I think its more for my sister, and maybe for my younger brother. And the feeling from my mother is sort of that it is almost a hassle. And my feeling, my feeling coincides with both. Which is that in some ways it is a show, and in some ways it's a hassle, and in some ways it's just a very real problem. Um, and that's that part of the situation. Do you want me to keep going?

DME: Yeah, what's the emotional part of this? That's just a little conflict you're talking about there.

P: Uhm.

DME: Are you feeling guilty that maybe you're making more out of it, that it is a show?

P: Actually, I think more in a way excited.

DME: Because of the attention?

P: Yeah. Um. Feeling more important. Sort of more that I am get-ting more attention than my sister. Than my older sister. But also almost that I wish I didn't have to bother my mother about it. Or scare anyone about it.

DME: Are you having any trouble breathing?

P: I think, on and off. On and off.

DME: Is it more than usual? You've had it before.

P: Um.

DME: Why a hospital <u>this</u> time?

P: I don't know. I think it's the prospect of it not stopping. Or, the possibility of having to try to sleep with it. I think that's why.

DME: Go ahead, so what happens?

P: So my mother and I get on our coats, and walk down. I remem-ber . . . sitting on a couple benches along the way, although I don't think there actually are any.

DME: Is it because you are short of breath?

P: It's partly . . . partly short of breath, and partly sort of the same feeling of almost a show to illustrate the desperation of the situ-ation.

DME: And from there, what happens at the emergency?

P: Actually, I didn't go that far. I suppose it's just waiting, and playing pac-man in the waiting room, and going in for breath treat-
ments.

DME: You signaled that there was something emotional, an emotional
factor in all of this. Is that so? What was the most emotional part
of all of this?

P: Uhm, I think just all the feelings in the first . . . in the upstairs
scene I described, was the most emotional thing and seeing all
the . . .

DME: Ok, now all that was a long time ago, wasn't it? And you've gotten older, and stronger, and a lot healthier since you've gone
clean, haven't you?

IM: Yes.

DME: Would it be all right to let that show up in your immune system
and in your breathing? Does your deepest mind know that you
don't need to horde air anymore—that you can let it out, you can
just let it blow out, because there is more air for the next breath?

P: Raises yes finger.

DME: Good, lock in on that with every cell in your mind, and your
body, and your feelings. And each time you breathe, it gets easier and easier, because the past is past. You're getting healthier
and stronger every day.

[Ego-strengthening suggestions]

DME: I wonder what would be needed to let your wish come true. You
said you would really like to feel good with yourself, and others,
and with what's out there. I think you were kind of talking about
whatever God is. Is this a spiritual sense?

IM: Yes.

DME: Well, you're getting a little more spiritual as you get older. Do
you find there is some strength in that?

P: When I am feeling it, definitely.

DME: Well, yeah, okay. Would it be all right to plug into that strength?
You know, the nature of that strength is what we call love. Love
is all around us. It takes a lot of effort to push it away. To be
angry and to reject it. And, if you don't push it away, it's just
there. What is your religious background?

P: I haven't really got one.

DME: You haven't had any background training in—?

P: No.

DME: In any religion? Okay.

DME: There is a three word sentence in the Bible. It's at the end of John, and it says "God is love." In Greek, it was "God is agape" which is charitable love. That is a pretty good concept of what most people worship. It's an energy concept. Love is an energy concept. Speaking of his light all the time, of kindly light and all those things. Charitable love is loving us because we need it; when you give charity to somebody if you expect something back in return it's not charity. You give it because they need it, not because they deserve it. It's kind of nice to think that that is all around us. You can breathe it in, and if you blow it out, there is more to come.

And you feel precious, and valuable, and just as good as anybody else. You don't have to prove that to anyone, you can just be you. You're just as good as anybody else, perhaps even better. When I asked if there is anything else I should know about you, you said "I do try to live my life in constant self improvement." Yes or no, would it be all right to reword this a little bit? Instead of saying "I try to live my life in constant self improvement," would it be all right to take the word "try" out of it. And just say "I live my life in self-improvement." You know the Nike ad does not say "try hard," the Nike ad says "Just do it."

DME: Just do it, huh. Okay? Wouldn't that be okay, wouldn't that be better?

IM: Raises yes finger.

DME: Yeah, okay. Let's "just do it." Now, about the medicines, you said you would like to be free of medicine. Maybe you cannot be free, maybe you can cut it down a little bit. Would it be all right–you never stop any sort of medicine all of a sudden– would it be all right to test a little bit, and see what happens if you use a little bit less over a period of time?

IM: Raises yes finger.

DME: Yeah, wouldn't it be interesting to find–you know people talk about "Growing out of Asthma." Wouldn't it be nice to realize you have just grown out, that it's not necessary to worry about medicine all day long. It's all right to have some in your bag when you go to Chile, but there is no reason to worry about it. You don't have to worry about it, just be <Name>. <Name>, the fine person. Living his life, and growing every day in self-improvement. Just do it.

Is there anything else you think we should talk about before we end this session? Is there anything else you think you want to deal with?

P: Raises hand.

DME: Speak to me.

P: Do you mean apart from the asthma? Or, aspects of it?

DME: Aspects of it. Is there something else on your mind that is troubling you in some way? Is there something else you would like to deal with right now?

P: Within it?

DME: Yeah.

P: I think that I would like to deal with the way that anxiety triggers it, and the way that when I start getting anxious and it gets worse.

DME: You would like to deal with the way anxiety triggers it, and how when you get anxious it gets worse. When you start having asthma does it cross your mind that you may not be able to breathe? Anxiety is just fright. It's very frightening. That is a lot of reality isn't it. To feel that you're having difficulty breathing, to have some fright. But you can be strong and not afraid because you have dealt with this through many many years. And, I brought along a self-hypnosis tape that you can use at home to practice learning self-hypnosis and self-control.

Let me ask you right this moment to go to your laughing place. You found your laughing place, so, when you get there, your yes finger will rise.

IM: Raises yes finger.

DME: Do you sense that as you see that, hear it, feel it, know it, that there is a calmness? That this is anxiety reducing?

P: Raises hand.

DME: Speak to me.

P: Do you mean that–?

DME: I want you to be able to use your ability to daydream going to your laughing place. If you need to calm yourself, and control your anxiety, what can you do at the time? And I'm suggesting that one of the things you can do is, "Geeze, I'm just going to stop a minute and even though I am having trouble breathing, I am going to go to my laughing place where nothing can bother, nothing can disturb."

P: Raises hand.

DME: Speak to me.

P: I think that—I think I may have to just . . . maybe move back to the laughing place because even there, I feel that there is anxiety and fear that creeps into it.

DME: There may be other laughing places. People have lots of laughing places. You don't have to have just one. But I think we are going to have to deal with what you're saying by having you learn some self-hypnosis. And doing it with a tape is without even trying. You just lay back and let it happen. Okay?

IM: Yes finger rises.

DME: In fact, we can play this tape in a little while, and see how it goes. Is there anything else you want to talk about before we end?

IM: Raises no finger.

DME: No? Okay. Way, way, way down deep. Calm, and safe. Each breath you take, more and more relaxed. And when your deepest mind knows that you can keep right on processing this information, keep on living your life in self-improvement. Feeling strong and unafraid. When your deepest mind knows you can keep on processing this, you'll blink your eyes, and open them and come back fully alert. Sound in mind, and sound in body, and in control of your feelings. How you feeling?

P: Uh, very relaxed.

[**Comment:** Dr. Ewin uses an alerting suggestion that created a win-win double bind. That is, it is suggested that the patient will not rouse back up until his subconscious (deepest mind) knows that they have just initiated the process of positive change.]

DME: Would you be willing to answer some questions?

Follow-Up

After the workshop demonstration transcribed above, he had no more asthma attacks for six months, but had not solved his problem of wanting "to get rid of my medicine," and was still carrying it and using it prophylactically. He was seen for another visit and given suggestions that it is perfectly okay to carry the medicine if it gives a sense of safety, but why not just use it if you have symptoms and know you need it? Eight months later, I (DME) received this E-mail:

Hello Dabney:

Great to hear from you. I've been feeling great since our session in Chicago. I cut down on medications for about a week or ten days and then went off completely. I've been completely off the stuff ever since, and have never felt better in my life. When I get a bit of tightness, I use your prescribed mantra, 'There's so much air.' This helps to quiet the anxiety around not being able to breathe. I also keep in mind (as we discussed) that if I do need to use the medication that's all right too. One of the best things is that for the first time in my life I don't carry it around with me in a day-to-day setting. If you recall, I used to be so worried if I forgot my inhaler that I would bring on a mild asthma attack! It's a great change.

Thank you so much, Dabney, for the help you've given me and the freedom and peace that you've allowed me. Please write anytime with questions, comments, or anything else.

Sincerely,"

Chapter 16

TRANSCRIPT OF PARTS OF TWO OFFICE SESSIONS WITH A DYSTONIA PATIENT

This transcript begins with a segment of a previous office session with the patient before the second hypnoanalysis session. In the first session, she had made the point that she made such an effort to be a good Christian, and why did this happen to her? It provides some essential background information on the problem. In the first intake session, the history was taken, the patient was hypnotized, and some direct suggestion for healing in hypnosis (DSIH) and in the waking state were given. The patient's permission was obtained to help her with her problem.

DME: You were in the hospital?

P: Yes, Sir, I was in a head-on collision five years ago.

DME: Were you unconscious?

P: Yes, Sir, I went into a coma . . . they said probably on impact. And I was in a coma for eight days.

DME: Were you paralyzed at all?

P: No, Sir.

DME: Where you driving?

P: Yes, Sir.

DME: What do you know about being hit in the head?

P: It took me . . . Probably last year was the first time I remembered anything about the actual hit–the actual collision. But um– I just remember it hurting real, real bad and I closed my eyes, and that must have been when I went into my coma.

DME: Uh-huh. And it's been five years now?

P: It will be five years this December 15th.

DME: This December.

P: Yes, Sir.

DME: And what kind of treatment have you had for this?

P: Well, none. . . . I've been to–I went to physical therapy for like a year–and it was not getting better. They didn't think it could help me you know–it wasn't getting any better. And then I went to a lot of different doctors who said "well, it might be *this* and we will put you on *this* medicine" . . . and then a totally different doctor would say, "Oh no, it's not *that,* it's *this*. And why don't we put you on *this* kind of therapy." You know, nobody was able to tell me "*This* is what it is." Nobody had any idea.

DME: You've been to a neurosurgeon?

P: Yes, Sir, I think so.

DME: And a Neurologist?

P: Yes, Sir.

DME: And have you had a CAT Scan or an MRI?

P: Yes, Sir, I have.

DME: And what did they say about them?

P: Well, uh, I was hit on the right side of my head by a ladder that actually came through my windshield and hit me on the head. And they said that there is one part of my brain on the right side that is a little smaller than on the left side. But even that small size difference, and that part of the brain that is smaller should not . . . you know a lot of people who are born right-handed–the right side of their brain is smaller–so it wasn't anything out of the ordinary.

DME: Um-hum. Can you show me that hand–what it looks like, what happens when it goes into a spasm?

P: *Patient lifts left hand up and it clenches shut.*

DME: Is that what it does?

P: It just did that by itself.

DME: And when it does that, you have to straighten it out?

P: If um–if I pick it up, it closes. And I can't open it, I can't force myself to open it. You can see the muscles. I can't force myself. I have to shake it like that until it kinda gets loose and then I pull my hand out and spread my fingers down and I rest it.

DME: How has this affected your daily living?

P: Well, you wouldn't think it would be any big deal because I am naturally right-handed but it affects everything I do. Sometimes, I mean it makes it real hard for me when I am driving–sometimes my hand will get clenched on the steering wheel and that isn't very safe. And then, anything . . . if I go to write something down and I pick up a drink with my left hand, I have to put down my pencil and remove my hand from the cup. I mean, anything I do, if I brush my hair . . . if I'm putting on mascara, if I do anything, I can't use my left hand–which makes my right arm tired all the time because it's the only one I use.

Second Hypnoanalysis Office Session

DME: Today is March the 8th, the last time I saw you was a month ago. Tell me what has happened since I saw you last.

P: Well, it still does the same thing as before. It's a lot easier to open–it's a whole lot easier to open when it closes. You know, it's not too hard to open but it still closes on me. It still. I mean, I'm finding–I'm finding that it doesn't close as much as it did. I'm finding it doesn't close as much as it did, but it still closes. It's just when it closes, whereas before I would have to shake it out, now I can concentrate and I can open it better by myself. So it's way better than it was before, it's not closing quite as much and when it does close, I can open it without having to shake it open. But it still closes a little bit.

DME: What about if you–uh–pick up a glass?

P: You know that, you see I have been doing pretty good with that. If I pick up a glass you know, I can easily open it.

DME: Good.

P: I can easily open it. You know, if I point at you, I can easily get it back to as relaxed as it gets.

DME: Uh-huh .

P: But it still every once in a while . . . it will jerk and close, or it will jerk you know and do that *(makes a claw-like gesture with her right hand),* and when I do certain things, like if I were to–you know I–there is no way I could tap the table like that *(demonstrating with right hand, then switches to left hand).* See, its trying to close. It's still… little things I try to do, it still closes on me. You know, it's just a lot easier to open now.

DME: What about if you're driving? Does it get locked on the wheel?

P: It'll . . . it'll close. It does that a lot, you know it will close. It will grip the steering wheel–the steering wheel real tight, and I mean it's easier, you know. I have to concentrate, and I will just do it finger by finger and I can open it off the steering wheel, but it still closes on me.

DME: Um-hum. How about your toe? Has it been better?

P: Uh—its better, you know it's gotten a bit better. It still sticks up, but I don't notice it as much because the pain is not there as bad as it used to be. You know, my hand still closes and my toe still sticks up, but it's not hurting near as much as it used to.

DME: The pain is not as bad?

P: Right, and I can still feel it and it still hurts whenever I open it and when it does close, it still hurts, but it's not near as bad as it was when it was constant opening and closing.

DME: How many times a day is it likely to do this now?

P: I mean, if I go to pick up a glass, of course it will close—but if I were to just keep it in my lap it might close about 20–30 times.

DME: It will close that often? As compared to how often before?

P: Before, you know, it might have been *not* closed 20-30 times. It was closing—I mean, if I had it like this *(places right hand on right leg)*, and I moved it over *(moves hand over to left leg, and closes fist)*, you know it jerked shut real bad. So it's a lot better than it used to be.

DME: Would you say its 50% better?

P: Yes, Sir.

DME: Is that about a good estimate?

P: Yes, probably about 60–65% better than it was before.

DME: All right. You have made a lot of progress. Are you aware of anything that seems to make it better or worse? Any time of a day, or any activity, or weekends?

P: Sometimes when it's real cold it closes more than when it's just— and I mean, I don't know if it's just because it's been real cold this past winter or whatever, but sometimes when it's cold, it will close on me. But then, that's everything, you know sometimes if you're cold, your body just *(she contracts her whole body a bit)*—but you know sometimes when it's cold, I notice it closes more often.

DME: Uh-huh. Let's uh, lean back. Get comfortable.

Patient leans back in easy chair, closes eyes and folds hands on stomach.

DME: Keeping your eyelids closed just as if they were glued together, roll your eyeballs up as if you were looking at the top of your forehead. Looking way, way up. Way up <Name>. Now take a deep breath—the deepest breath you have ever taken. Deep breath, deep breath; and hold it, and feel it pressing against your chest, and as you let it all out, just like a balloon collapsing, draining all the tension from every nerve and fiber in your body. Your eyes relaxed. Jaws unclenched, shoulders droopy. Paying attention only to the sound of my voice. Any other sound that you hear will be very pleasant in the background, and will just help you to go deeper, deeper relaxed.

Your arms all limp and floppy, abdomen soft. Each breath, as you exhale, just imagine you are blowing out stress and tension into the atmosphere. Never to return. Your legs, loose and limp and lazy-like and relaxed. And your mind as relaxed as your body. Feeling calm. And safe. And peaceful. And comfortable. Way, way, way down deep. Now, with your permission, I am going to move your right hand, and you'll find that it is more comfortable in this position.

Now, I want to teach you a way to signal to me without even talking. If I ask you a question and it feels OK, it feels yes, it feels agreeable, this finger will just slowly rise. to signal yeah, that's all right. Is your name (name)?

IM: Yes finger lifts.

DME: Just like that, every time you feel your answer to a question, you go inside even deeper, and get more in touch with your deepest and most heartfelt feelings.

Now, if I ask you a question and you disagree with it, you don't even have to know why, it just feels wrong, this finger will just slowly rise. Just come on up like it's coming up all by itself, just like you would shake your head yes or no. Is today the fourth of July?

IM: No finger rises.

DME: No, of course not. Today is the 8th of March. That's it, way, way, way down deep. Calm and safe.

DME: And if I ask a question that you're NOT ready to answer yet, or you don't want to answer, signal with your thumb and that's all right. And if something crosses your mind and you want to ask me a question, raise your hand and we will talk.

DME: And my first question to your feeling mind is, is it okay for me to help you with this?

IM: Yes finger rises.

DME: All right good. <Name>, there are various things that we do sub-consciously; or feel that affect our muscles and our body move-ments. And one of them is called "conflict." A conflict occurs when a person feels like "I want to do one thing, but I ought to do the opposite." It's being pulled in two different directions. We call that a conflict. Do you sense that the symptoms of your hand going into unconscious spasms, that they are, that you may be being affected by conflict? That you're being pulled in two direc-tions?

IM: Yes finger lifts.

DME: The answer's yes. Would it be all right for you to know at a con-scious level what the conflict is?

[**Comment:** Dr. Ewin reflects back to the patient what her fingers answered. He then asks her subconscious mind for permission as to whether it feels all right to become consciously aware of the nature of her conflict.]

IM: Yes finger rises.

DME: Okay. I'm going to be quiet now for a moment, while you do this. And when it comes up to you, when it comes to a conscious level. That you sense the nature of this conflict, your yes finger will rise as you review those feelings. . . .

After a while, Patient raises finger assigned to "yes."

DME: Speak to me and tell me what do you sense? What is the conflict, what is the nature of this?

P: I think I'm mad about it. I'm still mad about it. I feel like I ought to let go and forget all about it, but when I think about it, some-times I get so mad. But I don't need to be mad, enough to just you know, and I should just forget about it. If I keep on being mad, and angry, and sad and remembering all that, I'm never going to get any better.

DME: So you feel like you want to forget about it, but you have been holding onto your anger. Did you hear what you said? You said "I need to . . ." what?

P: "Let go."

DME: You certainly do need to let go of that left hand. And this will fit all kinds of ways. To let go of anger. You have already made your decision, haven't you?

IM: Yes finger rises.

DME: You know that's not the part of you that you like. You don't like the angry part of you. You like the loving part of you, don't you?

P: Yes.

DME: That's the kind of person you are. I wonder if you have a clear idea of what you are angry about? Are you angry because there was a wreck? Are you angry because they sued you? Are you angry because you got hurt so badly, and scared so much? Are you angry at yourself? Is this self-punishment? You know you were just learning how to drive. You had just gotten your license. I would like you to think clearly about what it is that you're angry about. Speak to me and tell me what it is.

P: I wonder why it happened to me.

DME: So you're angry at God?

P: No.

DME: Well, who makes things happen?

P: No! I'm just mad.

DME: You're either mad at yourself, or you're mad at God. Nobody else made you do this, right?

P: No.

DME: No, Okay. This is a real common deal you know, "Why me?" Here you are trying to be good and trying to do right. And you've been a good person, and you still are. You certainly did-n't intend for this to happen, did you?

IM: No finger lifts.

DME: Of course, you didn't. So you're not really guilty in that respect. Guilt requires intent. Somebody goes out hunting, and sees some deer antlers and takes a shot at it and it turns out that it is anoth-er hunter carrying a deer, and he kills the guy. The intent wasn't to kill the guy, it was to kill the deer wasn't it? That's not murder. There is no intent in it. They call that involuntary manslaughter, accidental manslaughter.

This was an accident. You didn't want it to happen, but it hap-pened. This kind of thing usually happens when we are in too much of a hurry.

DME: I wonder if it would be all right to forgive God. Have you ever thought of forgiving God for making you a human being who makes mistakes?

IM: Yes finger rises.

DME: If you thought about it, than why didn't you do it? Speak to me.

P: I don't think it's God that I am mad at. I was mad at him for a long time, but I was able to forgive him. I know he didn't do it to me, but if he didn't do it, then it puts all the blame on me. So, why did I do it? If I had only known, I wouldn't have done it, but I can't go back, and it will be with me for the rest of my life.

DME: No, it won't. The fact will be there, but the anger does not have to be there for the rest of your life. You learned a good lesson. You're not going to get into too big of a hurry again are you? No, I bet you are one of the safest drivers your age in town. Something good can come out of something that seems bad at the time. I would trust you to drive me. There is a story in the Bible I am going to want you to read, and I bet you may even remember it. Jesus was talking about the people in the synagogue and the Pharisees in the front row who was saying very proudly 'I've been a very good Jew, and I have paid all my tithes, and kept all the religious rites, and all the holidays and I've been good."

And way back in the back there was a poor man who simply said, "God forgive me, a sinner." And Jesus said, "the man in the back room will go to Heaven before the people who are so proud of how good they have been." Because we don't really earn our way into Heaven, in the Christian tradition. God made us all with shortcomings, and the way we get to Heaven is with his love and grace. He loves us because we are his children, even though we are imperfect. You know he could have made us all robots, and we would have been perfect. I expect someday you will be married and will have a few children. If you had two or three children, would you want them to be robots?

IM: No.

DME: Of course not, you don't want robots. How do you love a robot? You have two or three kids, they will screw up all the time. They don't wash their hands before supper, and they don't get their homework the way you want it, and they don't say "yes ma'am." They do all sorts of things. But if they will just come back and say "but Mom, I am sorry and I will try to do better," are you going to throw them out of the house? Or, are you going to put your arm around them?

IM: Yes finger lifts.

DME: You're going to put your arm around them. Well, that is what our Father in Heaven does with us. Do you know the story of

King David? Everybody knows how he killed Goliath, but when he got to be King, he was a terrible sinner. He committed adultery with Uriah's wife, Bathsheba. Got her pregnant. And he ordered the captain to leave Uriah at the battlefield to be killed by the enemy. And that's murder, and that is against the Ten Commandments. And adultery is against the Ten Commandments.

His troops got hungry, and he took the show-bread and desecrated the Temple. He was a terrible sinner. Do you remember what Saint Paul said about David? Saint Paul is quoting God. He said, "He is a man after mine own heart." And the Messiah, that Jesus, would come from the house of David. I think, "My gosh, how could someone who sins like David be a man after God's own heart?" And the answer is that every time he messed up, he came back home and said, "God I'm sorry, I've messed up again. I will try to do better." He had a contrite heart about it, and he repented.

DME: And what did you do when you messed up? Did you go home and tell your folks "Gee, I'm sorry. I didn't mean to bust up the car." And "I'm going to try to do better"? Isn't that what you did?

IM: Yes.

DME: I know damn well that that's what you did. And didn't they tell you they still love you?

IM: Yes.

DME: That's what our Father in Heaven has to say about us being imperfect. That if we care, we're forgiven. If we asked, we're forgiven. And so, if God forgives you, after all this mess, does it make much sense for you to know more than God does, and not be able to forgive yourself? It doesn't make much sense to me.

DME: I wonder if it would be all right for you to forgive yourself. You know it's been five years now . . . to drop the issue and get on with life? You can't change the fact that it happened, but you can change how you feel about it. You can change your attitude about it. I am going to ask you right now, and beg you to realize that you are a child of God and you're a child of your parents, and you're also a full adult, with good sense, and a warm heart.

And I'm going to ask you to forgive yourself, at a feeling level. Really mean it, as if you were forgiving your own child after your own child messed up. Take all the time you need, and when you really feel that you have forgiven yourself, finger signal "all right," because that is when the anger can go.

That's why you can't control your life anymore. Once you forgive, it doesn't control your life anymore.

IM: Yes.

DME: Lock in on that with every cell in your mind, and your heart, and your spirit. You're just as good as anyone else, maybe sometimes just as bad as everyone else. But that's all right. You're one of God's children, and all of God's children are precious.

DME: I want to ask your left hand, if it's become aware of what you said earlier. "That I have to let go of my anger." I want to ask your left hand, the fingers of your right hand can answer this. Would it be all right now to let go of all of this and be through with it? And let your hand become normal again in every way because you have let go of the anger and you have forgiven yourself and forgiven God and forgiven everyone about it. Even the man who sued you, he had a right to be compensated. That's the law of the Bible and it's over now. Would it be all right to let go? Because when you let go, that hand doesn't have to grip and lock anymore does it?

IM: (After some time . . .) Yes finger rises.

DME: Oh how nice, lock in on that. Ask your deepest mind, if your left hand is going to let go. Let your whole mind, body and spirit let go of the anger. Is there anything else, any other problem that you have to resolve? Is there anything that would keep you from getting completely well now?

IM: No finger rises.

DME: No? Okay. Lock in on that with every cell in your mind and your body and your feelings. And when your deepest mind knows that you can keep on processing this and every day, every hour, every minute get more normal in every way so that this is actually just a fact that happened in the past and is over now, and you have a whole new life ahead of you, of just being you. When your deepest mind knows you can do that, you will blink your eyes, and open them wide, and be wide awake, fresh alert, and comfortable. Sound in mind, and sound in body, and in control of your feelings.

P: After a time, Patient blinks and opens her eyes.

DME: That sounds good to me. Let me see what you can do with that hand now. Move it all around, move your wrist, and you can make a fist and. . . . Uhuh. How does it feel?

P: My hand doesn't hurt!

DME: Good. All right.

[**Comment:** This patient centered her complaint around the fact that she was a good Christian, so the therapy centers around her acknowledged authority, the Bible. This is utilitizing what the patient brings to you.]

REFERENCES

Alexander, L. (1971). The prehypnotic suggestion. *Comprehensive Psychology, 12,* 414–418.

Beecher, H.K. (1946). Pain in men wounded in battle. *Annals of Surgery, 123,* 96–105.

Bennett, H.L. (1987). Learning and memory in anaesthesia. In Rosen, M. and Lunn, J.N. (Eds.), *Consciousness, Awareness and Pain in General Anaesthesia,* Chapter 15. London: Butterworths.

Bennett, H.L. (1988). Perception and memory for events during adequate general anesthesia for surgical operations. In Pettinati, H.M. (Ed.), *Hypnosis and memory.* New York: Guilford Press.

Bennett, H.L., Davis, H.S., & Giannini, J.A. (1985). Non-verbal response to intraoperative conversation. *British Journal of Anaesthesiology. 57,* 174.

Bensen, V.B. (1971). One hundred cases of post-anesthetic suggestion in the recovery room. *American Journal of Clinical Hypnosis, 13,* 273.

Bonke, B., Schmitz, P.I.M., Verhage, F., & Zwaveling, A. (1986). Clinical study of so-called unconscious perception during general anaesthesia. *British Journal of Anaesthesiology, 58,* 957.

Breckenridge J.L., & Aitkenhead, A.R. (1983). Awareness during anaesthesia: A review. *Annals of the Royal College of Surgeons, 65,* 93.

Brown, D., Scheflin, A.W., & Hammon, D.C. (1998). *Memory, trauma, treatment and the law: An essential reference on memory for clinicians, researchers, attorneys, and judges.* New York: W.W. Norton & Company.

Buchheimer, A. (1987). Memory-preverbal and verbal. In T. Verny (Ed.), *Pre- and perinatal psychology: An introduction.* New York: Human Sciences Press.

Cheek, D.B. (1958). Hypnosis, an additional tool in human reorientation to stress. *Northwest Medicine, 57,* 177–182.

Cheek, D.B. (1959). Unconscious perception of meaningful sounds during surgical anesthesia as reviewed under hypnosis. *American Journal of Clinical Hypnosis, 1* (3), 101–113.

Cheek, D.B. (1960a). What does the surgically anesthetized patient hear? *Rocky Mountain Medical Journal, 57,* 49–53.

Cheek, D.B. (1960b). Use of pre-operative hypnosis to protect patients from careless conversation (during anesthesia). *American Journal of Clinical Hypnosis, 3,* 101–102.

Cheek, D.B. (1960c). Removal of subconscious resistance to hypnosis using ideomotor questioning techniques (recognize the flashback phenomenon). *American Journal of Clinical Hypnosis, 3,* 103–107.

Cheek, D.B. (1962a). Importance of recognizing that surgical patients behave as though hypnotized. *American Journal of Clinical Hypnosis, 4,* 227.

Cheek, D.B. (1962b). Ideomotor questioning for investigation of subconscious "pain" and target organ susceptibility. *American Journal of Clinical Hypnosis, 5*, 30–41.

Cheek, D.B. (1962c). Areas of research into psychosomatic aspects of surgical tragedies now open through use of hypnosis and ideomotor questioning. *Western Journal of Surgery, Obstetrics & Gynecology, 70*, 137–142.

Cheek, D.B. (1962d). Some applications of hypnosis and ideomotor questioning methods for analysis and therapy in medicine. *American Journal of Clinical Hypnosis, 5*, 92–104.

Cheek, D.B. (1964). Surgical memory and reaction to careless conversation. *American Journal of Clinical Hypnosis, 6*, 237–240.

Cheek, D.B. (1965). Emotional factors in persistent pain states. *American Journal of Clinical Hypnosis, 8*, 100–110.

Cheek, D.B. (1966a). The meaning of continued hearing sense under general anesthesia: A progress report and report of a case. *American Journal of Clinical Hypnosis, 8*, 275-280.

Cheek, D.B. (1966b). Therapy of persistent pain states, Part I: Neck and shoulder pain of five years duration. *American Journal of Clinical Hypnosis, 8*, 281–286.

Cheek, D.B. (1969). Communication with the critically ill. *American Journal of Clinical Hypnosis, 12* (2), 75–85.

Cheek, D.B. (1974). Sequential head and shoulder movements appearing with age regression in hypnosis to birth. *American Journal of Clinical Hypnosis, 16*, 261–266.

Cheek, D.B. (1975). Maladjustment patterns apparently related to imprinting at birth. *American Journal of Clinical Hypnosis, 18*, 75–82.

Cheek, D.B. (1980a). Ideomotor questioning revealing an apparently valid traumatic experience prior to birth. *Australian Journal of Clinical & Experimental Hypnosis, 8*, 65–70.

Cheek, D.B. (1980b). Two approaches to causal events in disease using ideomotor responses and light hypnosis. *Hypnos: Swedish Journal of Clinical & Experimental Hypnosis*, August, 80–86.

Cheek, D.B. (1981). Awareness of meaningful sounds under general anesthesia: Considerations and a review of the literature 1959–1979. In Wain, H.J., (Ed.), *Theoretical and clinical aspects of hypnosis*, p. 87. Miami: Symposia Specialists.

Cheek, D.B. (1989). An indirect method of discovering primary traumatic experiences: Two case examples. *American Journal of Clinical Hypnosis, 32* (1), 41–47.

Cheek, D.B. (1994). *Hypnosis: The application of ideomotor procedures*. Boston: Allyn & Bacon.

Cheek, D.B., & LeCron, L.M. (1968). *Clinical hypnotherapy.* New York: Grune & Stratton.

Clawson, T.A., Jr, & Swade, R.H. (1975). The hypnotic control of blood flow and pain: The cure of warts and the potential for the use of hypnosis in the treatment of cancer. *American Journal of Clinical Hypnosis, 3,* 160.

Coué, E. (1922). *Self-mastery through conscious autosuggestion.* New York: American Library Service.

Cousins, N. (1979). *Anatomy of an illness as perceived by the patient.* New York: W.W. Norton.

Crasilneck, H.B., & Hall, J.A. (1975). *Clinical hypnosis: Principles and applications.* New York: Grune & Stratton.

Crile, G., & Lower, W.E. (1914). *Anoci-association,* p. 98. Philadelphia: W.B. Saunders.

Daniels, E. (1962). The hypnotic approach in anesthesia for children. *American Journal of Clinical Hypnosis, 4,* 244.

DeCasper, A.J., & Fifer, W.P. (1980). Of human bonding: Newborns prefer their mothers' voices. *Science, 208,* 1174–76.

DeCasper, A J. and Spence, M.J. (1986). Prenatal maternal speech influence on newborns' perception of sounds. *Infant Behaviour and Development, 9,* 133–150.

Drislane, F.W. (1996). Status epilepticus. In M.A. Samuels, & S. Feske (Eds.), *Office practice of neurology,* pp. 758–765. London: Churchill Livingstone.

Dubovsky, S.L. and Trustman, R. (1976). Absence of recall after general anesthesia: Implications for theory and practice. *Anesthesia and Analgesia, 55,* 696.

Eastwood, J.D., Gaskowski, P., & Bowers, K.S. (1998). The folly of effort: Ironic effects in the mental control of pain. *International Journal of Clinical and Experimental Hypnosis, XLVI* (1), 77–91.

Eimer, B.N. (1988). The chronic pain patient: Multimodal assessment & psychotherapy. *International Journal of Medical Psychotherapy, 1,* 23–40.

Eimer, B.N. (1989). Psychotherapy for chronic pain: A cognitive approach. In A. Freeman, K.M. Simon, L. Beutler, & H. Arkowitz, (Eds.), *Comprehensive handbook of cognitive therapy,* pp. 449–465. New York: Plenum Press.

Eimer, B.N. (2000a). Clinical applications of hypnosis for brief and efficient pain management psychotherapy. *American Journal of Clinical Hypnosis, 43* (1), 17–40.

Eimer, B.N. (2000b, Summer). Hypnosis for the relief of pain: What's possible and what's not. *Psychological Hypnosis, 9* (2).

Eimer, B.N. (2002). *Hypnotize yourself out of pain now!* Oakland, CA: New Harbinger.

Eimer, B.N., & Freeman, A. (1998). *Pain management psychotherapy: A practical guide.* New York: John Wiley and Sons.

Elliotson, J. (1843). *Numerous cases of surgical operations without pain in the mesmeric state.* Philadelphia, PA: Lea and Blanchard.

Elman, D. (1970). *Hypnotherapy.* Glendale, CA: Westwood Publishing.

Erickson, M. (1961). Historical note on the hand levitation and other ideomotor techniques. *American Journal of Clinical Hypnosis, 3,* 196–199.

Erickson, M. (1986). Symptom-based approaches in mind-body problems. In E.L. Rossi, & M.O. Ryan (Eds.), *Mind-body communication in hypnosis* (Vol. III). (pp. 67–202). New York: Irvington Publishers, Inc.

Erickson, M., & Rossi, E.L. (1981). *Experiencing hypnosis: Therapeutic approaches to altered states.* New York: Irvington.

Esdaile, J. (1846). *Mesmerism in India.* London: Longman, Brown, Green, and Longmans.

Evans, F.J. (1991). Hypnotizability: Individual differences in dissociation and the flexible control of psychological processes. In S.J. Lynn & J.W. Rhue (Eds.), *Theories of hypnosis,* pp. 144–168. New York: Guilford.

Evans, F.J. (2001). Hypnosis and the management of chronic pain. In L.F. Fredericks (Ed.), *The use of hypnosis in surgery and anesthesiology: Psychological preparation of the surgical patient,* pp. 31–56. Springfield, IL: Charles C Thomas.

Evans, J.M. (1987). Patients' experiences of awareness during general anaesthesia. In Rosen, M. & Lunn, J.N. (Eds.), *Consciousness, awareness and pain in general anaesthesia,* Appendix. London: Butterworths.

Ewin, D.M. (1973). Hypnosis in industrial practice. *Journal of Occupational Medicine, 15,* 586–589.

Ewin, D.M. (1974). Condyloma acuminatum: Successful treatment of four cases by hypnosis. *American Journal of Clinical Hypnosis, 17,* 73–78.

Ewin, D.M. (1978a). Relieving suffering and pain with hypnosis. *Geriatrics, 33* (6), 87–89.

Ewin, D.M. (1978b). Clinical use of hypnosis for attenuation of burn depth. In F.H. Frankel, & H.S. Zamansky (Eds.), *Hypnosis at its bicentennial: Selected papers from the Seventh International Congress of Hypnosis and Psychosomatic Medicine.* New York: Plenum Press.

Ewin, D.M. (1979). Hypnosis in burn therapy. In G.D. Burrows, D.R. Collison, & L. Dennerstein (Eds.), *Hypnosis 1979.* New York: Elsevier/North-Holland.

Ewin, D.M. (1984). Hypnosis in surgery and anesthesia. In W.C. Wester, II, & A.H. Smith (Eds.), *Clinical hypnosis: A multidisciplinary approach,* pp. 210–235. Philadelphia: J.B. Lippincott Company.

Ewin, D.M. (March/April, 1985). Hypnosis in medical practice: Putting the mind to work. *Medical Student,* 4–6.

Ewin, D.M. (1986a). Hypnosis and pain management. In B. Zilbergeld, M.G. Edelstien, & D.L. Araoz (Eds.), *Hypnosis: Questions & Answers,* pp. 282–288. New York: W.W. Norton & Company.

Ewin, D. (1986b). Emergency room hypnosis for the burned patient. *American Journal of Clinical Hypnosis, 29* (1), 7–12.

Ewin, D. (1986c). The effect of hypnosis and mental set on major surgery and burns. *Psychiatric Annals, 16* (2), 115-118.

Ewin, D.M. (1989). Hypnotic recall of sounds heard under general anesthesia. In Bonke, B., Fitch,W., & Millar, K. (Eds.) *Memory and Awareness in Anesthesia: Proceedings of the First International Symposium on Memory and Awareness in Anesthesia.* Elsevier/North Holland Press.

Ewin, D.M. (1990). Hypnotic technique for recall of sounds heard under general anesthesia. In B. Benno, W. Fitch, & K. Millar (Eds.), *Memory and awareness in anesthesia.* Amsterdam: Swets & Zeitlinger.

Ewin, D.M. (1992a). Constant pain syndrome: Its psychological meaning and cure using hypnoanalysis. *Hypnos, XIX* (1), 57–62.

Ewin, D.M. (1992b). The use of hypnosis in the treatment of burn patients. *Psychiatric Medicine, 10* (4), 79–87.

Ewin, D.M. (1992c). Hypnotherapy for warts (Verruca Vulgaris): 41 consecutive cases with 33 cures. *American Journal of Clinical Hypnosis, 35* (1), 1–10.

Ewin, D.M. (1994). Many memories retrieved with hypnosis are accurate. *American Journal of Clinical Hypnosis, 36* (3), 174–176.

Ewin, D.M. (1998). Rapid eye roll induction. In D.C. Hammond (Ed.), *Hypnotic induction & suggestion,* p. 49. Des Plaines, IL: American Society of Clinical Hypnosis.

Ewin, D.M. (1999). Hypnosis in the emergency room. In R. Temes (Ed.), *Medical hypnosis: An introduction and clinical guide.* Philadelphia, PA: Churchill-Livingstone.

Ewin, D.M. (2001). The use of hypnosis in the treatment of burn patients. In G.D. Burrows, R.O. Stanley, & P.B. Bloom (Eds.), International handbook of clinical hypnosis. Chichester, England: John Wiley.

Finney, J.M.T. (1934). Discussion of papers on shock. *Annals of Surgery, 100,* 746.

Fredericks, L.E. (1980). The value of teaching hypnosis in the practice of anesthesiology. *International Journal of Clinical and Experimental Hypnosis, 28,* 6.

Fredericks, L.E. (2001). *The use of hypnosis in surgery and anesthesiology: Psychological preparation of the surgical patient.* Springfield, IL: Charles C Thomas.

Gatchel, R.J. (2005). *Clinical essentials of pain management.* Washington, D.C.: APA Press.

Gazzaniga, M.S. (1998). *The mind's past.* Berkeley, CA: University of California Press.

Gidro-Frank, L., & Bowers-Buch, M.K. (1948). A study of the plantar response in hypnotic age regression. *Journal of Nervous and Mental Disease, 107,* 443–458.

Goldmann, L. (1986). Awareness under general anaesthesia. PhD dissertation. University of Cambridge. Referenced in Goldman, L. (1988). Information-processing under general anesthesia: A review. *Journal of the Royal Society of Medicine, 81,* 224.

Goldmann, L. (1988). Information-processing under general anaesthesia: A review. *Journal of the Royal Society of Medicine, 81,* 224.

Goldmann, L, & Levey, A.B. (1986). Orienting responses under general anaesthesia. *Anaesthesia, 41,* 1056.

Goldmann, L., Shah, M.V,, & Hebden, M.W. (1987). Memory of cardiac anaesthesia: Psychological sequelae in cardiac patients of intra-operative suggestion and operating room conversation. *Anaesthesia, 42,* 596.

Gravitz, M.A. (1988). Early uses of hypnosis as surgical anesthesia. *American Journal of Clinical Hypnosis, 30* (3), 201–208.

Hammond, D.C (Ed.). (1990). *Handbook of hypnotic suggestions and metaphors.* New York: W.W. Norton.

Hammond, D.C., & Cheek, D.B. (1988). Ideomotor signaling: A method for rapid unconscious exploration. In D.C. Hammond (Ed.), *Hypnotic induction and suggestion: An introductory manual,* pp. 90–97. Des Plaines, IL: American Society of Clinical Hypnosis Press.

Hammond, D.C., Garver, R.B., Mutter, C.B., Crasilneck, H.B., Frishcolz, E., Gravitz, M.A., Hibler, N.S., Olson, J., Scheflin, A.W., Spiegel, H., & Wester, W. (1995). *Clinical hypnosis and memory: Guidelines for clinicians and for forensic hypnosis.* Des Plaines, IL: American Society of Clinical Hypnosis Press.

Hilgard, E.R. (1986). *Divided consciousness: Multiple controls in human thought and action.* New York: John Wiley.

Hilgard, E.R. (1991). A neodissociation interpretation of hypnosis. In S.J. Lynn & J.W. Rhue (Eds.), *Theories of hypnosis: Current models and perspectives,* pp. 83–104. New York: Guilford.

Hilgard, E.R., & Hilgard, J.R. (1994). *Hypnosis in the relief of pain* (Rev. ed.). New York: Brunner/Mazel.

Hoptman, M.J., & Davidson, R.J. (1994). How and why do the two cerebral hemispheres interact? Psychological Bulletin, 116(2), 195-219.

Hutchings, D. (1961). The value of suggestions given under anesthesia: A report and evaluation of 200 consecutive cases. *American Journal of Clinical Hypnosis, 4* (1), 26–29.

Ivry, R.B., & Robertson, L.C. (1998). *The two sides of perception.* Cambridge, MA: MIT Press.

Johnston, M., & Vogele, C. (1993). Benefits of psychological preparation for surgery: A meta-analysis. *Annals of Behavioral Medicine, 15,* 245–256.

Kessler, R., & Whalen, T. (1999). Hypnotic preparation in anesthesia and surgery. In R. Temes (Ed.), *Medical hypnosis: An introduction and clinical guide,* pp. 43–58. New York: Churchill Livingstone.

Kolb, B., & Wishaw, I.Q. (1996). Disconnection Syndromes. In *Fundamentals of Human Neurology* (3rd Ed.) (pp. 502–521). New York: W.H. Freeman and Company.

Kolough, F.T. (1964). Hypnosis and surgical convalescence: A study of subjective factors in postoperative recovery. *American Journal of Clinical Hypnosis, 7,* 120.

Levinson, B.W. (1965). States of awareness during general anaesthesia. *British Journal of Anaesthesiology, 37,* 544.

Levinson, B.W. (1967). States of awareness during general anesthesia. In Lassner. J. (Ed.), *Hypnosis and psychosomatic medicine.* New York, Springer Verlag.

Madrid, A., & Schwartz, M. (1991). Maternal-infant bonding and Pediatric asthma: An initial investigation. *Pre- & Perinatal Psychology Journal, 5* (4), 347–358.

Melzack, R. (1975). The McGill Pain Quesionnairre: Major properties and scoring methods. *Pain, 1,* 277–299.

Melzack, R. (1996). Gate control theory: On the evolution of pain concepts. *Pain Forum, 5* (2), 128–138.

Melzack, R., & Wall, P. (1965). Pain mechanisms: A new theory. *Science, 50,* 971–979.

Melzack, R., & Wall, P. (1982). *The challenge of pain.* New York: Basic Books.

O'Hanlon, W.H., & Martin, M. (1992). *Solution-oriented hypnosis: An Ericksonian approach.* New York: W.W. Norton.

Osler, W. (1904). *Aequanimitas.* Reprinted 1953. New York, Blakiston.

Pedersen, D.L. (1984). Hypnosis and the right hemisphere. *Proceedings of the British Society of Medical and Dental Hypnosis, 5,* 2–14.

Pedersen, D.L. (1994). *Cameral analysis: A method of treating the psychoneuroses using hypnosis.* New York: Routledge.

Penfield, W. (1974). *The mystery of the mind: A critical study of consciousness and the human brain.* Princeton, N.J.: Princeton Univ. Press.

Querleu, D., Lefebvre, C., Titran, M., Renard, X., Morillion, M., & Crepin, C. (1984). Reaction of the newborn infant less than 2 hours after birth to the maternal voice. *Journal of Obstetrics & Gynecology and Reproductive Biology, 13* (2), 125–134.

Raine, A., Brennan, P., & Mednick, S. (1991). Birth complications combined with early maternal rejection at age 1 year predispose to violent crime at age 18 years. *Archive of General Psychiatry, 51,* 984–988.

Rementer, S.R., & Eimer, B.N. (2005). *Essential guide to handguns: Firearm instruction for personal defense and protection.* Flushing, NY: Looseleaf Law Publications.

Rodger, B.P. (1961). The art of preparing the patient for anesthesia. *Anesthesiology, 22,* 548.

Rossi, E.L. (2002). *The psychobiology of gene expression: Neuroscience and neurogenesis in hypnosis and the healing arts.* New York: W.W. Norton & Company.

Rossi, E.L. (1993). *The psychobiology of mind-body healing: New concepts in therapeutic hypnosis.* New York: W.W. Norton & Company.

Rossi, E.L., & Cheek, D.B. (1988). *Mind-body therapy: Methods of ideodynamic healing with hypnosis.* New York: W.W. Norton and Company.

Sperry, R.W. (1964). The great cerebral commissure. *Scientific American,* 42–52.

Spiegel, H., & Spiegel, D. (1978/1987). *Trance and treatment: Clinical uses of hypnosis.* Washington, DC: American Psychiatric Press, Inc.

Thali, A. (1989). Sudeck syndrome and its "psychosomatic disposition": A comparative clinico-psychological study of the etiology in accident patients. *Psychotherapy and Psychosomatic Medical Psychology, 39,* 260.

Tramo, M.J., Baynes, K. Fendrich, R., Mangun, G.R., Phelps, E.A., Reuter-Lorenz. P.A., & Gazzaniga, M.S. (1995). Hemispheric specialization and interhemispheric integration. In A.G. Reeves & D.W. Roberts (Eds.), *Epilepsy and the Corpus Callosum* (2nd Ed.). New York: Plenum Press.

Trevathern, C.B. (Ed.) (1990). *Brain circuits and functions of the mind: Essays in honor of Roger Wolcott Sperry.* Cambridge, England: Cambridge University Press.

Turk, D.C. (2002). Clinical effectiveness and cost effectiveness of treatment for patients with chronic pain. *Clinical Journal of Pain, 18,* 355–365.

Verny, T., & Kelly, J. (1981). *The secret life of the unborn child: How you can prepare your baby for a happy, healthy life.* New York: Dell Publishing.

Watkins, J.G., & Watkins, H.H. (1997). *Ego states: Theory and therapy.* New York: W.W. Norton.

Watzlawick, P. (1978). *The language of change: Elements of therapeutic communication.* New York: W.W. Norton.

Weinberger, N.M., Gold, P.E., & Sternberg, D.B. (1984). Epinephrine enables Pavlovian fear conditioning under anesthesia. *Science, 223,* 605–607.

Wolfe, L.S., & Millet, J.B. (1960). Control of post-operative pain by suggestion under general anesthesia. *American Journal of Clinical Hypnosis, 3,* 100–112.

Zarren, J.I. & Eimer, B.N. (2002). *Brief cognitive hypnosis: Facilitating the change of dysfunctional behavior.* New York: Springer Publishing Company.

Appendix 1

AUTHORS' CREDENTIALS

Dabney M. Ewin, M.D., FACS, ABMH

Past President, American Society of Clinical Hypnosis (ASCH)
Past Vice President, American Society of Clinical Hypnosis
Past Secretary, Society for Clinical and Experimental Hypnosis (SCEH)
Past President, American Board of Medical Hypnosis (ABMH)
Fellow and Approved Consultant, American Society of Clinical Hypnosis
Fellow and Past Secretary, Society for Clinical and Experimental Hypnosis
Fellow, American College of Surgeons (FACS)
Advisory Scientific Editor, American Journal of Clinical Hypnosis
Editorial Consultant, International Journal of Clinical and Experimental Hypnosis
Clinical Professor of Surgery and Psychiatry, Tulane University School of Medicine
Clinical Professor of Psychiatry, Louisiana State University School of Medicine
Private Practice, Occupational Medicine and Hypnosis, Concentra Medical Centers, New Orleans, LA.

Bruce N. Eimer, Ph.D., ABPP, FAABehP

Licensed Psychologist in Pennsylvania
Certified School Psychologist in Pennsylvania and New York
Fellow and Approved Consultant, American Society of Clinical Hypnosis
Board Certified Diplomate in Behavioral Psychology with the American Board of Professional Psychology
Board Certified Diplomate in Pain Management of the American Academy of Pain Management
Fellow, Pennsylvania Psychological Association
Life Member, American Psychological Association
Private Practice, Clinical Psychology, Clinical Neuropsychology and Clinical Hypnosis, Alternative Behavior Associates, Huntingdon Valley and Abington, PA.

Appendix 2

RAPID HYPNOANALYSIS INTAKE
AND WORKSHEET

DEMOGRAPHIC AND MEDICAL INFORMATION SHEET
[Asked in face-to-face interview by BNE]

PATIENT NAME: **TODAY'S DATE:**

Start time: **Stop time:**

What's your home address and home, cell and work #s?   Age/DOB:

What kind of work do you do and where do you work?

Job satisfaction?

Marital status?   Spouse's first name?

How old is he/she?   Does he/she smoke?

First, second . . . marriage?   How long married?

Marital satisfaction?

Do you have any children?

Anyone else living in your household?   Problems?

Highest level of education: Do you wear contact lenses or glasses?

Who referred you?   What exactly did they say to you?

What exactly drew you to my Ad and prompted you to make an appointment with me as opposed to someone else?

Do you smoke?   What and how much?

Who else important to you smokes?

Do you drink coffee?   Y   N

How many cups or mugs a day might you have? # = _____   How taken?

Do you drink tea?   Y   N   How much a day? # = _____   How taken?

Do you drink soda?   Y   N   How much per day? # = _____

246

What alcoholic beverages do you drink? When was your last drink? How often do you drink? How much at one time? When were you last drunk? How often does this occur? Have you ever been in trouble while drinking as a result of drinking? Might there be any reason to believe you have a problem with your drinking behavior?

Any history of alcohol or drug problems in your family of origin? Ever been treated for abusing alcohol or drugs?

Do you engage in any recreational drug use such as marijuana?   Y   N   What drugs do you use?

Approximately how much? How often? Who are you usually with? When and where do you use?

What do you do to maintain your health?

MEDICATIONS:

Do you take any prescription meds?

Any nonprescription medication on a frequent basis?

MEDICAL HISTORY:

Do you have any sleeping problems?

Any headaches on a frequent basis?

Pain in back of your neck, shoulders, low back?

Coughing?   Allergies?   Sinuses?   Bronchitis?   Asthma?   Emphysema?

Any pressure in your chest or breathing problems?

Any heartburn or indigestion?

Any stomach cramps?   Problem with bowel movements or urination?

Pain or cramping in your feet or legs?

Serious illnesses, hospitalization, surgery in last 5 yrs?

Any major health problems?   Any history in your family of diabetes?

High blood pressure in your family?   Heart problems in your family?

Cancer in your family?

Ever had or been treated for any emotional problems?

How about other people in your immediate family?

Ever hospitalized for Psychiatric treatment?   Y   N

DME uses a sign-in worksheet for demographic information, etc. We share the following intake questions:

1. Tell me about your problem. Many patients will answer this in a way that if taken literally, describes the <u>subconscious</u> diagnosis.

2. **When did it start?** If the patient gives an exact date, follow up with, **What was going on in your life at that time?** Often instead of a date, there's an association (e.g., "ever since my tonsillectomy"). Note this. If the patient relates it to an incident, ask, **What change took place in your life at that time?**

3. **When did it become a problem?** Particularly important with incorrigible smoking problems. Gives useful insight into motivation to stop.

4. **What makes it better?** Aside from medicine, note circumstances, times, dates, etc.

5. **What makes it worse?** If NOTHING makes it better or worse, look for a near-death experience.

6. **If you were cured, what would you do that you cannot do now?** i.e., What problem does it solve for you? "Secondary gain." If several things are mentioned the last is most important.

What do you like for your friends to call you? May I call you that? We want the patient to feel comfortable with us, as we're about to ask some very intimate questions.

7. **<Name>, in your entire life . . . , what's the WORST THING THAT EVER HAPPENED to you?** Helplessness leaves a highly emotional imprint, often causing symptoms.

8. **<Name>, in your entire life . . . , what's the WORST THING YOU EVER DID?** What kinds of things make you feel guilty? Later, ideomotor questioning will ask if the symptom is a form of self-punishment.

9. **<Name>, in your entire life . . . , what's the most FRIGHTENED you've ever been?** Often leads to a phobia as a protection against the same thing happening again.

10. **<Name>, in your entire life . . . , what's the most ANGRY you've ever been?** The emotional energy of fear is often transduced into anger, because we're more comfortable with anger. At least we can curse!

11. **<Name>, in your entire life . . . , what's the most EMBARRASSED you've ever been?** Children are often cruel to each other. If a child limped, stuttered, etc., some incident may have been devastating.

12. **<Name>, have you ever known anyone with the same or a similar problem?**

13. **<Name>, in your entire life . . . , what's the BEST thing that ever happened to you?** "Nothing" is the mark of depression. A healthy ongoing relationship is a useful predictor of a good outcome.

14. **<Name>, if ONE WISH would come true, what would you wish for?** Very valuable information. Give up to three wishes. And finally ask: **How many wishes would I have to give you before you would wish to get well?**

15. **Is there ANYTHING ELSE you think I should know?** The most important question of them all! If the patient answers it, he is telling us the subconscious problem. If the answer is NO, we hope we took good notes, because the subconscious is saying "I've already told you."

Preparing The Patient For Hypnosis Induction

Do you have any questions before we start?

Are you afraid of hypnosis?

Do you know what it is that you are most likely to do that will interfere with this?

You are likely to try too hard. If you start trying to be the best patient I ever had, or wondering if you are doing it right, or if you start thinking things like should I feel like I am floating, or should I hear other noises, you have to be out of trance to analyze if you are in trance, and that is my job. Your job is to just do what I ask you to do, and shift into daydream-type thinking, and don't give a hoot whether you do it right or not.

Mind Wandering? That means you are shifting into daydream-type thinking which can wander anywhere it likes!

Trance Induction

Get comfortably relaxed. Close your eyes, and keeping your eyelids closed just as though they are glued together, roll your eyeballs up as though you are looking at the top of your forehead, looking way, way up. Now, take a deep, deep breath, the deepest breath you've ever taken, and hold it . . . hold it. Feel it pressing against your chest. One . . . Two . . . Three [about a 5 second pause concentrates the patient's mind now on holding the breath] . . . And as you let it all out . . . [drop your voice tone as you also pace by exhaling a deep breath] . . . just like a balloon collapsing, draining all the tension out of every nerve and fiber in your body. . . Your eyes relaxed and going deeper, deeper relaxed than you've ever been . . . Paying attention only to the sound of my voice. Any other sounds you hear will be very pleasant in the background and just help you to get more comfortably relaxed. It's comforting to know that the rest of the world is going on about its business while you and I are doing ours . . . Eyes relaxed . . . jaws unclenched . . . shoulders droopy . . . arms limp and floppy . . . your neck and back comfortably supported by the chair . . . And you can let all those muscles relax . . . abdomen soft . . . each breath you take as you exhale, just blowing stress and tension out into the atmosphere, never to return . . . your legs all loose and limp and lazy-like, and your mind as relaxed as your body . . . (shifting to a positive emotion) feeling calm . . . safe . . . peaceful . . . comfortable . . . precious . . . confident . . . Confident because you own your own mind, and it must think what you tell it to think. Confident because you own your own body and it must do what you tell it to do. Confident because you own your own feelings and they have to feel what you tell them to feel. Way, way, way down deep.

Laughing Place

For starters, I want to help you find your "Laughing Place," because laughing is healthy and drives out misery. Everybody has a laughing place. You can start by making a smile come onto your face. Even if you don't feel like it, see what happens if you tell the muscles in your face to make a smile . . . [pause and wait and validate the patient's response]. . . . See what happens. You can do it. That's right. And as the smile comes on to your face, notice the feeling that goes along with it. And just let that feeling go down to your heart [pause] . . . and spread over your entire body. . . . And as you begin to feel this pleasant sensation, just let it happen . . . just let it happen. . . .

Now, I wonder if you can make yourself feel like laughing even if you haven't felt this way in a while. . . . Because laughing is healthy and drives away misery. . . . Just do it and see what happens . . . Just do it and see what happens. That's right. You may even enjoy that feeling more than you expected. . . .

And as you feel more like laughing, it may bring up a happy memory of a time when you felt like laughing. . . . And you may begin to experience some of the sensations that go along with these feelings . . . the scene, the place, the colors, the shapes, the people you are with, or the quiet peacefulness of solitude . . . the sounds . . . the shared laughter, the music, or perhaps the voice of someone who loves you . . . the smells that are here . . . the scent of perfume or flowers, the smell of clean fresh air in the outdoors, the delicate aroma of a good wine . . . the taste of your favorite food or drink . . . the touch and caresses of someone who loves you . . . all the things that make your laughing place, your laughing place, so good . . . so free of any cares, or worries, or duties. . . . And while you are enjoying your laughing place, nothing can bother, nothing can disturb you. . . . When your inner mind knows that you are so concentrated on your laughing place that nothing can bother, nothing can disturb, just give me a little nod of your head so I'll know you've found it. . . .

And having found it, take a mental snapshot of it now, so that at any time when we're doing therapy together, we can instantly shift back to this picture for comfort (it usually takes 30 to 60 seconds for a confirming head nod response, and then you can go on with the ideomotor set-up procedure).

Alerting

In a moment, I am going to rouse you up by counting slowly from one to three. When I say three, blink your eyes and open them, and come back fully alert, sound in mind, sound in body and in control of your feelings. One . . . rousing up slowly . . . two . . . and three. Wide awake, alert, refreshed, and feeling great.

Appendix 3

IDEOMOTOR SETUP

PATIENT: **DATE:**   **SESSION#:**

Induce Trance

After inducing trance . . .

I'm going to move your hand–(positions hand nearest therapist with wrist flexed). You'll find it more comfortable in this position, and hold it right here. Now I am going to teach you a way to signal how you feel without even talking.

"YES" SIGNAL

You know that if we were just having a conversation, and I asked "is your name . . . , you could simply nod your head up and down without talking and I would know you were feeling "yes."

If I ask you a question, and you feel the answer is YES, you have a "yes" feeling about it, you agree, this finger will slowly rise to signal that you agree, that it feels okay, that it feels yes.

Do you like for your friends to call you [say name]? That's right. Of course, you've already told me that you like for your friends to call you . . .

Every time your feelings answer a question, you'll go deeper inside and get even deeper in touch with your deepest and most heartfelt feelings.

"NO" SIGNAL

If I ask you a question and you disagree, you have a NO feeling about it, it just doesn't feel right, this finger will slowly rise to signal that you disagree. You don't have to know why, it just doesn't feel right, the answer is "no."

Is today the Fourth of July? Of course not, the answer is no, today is [state today's date].

"I DON'T WANT TO ANSWER" SIGNAL

If I should ask a question that you're not ready to answer yet, or don't want to answer, just signal with your thumb and that's all right.

"SPEAK TO ME" SIGNAL

If something crosses your mind that you want to tell me, or you want to ask a question, just raise your hand and we'll talk. [If you get a hand signal, say:] Speak to me and tell me what's on your mind.

My first question to your feeling mind is, is it all right for me to help you with this problem? [If "yes,"] Okay. Very good.

Appendix 4

IDEOMOTOR ANALYSIS WORKSHEET

PATIENT: **DATE:**   **SESSION#:**

CONFLICT

One of the things that causes symptoms is what we call a <u>conflict</u>. A conflict occurs when you feel like you want to do one thing, but you ought to do the opposite. You're pulled in two directions. That uses up a lot of energy. [Patient is asked to answer with his fingers:] So, my question to you is do you sense that you are being affected by a conflict? That you're being pulled in two directions? [NO, we pass on.]

[YES, ask:] Would it be all right for you to know at a conscious level what the conflict is?

[YES, say:] I'll be quiet while you scan your feelings, and when it comes to your conscious mind, your yes finger will rise. [When the yes finger rises, ask:]

Is it all right for you to tell me what it is?

Speak to me and tell me what you're experiencing.

[Once the patient has identified and verbalized the stressful conflict, we typically point out:] A conflict is a problem in indecision. You are being pulled in two directions and you are suffering from a problem in indecision. So, you need to decide which choice to make, abandon the thoughts about the opposite choice, and get on with your life. Which choice you make has to be your own. But having made one, I can help you feel comfortable carrying it out.

REFRAME–The treatment for "a conflict" is to make a decision.

The conflict is resolved when you make a choice and start carrying out your decision. There are changes that go with making a choice, and I can help you stick to your decision. Another choice you can make is to decide to put off choosing until a more appropriate later date. Sometimes you don't have enough information to make a wise decision. So, it's sensible to postpone making a serious choice until you have more factual information. If you decide this is not the right time to make a decision, then DECIDE to put the issue out of your mind until a more appropriate time to make a decision. This is still a choice, and it will give you relief from the symptom in the mean time. When you let a conflict go on and on, you use up your nervous energy that

255

should be used for improving your health and your joy and your life. So it's important to resolve conflicts.

ORGAN LANGUAGE

One thing that can cause symptoms is what we call "organ language." This refers to phrases in our everyday conversation that include mention of a body organ in a negative way. For instance, we might hear people say things like: "My job is a real headache," or "My boss is a pain the neck." If taken literally by your subconscious, these types of phrases can be converted into an actual symptom!

Do you sense that you are being affected by organ language?

[If YES,] Would it be all right to bring your specific phrase that's affecting you to a conscious level?

[If YES,] Would it be all right to tell me the phrase?

[If YES,] Speak to me and tell me how it's affecting you.

REFRAME – The treatment for "organ language" is to accurately re-word the phrase omitting mention of an organ. For example . . .

Your job may be difficult or unpleasant . . . , OR, Your boss may be an arrogant SOB.

ALTERNATIVELY, LET THE PATIENT RE-WORD IT IN THE FOLLOWING MANNER:

Would it be all right with your subconscious to come up with another way to deal with . . . still maintain your comfort? [If YES,]

Let your subconscious review this issue, and I'll be quiet, and when you come up with a way to cope with this problem and still be comfortable, your yes finger will rise.

[When YES finger rises,] Now lock in on that with every cell in your mind, and body and feelings. Want it to happen, let it happen, and it will happen.

MOTIVATION (a.k.a., "SECONDARY GAIN")

A person can be motivated to have a symptom because it *seems* to solve a problem. One of the causes of symptoms may be that they serve a subconscious purpose. These symptoms may even be self-protective such as when students get sick around exam time, or when soldiers get sick when especially dangerous missions are about to be undertaken.

Do you sense that you are motivated to have this symptom? That it somehow serves a useful or protective purpose for you? Yes or No?

[If YES,} What possible good could come in your life from having this problem?

How is it possible that this symptom is helpful or protective to you?

REFRAME–The treatment for "motivation" is to find a better and healthier way to cope with the problem, or to change the way the problem is perceived.

PAST EXPERIENCE–IMMEDIATE ONSET

Do you sense this problem started with a significant experience in your past?

[YES?] Is it all right to go back and do a subconscious review of everything that was significant to you in this episode?

[YES?] Did it happen before age 20?

Before age 10?

Before age 5?

Before age 4?

Is it all right to orient your mind back to what happened at age 4?

[With a "yes," say:] Let your mind orient back to the very beginning. And when you start reviewing it, your yes finger will rise. Every time you encounter something emotionally important to you, your no finger will rise. And when you have completed reviewing the episode, you'll signal with your thumb.

Is it all right to bring it up to a conscious level and review it again and tell me what's happening? [If "yes," say:] Speak to me and tell me what's happening.

REFRAME–The treatment for "immediate past experience" is regression to the incident and reframing it.

PAST EXPERIENCE–PREVIOUSLY SENSITIZED

Did anything happen before this to emotionally sensitize you?

If "yes," then go on and identify and review the sensitizing event and reframe it. Count number times "no" finger rises because if there are three emotional instances, we need to regress and reframe each.

If there are several NO signals and it appears complicated, we will say to the patient . . .

You got through it all right, but let's go over it again as though you read the headlines last time and now you are going to read the fine print–all about it, the details, who's there, what they're saying, how you feel, and what's happening.

Is it all right to review it one more time and speak and tell me what is happening?

[With a YES,] Speak to me and tell me what's happening.

REFRAME–The treatment for "previously sensitized past experience" is regression to the sensitizing incident and reframing it.

IDENTIFICATION

Sometimes problems result from modeling another person we are or were close to in order to share a relationship and keep the relationship alive.

Did someone with whom you are or were emotionally close have the same or a similar problem? [If YES,]

Do you sense, "yes" or "no" that you are identifying with that person?

[If yes,] Is it all right to know who it is?

[If yes,] And the answer's yes. All right. When it comes to your mind, your yes finger will rise. [Yes finger rises]

REFRAME–The treatment for "identification" is to separate the identities. Everyone is unique.

You can keep the relationship alive by keeping your happy memories of what you had and make that person proud of you for taking better care of yourself than he did. You are a different person than your [the person's name] was.

You are not [your . . . .]. You do not have all the same genes, the same education, the same experiences, the same intellect, and so forth as your [father, mother, etc.]. You are an individual. Everyone is a separate individual responsible for his own behavior. You can stop [smoking or whatever] when you decide to do so. You are not helpless. Surely the person you care about would want you to keep your memories of the good times you had together and not to emulate harmful or self destructive habits of theirs.

SELF-PUNISHMENT

One of the things that causes symptoms is self-punishment. When we were children and got caught with our hands in the cookie jar, we got admonished or grounded and then it was over. As adults, we may hurt someone's feelings, or do something else we are not proud of, or think "bad thoughts," or fail to keep a promise, and no one punishes us. Something is missing and the subconscious mind can produce a symptom as a form of self-punishment.

Do you sense that this symptom is a form of self punishment for real or imagined guilt?

Yes or no? [If you get a yes:]

Would it be all right to know what you feel you shouldn't have done? Would it be all right to identify the offense? [If we get a yes:]

When it comes to your conscious mind so you can talk about it, your "yes" finger will rise.

[Yes rises.] Speak to me and tell me what it is.

REFRAME–The treatment for "self-punishment" is either to remedy the offense or forgive yourself.

If it is something that can be made up to somebody, then that may need to be done.

If it is imagined guilt, then the patient needs to feel innocent.

If the patient has been punished enough, he may need to realize this and let it go.

If it is real guilt for something that the patient didn't do, ask: Would the symptom go away if you did it?

If it's real guilt that cannot be remedied, the patient needs to forgive himself.

Ask: Was it so bad that you deserve to suffer indefinitely? Or, Do you deserve the death penalty?

Did you intend to . . . .?

Is it possible that you have already been punished enough? [If YES]

Then, would it be all right to let it go?

Is there anything to prevent you from letting it go right now? [If that answer is no,]

Great. Since this symptom has no more value, let it go right now. Say goodbye to the symptom.

[If the answer is yes,] Explore and find out what the reason is and resolve it using the IM questioning technique.

All of us can only do the best that we can with what we had at the time. Isn't that what you did?

Would it be all right to forgive yourself by knowing and recognizing that you really would have done things differently if you had known <u>then</u> what you know <u>now</u>?

Would it be all right to let the symptom go?

The Bible says: "Judge not, that ye be not judged." This is violating the command-ment, "Thou shall have no other Gods before me." Humans are the accused, not the judges, and self-judgment is putting oneself in the seat of God. The God of Abraham tells us that he will forgive anyone who is contrite, and if you feel bad enough or feel guilty enough to punish yourself, it's because you are contrite.

SUGGESTION

One of the things that causes symptoms is what we call a suggestion or imprint. It means that an idea has been accepted at a subconscious level. It is usually introduced at a highly emotional time and is from then on responded to automatically and uncritically.

Answer with your fingers. Do you sense that you are being affected by a suggestion? [If yes, ask:]

Was it given by some authoritative person? [If no, ask:]

Do you sense it is an idea that you gave yourself?

If either of these is "yes", then ask:]

Would it be all right to know what the idea is? [If "yes", say:]

Let it come to consciousness and tell me what it is.

REFRAME–The treatment for "suggestion" is to identify and remove it.

INDEX

Feeling mind

[handwritten note:] ch.
p. Waking state reframing
48

Charles C Thomas

PUBLISHER • LTD.

P.O. Box 19265
Springfield, IL 62794-9265

Book Savings* Save 10% , Save 15% , Save 20%!

- Brooke, Stephanie L.—**CREATIVE ARTS THERAPIES MANUAL: A Guide to the History, Theoretical Approaches, Assessment and Work with Special Populations of Art, Play, Dance, Music, Drama, and Poetry Therapies.** '06, 398 pp. (8 x 10), 34 il., 9 tables.

- Decker, Kathleen P.—**FIT, UNFIT OR MISFIT? How To Perform Fitness for Duty Evaluations in Law Enforcement Professionals.** '06, 240 pp. (7 x 10), 3 il., 43 tables.

- Olson, R. Paul—**MENTAL HEALTH SYSTEMS COMPARED: Great Britain, Norway, Canada, and the United States.** '06, 426 pp. (8 1/2 x 11), 10 il., 65 tables.

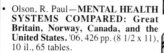

- Stack, Pamela J.—**MY RECOVERY ZONE: An Expressive Journal for Myself.** '06, 55 pp. (8 1/2 x 11), (2 in color), spiral (paper).

- Ewin, Dabney M. & Bruce N. Eimer—**IDEO-MOTOR SIGNALS FOR RAPID HYPNO-ANALYSIS: A How-To Manual.** '06, 296 pp. (7 x 10), 15 il., \$63.95, hard, \$43.95, paper.

- France, Kenneth, Kim Weikel, and Michelle Kish—**HELPING SKILLS FOR HUMAN SERVICE WORKERS: Building Relationships and Encouraging Productive Change. (2nd Ed.)** '06, 378 pp. (7 x 10), 6 il., \$73.95, hard, \$51.95. paper.

- Palmo, Artis J., William J. Weikel & David P. Borsos—**FOUNDATIONS OF MENTAL HEALTH COUNSELING.** (3rd Ed.) '06, 468 pp. (7 X 10), 5 il., 3 tables, \$85.95,hard, \$61.95, paper.

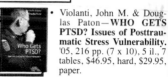

- Willis, Jerry W. & Seung H. Kim—**USING COMPUTERS IN EDUCATIONAL AND PSYCHOLOGICAL RESEARCH: Using Information Technologies to Support the Research Process.** '06, 274 pp. (7 x 10), 206 il., 10 tables, \$69.95, hard, \$44.95, paper

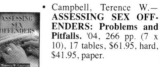

- Dennison, Susan T.—**A MULTIPLE FAMILY GROUP THERAPY PROGRAM FOR AT RISK ADOLESCENTS AND THEIR FAMILIES.** '05, 310 pp. (8 1/2 x 11), 62 il., 4 tables, \$49.95, paper.

- Horovitz, Ellen G.—**ART THERAPY AS WITNESS: A Sacred Guide.** '05, 246 pp. (7 x 10), 85 il., (3 in color), \$43.95, spiral (paper).

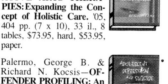

- Le Navenec, Carole-Lynne & Laurel Bridges—**CREATING CONNECTIONS BETWEEN NURSING CARE AND THE CREATIVE ARTS THERAPIES:Expanding the Concept of Holistic Care.** '05, 404 pp. (7 x 10), 33 il., 8 tables, \$73.95, hard, \$53.95, paper.

- Palermo, George B. & Richard N. Kocsis—**OFFENDER PROFILING: An Introduction to the Sociopsychological Analysis of Violent Crime.** '05, 284 pp. (7 x 10), 22 il., 2 tables, \$56.95, hard, \$38.95, paper.

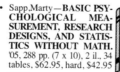

- Sapp,Marty—**BASIC PSYCHOLOGICAL MEASUREMENT, RESEARCH DESIGNS, AND STATISTICS WITHOUT MATH.** '05, 288 pp. (7 x 10), 2 il., 34 tables, \$62.95, hard, \$42.95 paper.

- Violanti, John M. & Douglas Paton—**WHO GETS PTSD? Issues of Posttraumatic Stress Vulnerability.** '05, 216 pp. (7 x 10), 5 il., 7 tables, \$46.95, hard, \$29.95, paper.

- Campbell, Terence W.—**ASSESSING SEX OFFENDERS: Problems and Pitfalls.** '04, 266 pp. (7 x 10), 17 tables, \$61.95, hard, \$41.95, paper.

- Marvasti Jamshid A.—**PSYCHIATRIC TREATMENT OF SEXUAL OFFENDERS: Treating the Past Trauma in Traumatizers-A Bio-Psycho-Social Perspective.** '04, 220 pp. (7 x 10), \$49.95, hard, \$39.95, paper.

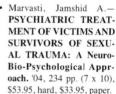

- Marvasti, Jamshid A.—**PSYCHIATRIC TREATMENT OF VICTIMS AND SURVIVORS OF SEXUAL TRAUMA: A Neuro-Bio-Psychological Approach.** '04, 234 pp. (7 x 10), \$53.95, hard, \$33.95, paper.

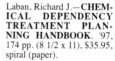

- Wodarski, John S., Lois A. Wodarski & Catherine N. Dulmus—**ADOLESCENT DEPRESSION AND SUICIDE: A Comprehensive Empirical Intervention for Prevention and Treatment.** '03, 186 pp. (7 x 10), 23 il., \$32.95, spiral (paper).

- Laban, Richard J.—**CHEMICAL DEPENDENCY TREATMENT PLANNING HANDBOOK.** '97, 174 pp. (8 1/2 x 11), \$35.95, spiral (paper).

---

5 easy ways to order!

PHONE: 1-800-258-8980 or (217) 789-8980

FAX: (217) 789-9130

EMAIL: books@ccthomas.com

Web: www.ccthomas.com

MAIL: Charles C Thomas • Publisher, Ltd. P.O. Box 19265 Springfield, IL 62794-9265

Complete catalog available at ccthomas.com • books@ccthomas.com

Books sent on approval • Shipping charges: \$7.50 min. U.S. / Outside U.S., actual shipping fees will be charged • Prices subject to change without notice

*Savings include all titles shown here and on our web site. For a limited time only.

Pg 89. WANT IT TO HAPPEN, LET IT HAPPEN, IT WILL HAPPEN

Cheek Re: surgery   preop suggestion to ignore any sound or
Pg 119   discussion unless they say your name 1st

afu. feeling mind.
    INNER mind 163
    deepest mind 164